The Legumes of Texas

Blue Bonnet, *Lupinus subcarnosus*

ANNE OPHELIA TODD

THE LEGUMES OF TEXAS

By B. L. Turner

UNIVERSITY OF TEXAS PRESS • AUSTIN

161162

TO PROFESSOR B. H. WARNOCK

inspiring teacher and friend

PREFACE

When I undertook a chromosomal study of the Leguminosae of Texas in the summer of 1953, it soon became apparent that very little planning and intelligent sampling could be accomplished unless some preliminary taxonomic survey was made with regard to the number of legume species present, their variability, and distribution. Since the only publication dealing with the Texas legumes as a whole was an incomplete check list replete with synonymy and errors, this necessitated a study from the ground up, including library, field, and herbarium work.

The present text is the outgrowth of such a study. Support for the initial field work and research time came largely from funds provided by the Clayton Foundation and the Plant Research Institute of the University of Texas, and the final writing and publication were made possible by a grant from the University Research Institute. For this support I am deeply grateful.

In addition to the financial support mentioned above, a number of individuals have contributed significantly to the completion of the present study. Especial appreciation is due the following: B. H. Warnock, Sul Ross State College, and L. H. Shinners, Southern Methodist University, for permitting free access to their herbaria and other favors too numerous to mention; R. C. Barneby, of Wappinger Falls, New York, for identification and treatment of the difficult genus *Astragalus*; M. C. Johnston for his many last-minute records; Lawrence Erbe for making the many dot maps included; and Olin Fearing for his contribution to the chromosomal study. The frontispiece is an original water color by Anne O. Todd, and it is reproduced here with her kind permission.

B. L. T.

Austin, Texas
June, 1959

Table of Contents

List of Illustrations

LEGUMINOSAE

Introduction

THE LEGUMINOSAE is one of the five largest families of flowering plants and is second only to the Gramineae in economic importance. It includes a number of such familiar food products as beans and peas, as well as important sources of grazing food for animals, of which alfalfa and clover are the better known. In the broadest sense and on a world-wide basis the family contains approximately 13,000 species, distributed into about 550 genera.

In the present text, 391 legume taxa occurring in 59 genera are recognized for Texas; this total includes 44 introduced species which have become established as weeds along roadsides and in yards. Altogether, 347 legume taxa are native in Texas, 304 species and 43 varieties occurring in 54 genera.

Texas is particularly rich in endemics (here defined as taxa of limited distribution within the state or but slightly exceeding its boundaries). Approximately 104 taxa may be classified as such, representing an endemism of about 30 per cent for the state's native legumes. Of these, 51 species and 3 varieties are not known to occur outside the state's boundary.

Fully one third of the Texas legumes (120 taxa, representing 102 species and 18 varieties) are not known to occur in any other state of the United States, though some of these are abundant and widespread in adjacent Mexico.

Astragalus, with 38 taxa (26 species and 12 varieties), is the largest legume genus in the state. This is followed by *Desmodium*, with 23 species, and *Dalea*, with 22 species and 4 varieties.

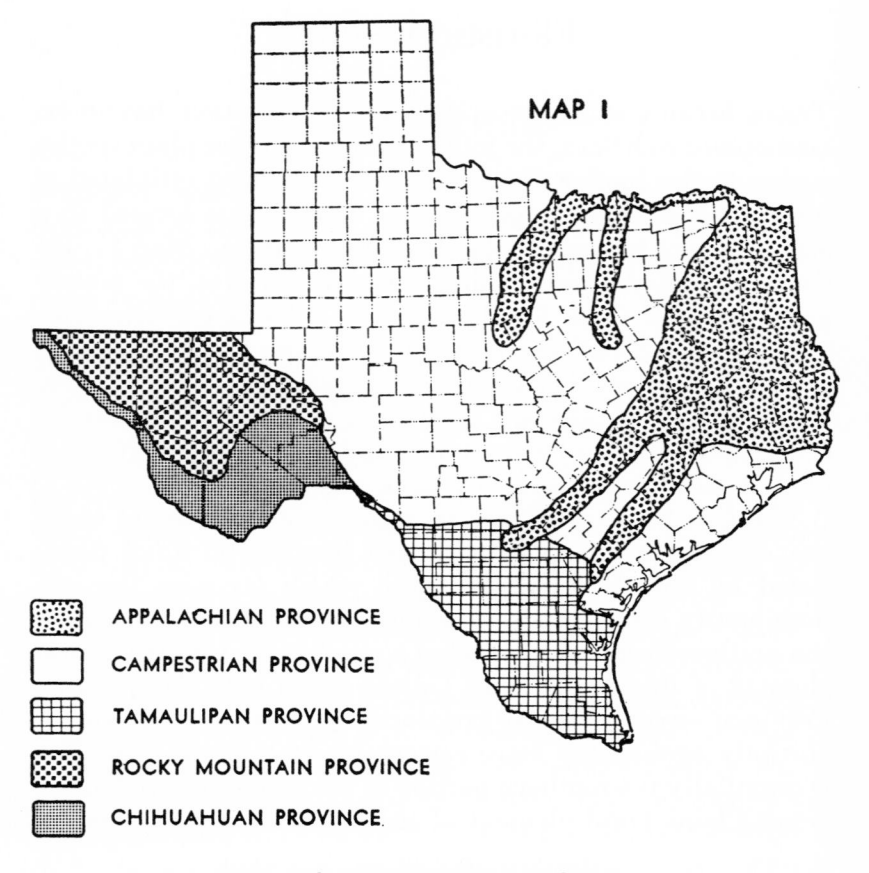

MAP 1

APPALACHIAN PROVINCE

CAMPESTRIAN PROVINCE

TAMAULIPAN PROVINCE

ROCKY MOUNTAIN PROVINCE

CHIHUAHUAN PROVINCE.

Major Floristic Provinces of Texas

Floristic Regions

TEXAS, because of its size and geographic position, has an exceptionally rich flora; the total number of higher plant species native to the land within its borders has been estimated at more than 5,000 (Harper, 1950). The state is located in a region where five major floral provinces[1] meet (Map 1). Because of edaphic and/or physiographic features, the boundaries between these floral provinces are often sharp (e.g., eastern Texas), but where such features are absent, there is a more or less gradual change between the vegetation or species characteristic of adjacent provinces; this transition usually occurs over a 50- to 100-mile belt and is probably a reflection of climatic changes across the area concerned.

The five floral provinces recognized in the present study are: (1) Appalachian Province—a mesophytic forest dominated by oak, hickory, and pine which occupies the predominantly sandy lands of eastern Texas; this is essentially the southwesternmost portion of a much more extensive floral element of the southeastern United States. (2) Campestrian Province—a drier, mostly grassland region which butts rather abruptly against the more eastern forest communities. This is essentially the southern portion of the much more extensive Great Plains floral element of the central United States. In

---

[1] Though the term "floral province" is used in the present discussion it is believed that the term "Biotic Province," as defined by Dice (1943), is equally applicable to these large regions. Nomenclature for the provinces is taken for the most part from Cooper (1859); though Cooper's work is one of the earliest attempts to recognize broad natural provinces within the United States, it is surprisingly sound, especially in regard to the recognition of major biotic regions of an equivalent nature.

eastern Texas the boundary between natural grassland and forest is usually dependent upon soils; grasslands normally occupy heavy clay or calcareous soils, whereas forest is confined to sandy or siliceous soils. The peculiar interdigitation of grassland and forest (or clays and sands) is a reflection of the distributional pattern of various geologic bases: calcareous rock types give rise to the former and siliceous parent material to the latter. (3) Rocky Mountain Province—at higher elevations of the trans-Pecos region where pine forests and low growths of juniper and oak occur. At successively lower elevations one passes into drier regions dominated by grasses. In the northern portion of the trans-Pecos area the legumes (and other plant species) are characteristically those of the southern Rocky Mountains of New Mexico and Arizona. The boundary between the Rocky Mountain Province and the Chihuahuan Province to the south is not sharp; the lines indicated on the map showing the major floristic provinces of Texas were determined by comparing distributional patterns of the legume species in this region. Species occurring in the Davis Mountains are seemingly about equally divided between those characteristic of the Rocky Mountain Province and those of the Chihuahuan Province. However, in terms of frequency and dominance the vegetation is more typical of the Rocky Mountain Province. Floristically, the vegetation of the Guadalupe Mountains is like that of the southern Rockies, while that of the Chisos Mountains in the Big Bend National Park is much closer to the Chihuahuan element of Mexico. (4) Chihuahuan Province—a predominantly desert region, dominated at lower elevations by the ubiquitous creosote bush and at somewhat higher elevations by short grasses and microphyllous shrubs. The legume flora is somewhat impoverished (only 54 species are known to occur in this province), but it is of a very distinct nature, most of the species belonging to genera characteristic of the Mexican plateaus and deserts. In Texas the province is but the northern extension of a much more extensive desert region of northern Mexico. (5) Tamaulipan Province—a region of low mimosaceous tree and shrub growth, apparently once supporting considerable stands of grassland, but now so badly overgrazed and disturbed that historical interpretation is difficult. This is a very distinct province; nearly all workers (zoological and botanical) agree as to its approximate boundary in Texas. The province is essentially a northern extension of a more extensive microphyllous shrubby region of northeastern Mexico.

Each of these floral provinces encompasses a number of vegetational types, and the reader is referred to the accounts of Tharp (1952, 1939) for the characteristics and distribution of the latter communities in Texas. Except for the mountainous portions of the trans-Pecos area, the floral provinces recognized here follow the same pattern-lines as those indicated by Tharp, but are of a more inclusive nature. In keeping with the definition of "province" (Dice, 1943), isolated grassland stands on calcareous soils within the forested sandy regions of deep east Texas and outliers of mountainous vegetation of the trans-Pecos area are not indicated on the map showing the major floristic provinces of Texas.

It is believed that the natures of the five major floral provinces recognized here are more or less equivalent. Data used to arrive at this conclusion were obtained in the following manner: Distributional (and ecological) information for each of the native legume species and varieties was assembled to show (1) the percentage of species restricted to a given region ("endemic" species) and (2) the percentage of species shared with other provinces ("shared" species). The percentage of restriction, expressed as that fraction of the total species known to occur in the province under consideration, was taken as a measure of the naturalness of that floral region. It is interesting that attempts to recognize clearly distinct, but smaller, subdivisions of a given broad floristic type usually resulted in a drastic lowering of "restriction" ratios; for example, if the deeper-soiled grassland regions of central Texas (Texan Biotic Province of Dice) were recognized as a

TABLE 1

Restriction to Floristic Provinces of the 347 Native Legume Taxa of Texas

Province	*"Endemic" Species*	*"Shared" Species*	*Total Species*	*Percentage Restriction*
Appalachian	61	38	99	61.6
Campestrian	59	76	135	43.7
Tamaulipan	35	51	86	40.7
Rocky Mountain	40	43	83	48.2
Chihuahuan	22	32	54	40.0

separate element from the Campestrian Province (recognized here), one would obtain a restriction percentage of 17.6 for the former and 25 for the latter. However, if this central Texas grassland floral element is included with that province to which it is most closely related floristically, then the restriction percentage for the Campestrian Province in this more inclusive sense becomes about 43. (Inclusion of the Texan Biotic element with the adjacent Appalachian Province would, in effect, lower the restriction percentage of this latter floristic region.)

This statistical information is summarized in Table 1. It should be noted that the restriction, or "endemic," element for the Appalachian Province is very high, perhaps a reflection of the very old age and long-time stability of this broad floristic type. This is also borne out by paleobotanical studies (Sharp, 1951).

As indicated by Table 1, recognition of the floral provinces coincides with a restriction figure for the legume species of about 40 per cent. Attempts to recognize the several ecological or vegetational subdivisions of each of these floral divisions, as circumscribed by Tharp, would result in such heterogeneous restriction figures that these regions, on a floristic basis, would not be strictly comparable.

Scope of the Text

Keys

THE KEY to genera in this text is based, for the most part, on vegetative and/or floral features. In a few instances, when these characters are not particularly diagnostic or when they show excessive variability, fruit characters are used. Except when acknowledgments are made, all keys are my own and were constructed from observations on both fresh and pressed material. The keys are strictly artificial and no attempt has been made to key closely related genera or species together.

It should be noted that the key to genera is arranged so that dichotomous choices always lie together, thus avoiding page-shuffling for comparative statements. Numbers in brackets at the end of appropriate key leads refer to the next lead to be consulted, which will be found slightly indented on the lower portion of the same page or as a major lead on the pages that follow.

Generic Treatments

Descriptions of genera are brief, giving only the easily observed and/or diagnostic features of the included plants. The characters listed are intended to be used primarily with Texas material, but the generic descriptions should apply equally well to species of these groups elsewhere (in some instances exceptions to the rule for exotic species have not been allowed for).

Specific Treatments

Species are not described except when populational heterogeneity or purposes of comparison make such descriptions desirable. However, descriptive matter can be obtained through the use of both the key leads and generic information. If one judiciously uses the characters indicated, along with the ecology, normal flowering dates (indicated by month only), and distributional maps, he should have little difficulty in "pinning down" a given species.

Every attempt has been made to include all the species known to occur in Texas, either native or established weedy types. Except for a few commonly cultivated plants, horticultural and rare exotic introductions are not included. In a few instances species are treated which have not been collected in the state as yet, but because most of these are found rather commonly in adjacent regions, their discovery in the state is anticipated.

In a state as large as Texas, with its many distinct habitats and several floristic provinces, it is inevitable that new species and records must come to light. Indeed, some of the taxa, as treated in the present text, are heterogeneous populations which may ultimately be fragmented into several infraspecific or specific taxa; but for the most part, these appear to be few, and where such a course has seemed likely, this has been clearly indicated in the comments accompanying the species treatment.

Effort has been made to treat all taxa uniformly with respect to their designation as species and varieties. The criteria for specific and varietal recognition and treatment have been: (1) that these taxa are of a populational nature; (2) that morphological discontinuities form the basis for their recognition; (3) that two varieties do not normally occupy the same habitat; and (4) that where predictable peripheral intergradation occurs between geographically adjacent taxa, this fact is often indicative of gene exchange (either past or present) and hence suggestive of exceptionally close relationship; such taxa are usually treated as intergrading varieties of a single species.

All the changes in nomenclature necessary in keeping with the above have not been proposed here; instead, where such changes seem desirable, these have been indicated by discussion under the appropriate taxon. The author does not normally subscribe to name-changing without adequate revisionary study, unless currently used names are clearly contrary to the International Code of Botanical Nomenclature.

Synonymy Included

There are only four well-known and/or recent authoritative publications which treat all or parts of the Texas Leguminosae. These are: Small's *Flora of the Southeastern United States* (1903–1913, various editions); *North American Flora* (published by the New York Botanical Garden—incomplete for the Leguminosae); Shinners' *Spring Flora of the Fort Worth–Dallas Area* (1958, privately published); and a *Check List of Texas Plants*, by Cory and Parks (Bulletin 550 of the Texas Agricultural Experiment Station, 1937). The last-named publication is a mere check list; yet, for Texas, it has been the only complete guide to its flora for the past twenty years. Indeed, there are few systematic workers in the state who do not cherish their much-thumbed copies and feel a sense of loss without it.

In the present text an effort has been made to account for all the species and varietal names used in the above four publications for Texas legumes. Complete synonymy has not been attempted. Space limitation has eliminated the inclusion of most long-established synonyms. Where differences of opinion exist with respect to nomenclature, discussion will be found under the species in consideration.

Maps

Distributional dot maps were compiled from plant specimens deposited in herbaria at the following institutions: Southern Methodist University, Dallas, Texas; Sul Ross State College, Alpine, Texas; and the University of Texas, Austin, Texas. Altogether, about 10,000 specimens were examined for this compilation. Master charts showing place of deposition of specimens mapped are on file at the University of Texas Herbarium.

When field and herbarium work has indicated that related taxa intergrade over a relatively broad geographical area, this has been shown by appropriate shading on the maps. For example, Map 40 shows the approximate region of intergradation between three varieties of *Cassia fasciculata;* elsewhere these infraspecific taxa are essentially of the typical form.

Chromosome Numbers

Chromosome numbers are listed for all those species for which counts are available (approximately 55 per cent of the 391 taxa treated). In addition, the basic chromosome number for each genus is given, along with the number of species from which this has been determined. Where counts are not available for the taxon listed, this has been stated. It is hoped that such accentuation will stimulate future workers to acquire this information.

Chromosome reports for most taxa are taken from Darlington and Wylie's recent edition of the *Chromosome Atlas of Flowering Plants* (The Macmillan Company, New York, 1956). Reference to this source is abbreviated throughout as D. & W. In many instances unreported numbers are given for the first time in the present text. To save cataloguers the trouble of searching these out, they are relisted here, along with the workers responsible:

Unpublished Chromosome Counts Reported for the First Time in the Present Text

SPECIES	NUMBER (n)	SOURCE
MIMOSOIDEAE		
Acacia berlandiera	13	Turner and Fearing
Acacia constricta	26	Turner and Fearing

SPECIES	NUMBER (*n*)	SOURCE
Acacia rigidula	13	Turner and Fearing
Acacia texensis	13	Turner and Fearing
Acacia vernicosa	13	Turner and Fearing
Mimosa emoryi	26	Turner and Fearing
Mimosa warnockii	13	Turner and Fearing
Pithecellobium pallens	13	Turner and Fearing
Schrankia hystricina	13	Turner and Fearing
Schrankia roemeriana	13	Turner and Fearing
Schrankia uncinata	13	Turner and Fearing
Prosopis glandulosa var. *velutina*	14	Turner and Fearing

CAESALPINIOIDEAE

Cassia aristellata	8	Irwin
Cassia bauhinioides	14	Irwin
Cassia fasciculata var. *rostrata*	8	Irwin
Cassia lindheimeriana	14	Irwin
Cassia marilandica	14	Irwin
Cassia texana	8	Irwin
Cercidium macrum	14	Turner
Hoffmanseggia drepanocarpa	12	Turner and Fearing
Hoffmanseggia oxycarpa	12	Turner and Fearing

PAPILIONOIDEAE

Aeschynomene viscidula	10	Turner
Astragalus brazoensis	11	Turner and Fearing
Astragalus distortus var. *engelmannii*	13	Turner and Fearing
Astragalus wootonii	12	Turner
Baptisia nuttalliana	9	Turner
Crotalaria sagittalis	16	Turner and Fearing
Dalea brachystachys	7	Turner and Fearing
Dalea lachnostachys	7	Turner and Fearing
Dalea pogonathera var. *walkerae*	7	Turner and Fearing
Dalea wrightii	7	Turner and Fearing
Desmodium wrightii	11	Turner and Fearing
Eysenhardtia texana	20	Turner and Fearing
Galactia texana	10	Turner and Fearing
Petalostemum griseum	7	Turner

The Legumes of Texas

SPECIES	NUMBER (n)	SOURCE
Psoralea cuspidata	11	Turner and Fearing
Psoralea digitata var. *digitata*	11	Turner and Fearing
Psoralea subulata	11	Turner
Rhynchosia difformis	11	Turner and Fearing
Rhynchosia latifolia	11	Turner
Rhynchosia texana	11	Turner
Trifolium bejariense	8	Turner and Fearing
Vicia leavenworthii var. *occidentalis*	7	Johnston

General Characteristics and Key to Genera

TREES, shrubs, or herbs with mostly alternate compound leaves and stipules.

Flowers perigynous or rarely hypogynous, in panicles, racemes, spikes, or globose heads, rarely, fasciculate or solitary in the leaf axils.

Calyx regular to irregular, composed of five separate or variously fused parts.

Corolla regular to slightly irregular to zygomorphic, depending on the subfamily or degree of specialization; petals basically 5 (rarely, less or absent through reduction), separate, or the lower two, representing the keel, fused for some portion of their distance; in bud the petals valvate or variously imbricate.

Functional stamens 1 to numerous, separate to fused or, rarely, absent in dioecious species.

Gynecium composed of a single, superior, unicarpellate pistil (rarely, some species having flowers with several unfused pistils); ovules 1 to numerous in a ventral position and arranged along the margin of the fused carpel.

Fruit a dehiscent or indehiscent pod or legume, of various shapes and texture. Seeds 1 to numerous, mostly with a hard seed coat, usually requiring some degree of scarification for germination.

The family is classically divided into three subfamilies, Mimosoideae, Caesalpinioideae, and Papilionoideae. A brief description of each of these groups is given in the appropriate portions of the text.

Artificial Key to Texas Legume Genera

1. Leaves, all of them, simple . . . . Key A (below)
1. Leaves compound with 2 or more leaflets [2]
   2. Leaves pinnately twice compound . . . Key B (below)
   2. Leaves pinnately once compound or palmate . Key C (p. 18)

Key A

1. Herbs or unarmed shrubs [4]
1. Trees or thorny shrubs [2]
   2. Leaves large, 3–10 cm. wide, cordate, or reniform . .
      . . . . 11. *Cercis*
   2. Leaves small, linear, or linear lanceolate [3]
      3. Flowers yellow; sepals united, forming a distinct calyx
         tube . . . . 46. *Alhagi*
      3. Flowers deep red; sepals separate . . 14. *Krameria*
4. Sepals separate; fruit a prickly bur . . . 14. *Krameria*
4. Sepals united, forming a distinct calyx tube; fruit without
   prickles [5]
   5. Shrubs; leaves narrow, 3 mm. wide or less, stems glandular-
      dotted . . . . 33. *Dalea*
   5. Annual or perennial herbs; leaves 8 mm. wide or more; stems
      not glandular-dotted [6]
      6. Leaves cordate or reniform, about as long as wide or
         less . . . . 65. *Rhynchosia*
      6. Leaves linear, lanceolate, ovate, obovate, or spatulate, three
         to eight times as long as wide [7]
         7. Leaves sessile or nearly so, without conspicuous retic-
            ulate veins, glabrous to pubescent . . 22. *Crotalaria*
         7. Leaves with petioles 4–20 mm. long, obviously retic-
            ulate-veined, glabrous [8]
            8. Flowers in terminal racemes; fruit constricted between
               the seeds (a loment) . . . . 51. *Desmodium*
            8. Flowers sessile in the leaf axils; fruit not constricted
               between the seeds . . . . . 61. *Galactia*

Key B

1. Flowers in dense or loose globose heads or spikes; petals very
   small, 2 mm. wide or less [6]
1. Flowers in open racemes or solitary, never in congested heads
   or spikes; petals large, 4 mm. wide or more [2]

2. Pinnae 8 cm. long or less; shrubs 8 feet tall or less [4]
2. Pinnae of well-developed leaves 10 cm. long or more; trees or shrubs 8–60 feet tall [3]
   3. Leaves with only 1 pair of pinnae; flowers yellow; small spinescent trees or shrubs . . . 17. *Parkinsonia*
   3. Leaves with 3–7 pairs of pinnae; flowers greenish-white, unarmed trees to 60 feet tall . . . 16. *Gymnocladus*
4. Plants thorny . . . . 18. *Cercidium*
4. Plants without thorns [5]
   5. Petiolules (stalk) of pinnae 4–20 mm. long; stems stiffly erect, decidedly woody; leaflets glabrate, without raised glands . . . . 19b. *Caesalpinia*
   5. Petiolules of pinnae 0.5–3 mm. long; stems herbaceous, or if somewhat woody, the leaves decidedly pubescent or with raised glands . . . . . . 19a. *Hoffmanseggia*
6. Stamens 10 or fewer to each flower [10]
6. Stamens numerous, more than 10 to each flower [7]
   7. Unarmed herbs or small shrubs 3 feet high or less; stipules membranous, not spinescent; flower heads loose, 2- to 15-flowered . . . . 3. *Calliandra*
   7. Spinescent or prickly shrubs or trees (rarely, the spines absent); flower heads congested, (10)15- to many-flowered [8]
   8. Stamens free to the base or nearly so . . 4. *Acacia*
   8. Stamens united at their base forming a tube 2–5 mm. long [9]
     9. Plants armed with paired spines (often much reduced); flower heads greenish-white, 1–3 cm. across; native plants of southern Texas . . . 1. *Pithecellobium*
     9. Plants unarmed; flower heads reddish to pink, 3–5 cm. across; introduced or cultivated plants (rarely, escaped), widespread . . . . 2. *Albizia*
10. Flowers globose or in short spikes 1–3 cm. long [12]
10. Flowers in spikes (3)4–8 cm. long; trees or shrubs usually armed with straight stout spines [11]
   11. Legume flattened, 1.5 cm. wide or more; larger spines often branched; leaves once pinnate and twice pinnate on the same tree . . . . 15. *Gleditsia*
   11. Legume terete or tightly coiled, 1.2 cm. wide or less; spines unbranched; leaves all twice pinnate . . 10. *Prosopis*
12. Unarmed trees, shrubs, or herbs [15]
12. Trees or shrubs (a briar in *Schrankia*) with spines, thorns, or recurved prickles [13]

13. Plant a weak-stemmed, wide-spreading briar; stems, leaves, and peduncles armed with numerous recurved prickles . . . . 6. *Schrankia*

13. Trees or shrubs with usually erect stems (straggling and briarlike in *Mimosa malacophylla*); plant variously spiny or prickly, but at least the peduncles without numerous recurved prickles [14]

    14. Pod twisted, springlike; anthers with apical glands; leaves with 1 pair of pinnae . . . 10. *Prosopis*

    14. Pod straight or nearly so (rarely, contorting, but never springlike); anthers without glands . . 7. *Mimosa*

15. Small trees . . . . 5. *Leucaena*

15. Prostrate herbs or low shrubs [16]

    16. Flower heads bright yellow; roots orange; fruits abruptly narrowed at the base, forming a distinct stipe . . . . 9. *Neptunia*

    16. Flower heads pink or pinkish to white, never bright yellow; roots not orange; fruits without a distinct stipe at base [17]

        17. Flowers bright pink, in dense heads or short spikes; stems prostrate; fruit with valves separating from the margin at maturity . . . . . 7. *Mimosa*

        17. Flowers whitish or greenish-white; stems erect to prostrate; fruit splitting along the margin at maturity, the valves not separating from the margin . . . . 8. *Desmanthus*

KEY C

1. Sepals united, forming a calyx tube; flowers usually very irregular (sometimes reduced to a single petal, or if appearing regular, then the petals 3 mm. wide or less) [3]

1. Sepals separate, not forming a calyx tube; flowers only slightly irregular; stamens separate [2]

    2. Flowers white or pinkish-red; leaflets 2; woody shrubs or small trees . . . . 12. *Bauhinia*

    2. Flowers yellow; if leaflets 2, then the plant herbaceous . . . . 13. *Cassia*

3. Leaves with 2 or 3 leaflets only [37]

3. Leaves, most of them, with 4 or more leaflets [4]

    4. Shrubs, trees, or woody vines, the stems persisting to produce new growth each year [28]

4. Perennial or annual herbs, the aerial stems dying back each
 year, any new stems arising from the previous year's root or
 underground stem [5]
  5. Leaves, most of them, pinnate, the leaflets arranged alternately or opposite along the rachis [9]
  5. Leaves palmate or digitate (the central leaflet stalked in
 Galactia grayi) [6]
    6. Plants with prostrate stems 3–6 feet long; leaves, at least
 some of them, with a leaflet having a distinct stalk 5–10
 mm. long   .   .   .   .   61. *Galactia*
    6. Plants erect to semierect or acaulescent (rarely, stems
 short and prostrate); leaflets all sessile or equally short-
 stalked [7]
      7. Leaves with 2–4 leaflets, never more; flowers yellow
 .   .   .   .   50. *Zornia*
      7. Leaves with 4–8 leaflets; flowers lavender to blue,
 never yellow [8]
        8. Leaves glandular-dotted; fruit 1-seeded, 2–6 mm.
 long   .   .   .   .   30. *Psoralea*
        8. Leaves not glandular-dotted; fruit several-seeded,
 20–60 mm. long   .   .   .   .   .   23. *Lupinus*
9. Leaves not glandular-dotted [12]
9. Leaves glandular-dotted (these often hidden beneath a
 dense pubescence, but readily seen when the hair is scraped
 off [10]
  10. Rachis of mature leaves 6–15 cm. long, fruit a prickly
 pod 1–2 cm. long   .   .   .   .   .   45. *Glycyrrhiza*
  10. Rachis of mature leaves mostly 0.5–6 cm. long; fruit included within the calyx, not prickly, 0.5 cm. long or
 less [11]
    11. Flower strongly irregular with well-developed ban-
 ner, wings, and keel; stamens 8–10   .   .   33. *Dalea*
    11. Flower not strongly irregular, at least 4 of the petals
 essentially alike, not differentiated into wings and
 keel; stamens 5   .   .   .   .   34. *Petalostemum*
12. Leaves odd-pinnate and without tendrils, the leaf rachis
 terminated by a leaflet [15]
12. Leaves even-pinnate or bearing tendrils, the leaf rachis
 not terminated by a leaflet [13]
  13. Stems stiffly erect, 40–200 cm. tall; leaves without
 tendrils; leaflets 20 to numerous; flowers yellow, red,
 or orange   .   .   .   .   .   .   40. *Sesbania*

13. Stems weak, climbing by tendrils, or if erect and without tendrils, then the stem 40 cm. tall or less; leaflets 4–20; flowers blue, violet, or purplish [14]
    14. Style with a dense ring of hairs just below the stigma . . . . 53. *Vicia*
    14. Style flattened, with a line of hairs down the inner surface . . . . 54. *Lathyrus*
15. Stamens, all of them, separate; flowers white; leaves densely pubescent; fruit indehiscent, torulose . . . 20. *Sophora*
15. Stamens, at least 5 of them, united by their filaments [16]
    16. Rachis of leaf 1.5–15 cm. long, if less, then the flowers in several-flowered racemes; leaflets 5 to numerous [18]
    16. Rachis of leaf 0.2–1.5(2) cm. long; flowers 1–3(4), terminal on slender peduncles, never racemose along a central axis; leaflets 3–9 [17]
        17. Stems and leaves densely pubescent with wide-spreading glandular hairs; plants of east Texas . . . . 47. *Aeschynomene*
        17. Stems and leaves appressed-pubescent or glabrate, plants of trans-Pecos Texas . . . . 28. *Lotus*
18. Stipules rigid, spinescent; flowers white; plants of trans-Pecos Texas . . . . 38. *Peteria*
18. Stipules membranous or absent, not at all spinescent [19]
    19. Fruit dehiscent or indehiscent, but not breaking into 1-seeded segments at maturity; stems mostly 40 cm. long or less, but if longer *and* stiffly erect, then the flowers numerous to each raceme [21]
    19. Fruit a loment, indehiscent, breaking into 1-seeded segments at maturity; stems stiffly erect, trailing, or twining, 40–200 cm. long; flowers yellow, 1–4 in axillary fasciculate clusters or short racemes, or solitary [20]
        20. Leaves with 6 to numerous leaflets; plants of eastern and south coastal Texas . . 47. *Aeschynomene*
        20. Leaves with 3–5(7) leaflets; plants of trans-Pecos Texas . . . . 48. *Nissolia*
    21. Plants annual or perennial, the stems prostrate to weakly ascending (often acaulescent); if stiffly erect and over 30 cm. tall, then the legume inflated and less than six times as long as wide [23]
    21. Plants perennial, the stems erect, 30–200 cm. tall; legume six to twenty times as long as wide, not inflated; plants of central and east Texas [22]

22. Stems, leaves, and legume densely long-pubescent with spreading hairs . . . . . . 36. *Tephrosia*

22. Stems, leaves, and legume appressed, short-pubescent to nearly glabrate . . . . . 29. *Indigofera*

23. Peduncle of flowering racemes 1–8(9) cm. long [24]

23. Peduncle of mature flowering racemes 8–30 cm. long; legume flattened [23a]

23a. Flowers white or cream-colored . . 43. *Astragalus*

23a. Flowers pink or reddish-tinged . . 36. *Tephrosia*

24. Flowers, when fresh, brick-red or reddish (often fading lavender); perennials [26]

24. Flowers of various colors, but not brick-red or reddish; annuals or perennials [25]

25. Keel petals acute, blunt, or rounded at the apex . . . . 43. *Astragalus*

25. Keel petals with the apex extending into a sharp erect point; plants acaulescent; flowers purple . . . . 44. *Oxytropis*

26. Fruit inflated, bladder-like; leaflets without raised reticulate veins, opposite along the leaf rachis . . . . 42. *Sphaerophysa*

26. Fruit flattened to somewhat turgid, but not inflated or bladder-like; leaflets with raised reticulate veins, or *if* without reticulate veins, then the leaflets arranged alternately along the rachis [27]

27. Leaflets mostly opposite along the leaf rachis, reticulate-veined; leaf petioles mostly 1 cm. long or more . . . . 36. *Tephrosia*

27. Leaflets mostly alternate along the leaf rachis, without reticulate venation; leaf petioles 1 cm. long or less . . . . 29. *Indigofera*

28. Leaves not glandular-dotted [31]

28. Leaves glandular-dotted (best seen on under surface of leaf) [29]

29. Flowers with only 1 petal present (the banner); leaves, most of them, 8 cm. long or more; if less, then the leaflets densely pubescent; leaflets (4)5–30 mm. wide . . . . 31. *Amorpha*

29. Flowers with 4 or 5 petals; leaves, most of them, 8 cm. long or less; if more, then the leaflets glabrate or nearly so; leaflets 1–5 mm. wide [30]

30. Rachis of leaf, on well-developed leaves, 3–9 cm. long;
    fruit three to six times as long as the calyx; flowers white
    . . . . *32. Eysenhardtia*
30. Rachis of leaf 0.5–2.5 cm. long; fruit not exceeding the
    calyx; flowers rose, reddish, or purplish (rarely, white)
    . . . . *33. Dalea*
31. Leaflets 2 mm. wide or less . . . . *35. Brongniartia*
31. Leaflets 4 mm. wide or more [32]
    32. Stamens, all of them, separate to the base; fruit indehiscent,
        cigar-shaped, torulose, 6–25 mm. in diameter . .
        . . . . *20. Sophora*
    32. Stamens united by their filaments into a tube; fruit flat-
        tened, or if somewhat terete, not as above [33]
        33. Rachis of leaf 8 cm. long or more; legume 3 cm. long or
            more; flowers 10 mm. long or more [35]
        33. Rachis of leaf 1–8 cm. long; legume 1.5–3.5 cm. long;
            flowers 5–10 mm. long [34]
            34. Shrubs or trees to 20 feet tall; rachis of leaf 1–3 cm.
                long . . . . . . *39. Coursetia*
            34. Suffruticose herbs, appearing shrublike, 6 feet tall
                or less; rachis of leaf mostly 3–8 cm. long
                . . . . *29. Indigofera*
        35. Herbaceous, perennial or annual, shrubs, 3–9 feet tall,
            the main stem mostly greenish and easily broken;
            flowers 8–20 mm. long, pale yellow, orange, or reddish
            . . . . *40. Sesbania*
        35. Woody shrubs, trees, or vines, the main stem develop-
            ing a tough brown bark; flowers 15 mm. long or more,
            white, lavender, or rose-purplish, never yellowish to
            red [36]
            36. Shrubs or woody vines, never prickly or spiny, the
                ultimate stems twining . . . *37. Wisteria*
            36. Erect trees or shrubs, often prickly or spiny, the
                ultimate stems never twining . . *41. Robinia*
37. Leaves with tendrils . . . . . . *54. Lathyrus*
37. Leaves without tendrils [38]
    38. Leaflets 3 [40]
    38. Leaflets 2 [39]
        39. Leaflets narrow, acute at apex, pubescent, 4–15 mm.
            wide . . . . *50. Zornia*
        39. Leaflets broad, obtuse or rounded at apex, 15–30 mm.
            wide . . . . *21. Baptisia*

40. Herbs or shrubs with erect or trailing stems, never twining [51]
40. Twining vines (often trailing when support is lacking) [41]
    41. Perennial or herbaceous vines, not at all woody; leaves mostly 20 cm. long or less [43]
    41. Woody or semiwoody, high-climbing vines, leaves, well-developed ones, 20 cm. long or more [42]
        42. Stipules conspicuous, 8–15 mm. long; flowering racemes 7–40 cm. long   .   .   .   63. *Pueraria*
        42. Stipules inconspicuous, 6 mm. long or less; flowering racemes 2–5 cm. long   .   .   .   62. *Dioclea*
    43. Flowers 1 to numerous on terminal peduncles or in short or elongate racemes [46]
    43. Flowers single, or 1–3 clustered in the axils of leaves and without a common peduncle, never 1 to several on terminal peduncles or in racemes [44]
        44. Flowers yellow, 4–7 mm. long; legume 14–30 mm. long   .   .   .   .   65. *Rhynchosia*
        44. Flowers not yellow, 10–30 mm. long; legume 40–100 mm. long [45]
            45. Flowers subtended by conspicuous membranous bracts 3–5 mm. wide; legume tapering into a slender beak 10–30 mm. long; plants of central and east Texas   .   .   .   .   56. *Centrosema*
            45. Flowers subtended by small subulate bracteoles 1 mm. wide or less; legume beakless or nearly so; plants of trans-Pecos Texas   .   58. *Cologania*
    46. Flowers yellow [50]
    46. Flowers of various colors, but never yellow [47]
        47. Flowers 1 to several at the apex of an elongate peduncle, not at all racemose; leaves with petioles 1–4 cm. long   .   .   .   .   .   66. *Strophostyles*
        47. Flowers several along the sides of a central axis, or if the flowers 1–2 at the apex of a peduncle, then the leaves sessile or nearly so [48]
            48. Flower pedicels subtended by conspicuous, persistent bracts about as long as broad (2–4 mm. long); calyx lobes 4; plants of east Texas   .   .   .   .   57. *Amphicarpa*
            48. Flower pedicels without conspicuous bracts, or bracts deciduous; if bracts are persistent, then

these two to three times as long as wide, with an acute
apex [49]
49. Calyx lobes 4, subulate, as long as the tube or longer;
    peduncles 1–6(7) cm. long   .   .   61. *Galactia*
49. Calyx lobes 5, obtuse or broadly acute, scarcely
    longer than wide, shorter than the tube; peduncles
    of mature racemes (4)7–25 cm. long .   67. *Phaseolus*
50. Peduncles of mature racemes 8–30 cm. long; legume 3–6
    cm. long .   .   .   .   68. *Vigna*
50. Peduncles 1–8 cm. long; legume 1.5–2.5 cm. long   .
  . . . . 65. *Rhynchosia*
51. Banner narrow, dark red, 3–5 cm. long; plant a shrub or sub-
  shrub, 3–10 feet tall .   .   .   .   .   .   60. *Erythrina*
51. Banner not dark red, or if reddish, then much smaller [52]
    52. Leaves and calyx not glandular-dotted [54]
    52. Leaves and/or calyx glandular-dotted (these often hidden
        beneath a dense pubescence, but readily seen when the
        hair is scraped off) [53]
        53. Flowers yellow   .   .   .   .   .   33. *Dalea*
        53. Flowers lavender or brick-red, never yellow   .   .
    . . . . 30. *Psoralea*
54. Leaflets entire, not at all toothed [57]
54. Leaflets toothed or denticulate, at least near the apex
    (sometimes minutely so) [55]
    55. Flowers in slender, elongate racemes, at least four to
        eight times as long as thick   .   .   .   26. *Melilotus*
    55. Flowers in short, thick racemes or umbels, three times
        as long as thick or less [56]
        56. Fruit coiled or curved, longer than the calyx; leaves
            trifoliate, not palmate   .   .   .   25. *Medicago*
        56. Fruit not coiled or curved, shorter than the calyx
        . . . . 27. *Trifolium*
57. Flowers 4–6 cm. long   .   .   .   .   55. *Clitoria*
57. Flowers 3 cm. long or less [58]
    58. Leaves with petioles 14 mm. long or less [68]
    58. Leaves, at least some of them, with petioles 15 mm. long
        or more [59]
        59. Annual or perennial herbs 2 feet tall or less, or the
            stems trailing, not stiffly erect [62]
        59. Perennial, stems stiffly erect, 3–7 feet tall [60]
            60. Flowers yellow; fruit a several-seeded pod, not
                breaking at maturity into 1-seeded segments;

known only from Big Bend area of trans-Pecos Texas .
. . . . 24. *Genistedium*
60. Flowers of various colors, but mostly violet or rose-tinged;
fruit 1- to several-seeded loment that breaks at maturity
into 1-seeded segments [61]
    61. Leaflets subtended by stipels; fruit a several-seeded
loment that breaks at maturity into 1-seeded segments
. . . . 51. *Desmodium*
    61. Leaflets without subtending stipels; fruit a 1-seeded
segment, never more . . . . 52. *Lespedeza*
62. Leaves trifoliate, the terminal leaflet distinctly stalked, the
stalk 5–40 mm. long [64]
62. Leaves palmate, the terminal leaflet sessile or nearly so [63]
    63. Flowers white; petioles glabrate; pod flattened . .
. . . . 61. *Galactia*
    63. Flowers yellow; petioles pubescent with long hairs; pod
inflated . . . . 22. *Crotalaria*
64. Stems prostrate, not at all erect, bearing subterranean fruit
near the lower part; leaflets leathery, elliptic to orbicular, with
raised reticulate veins beneath . . . . 61. *Galactia*
64. Stems erect, ascending, or trailing, but never bearing subterranean fruit; leaflets various [65]
    65. Fruit 2–2.5 cm. wide; seeds 12–16 mm. wide, trailing
plants on open beach sand . . . . 64. *Canavalia*
    65. Fruit 1.5 cm. wide or less; seeds 10 mm. wide or less [66a]
        66a. Flowers yellow, never rose or purplish . . .
. . . . 65. *Rhynchosia*
        66a. Flowers rose, violet, or purplish, never completely
yellow [66b]
            66b. Leaflets not subtended by stipels; fruit 1-seeded
. . . . 52. *Lespedeza*
            66b. Leaflets subtended by stipels; fruit several-seeded
[67]
                67. Fruit a loment, breaking at maturity into 2–6
1-seeded segments . . . 51. *Desmodium*
                67. Fruit a several-seeded pod, not breaking into
1-seeded segments; large trailing vines of
trans-Pecos Texas . . . 67. *Phaseolus*
68. Stipules fused to the petiole, often forming a tube around the
stem; flowers small, yellowish-orange . . 49. *Stylosanthes*
68. Stipules not, or but slightly, fused to the petiole, never forming
a tube; flowers variously colored [69]

69. Stamens separate; fruit an inflated or globose pod . .
. . . . 21. *Baptisia*
69. Stamens united, forming a tube; fruit a flattened 1- to several-
seeded pod or loment, never inflated or globose [70]
    70. Stipels present at the base of each leaflet; fruit a 2- to
several-seeded loment, breaking at maturity into 1-seeded
segments . . . . 51. *Desmodium*
    70. Stipels absent; fruit 1-seeded or several-seeded but not
breaking into segments at maturity [71]
        71. Stipules minute, reduced to glands; fruit several-
seeded . . . . 28. *Lotus*
        71. Stipules conspicuous, 2–10 mm. long; fruit 1-seeded
. . . . 52. *Lespedeza*

Subfamily Mimosoideae

TREES, SHRUBS, or less often herbaceous perennials (rarely, annual). Leaves mostly twice pinnate with several to numerous small leaflets (once pinnate in the tropical genus *Inga;* reduced to a simple condition in certain exotic species of *Acacia*). Flowers regular or nearly so, mostly in spikes, heads, or congested racemes; petals separate or variously united; sepals usually united, at least to the middle; petals valvate in the bud; stamens 4 to numerous, usually exceeding the petals.

The subfamily, if treated conservatively, contains about 2,000 species distributed in approximately 40 genera. Most of the species are without agronomic value, though some of the woody members are important browse plants in the more arid portions of the world. The subfamily is sometimes treated as a distinct family, Mimosaceae.

1. PITHECELLOBIUM   Ape's-earring

TREES or shrubs with spinescent stipules.

LEAVES twice pinnate with 2 to several pinnae; leaflets smooth or with raised veins; petiolar gland usually present.

FLOWERS in globose heads or spikes, yellow to greenish-white; stamens numerous, united into a tube at base.

FRUIT an extremely variable, elongate, indehiscent or dehiscent pod.

BASIC chromosome number, as determined from counts on 8 species, $x = 13$ (D. & W.).

A large genus with about 150 species widely distributed in the tropical and subtropical regions of North and South America. The genus is sometimes spelled *Pithecollobium.*

KEY TO SPECIES

1. Leaflets large, 3–6 pairs per pinna; petiolar gland elevated between the lowest pair of pinnae   .   .   .   1. *P. flexicaule*
1. Leaflets small, (6)7–20 pairs per pinna; petiolar gland depressed, usually below the lowest pair of pinnae   .   .
.   .   .   .   2. *P. pallens*

1. *Pithecellobium flexicaule* (Benth.) Coulter, Bot. Gaz. 15: 270. 1890. TEXAS EBONY
    Ebenopsis flexicaulis (Benth.) Britt. & Rose
    Siderocarpus flexicaulis (Benth.) Small
    Endemic to southern Texas and adjacent Mexico in sandy-loam or clay soils (Map 2); usually a small tree or large shrub growing with other woody species, forming dense thickets. April–July.
    Chromosome number, $2n = 26$ (Atchison, 1951; as *Siderocarpus flexicaulis*).

2. *Pithecellobium pallens* (Benth.) Standl., Tropical Woods 34:39. 1933. TENAZA

Havardia pallens (Benth.) Britt. & Rose
Havardia brevifolia (Benth.) Small

Southern Texas and adjacent Mexico in mostly alluvial, sandy-clay soils along stream bottoms (Map 3). May–August. Vegetatively, the species resembles *Acacia berlandieri*, but can be distinguished from that species by its straight and paired spines; *A. berlandieri* has infrastipular spines. *P. pallens* is reportedly a good browse plant, especially during winter months (Standley, 1922).

This species is the type of Small's proposed genus *Havardia*. Burkart (1949) has suggested that the species is best placed in the genus *Albizia*.

Chromosome number, $2n = 26$ (Turner and Fearing, unpublished).

2. ALBIZIA   Silk-Tree

UNARMED TREES or shrubs with smooth bark.

LEAVES twice compound, mostly deciduous; leaflets small and numerous; stipules herbaceous, usually deciduous.

FLOWERS yellow or reddish in globose heads or cylindric spikes; stamens numerous, fused near the base, exserted.

FRUIT a many-seeded, flattened, dry, linear pod.

BASIC chromosome number, as determined from counts on 8 species, $x = 13$ (D. & W.).

A genus with about 70 species mainly confined to tropical and subtropical regions of Asia, Africa, and Australia. Some of the species are valuable timber trees; in the United States, *A. lebbeck* Benth. and the species below are grown as yard ornamentals. The genus *Albizia* is sometimes spelled *Albizzia*.

Albizia julibrissin Durazz., Mag. Tosc. 3:11. 1772. SILK-TREE (also known locally as "Mimosa-tree")

Introduced from Asia; occasionally planted as a roadside

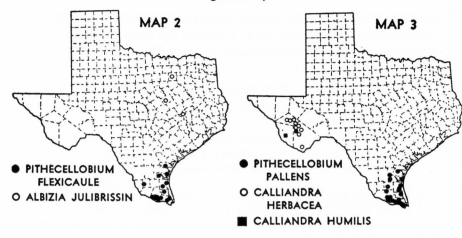

MAP 2

● PITHECELLOBIUM
   FLEXICAULE
○ ALBIZIA JULIBRISSIN

MAP 3

● PITHECELLOBIUM
   PALLENS
○ CALLIANDRA
   HERBACEA
■ CALLIANDRA HUMILIS

tree in eastern Texas (Map 2). May–July. Native to the warmer regions of eastern Asia, but elsewhere widely cultivated as an ornamental, often becoming naturalized.

Chromosome number, $2n = 26(52)$ (D. & W.).

3. CALLIANDRA   False-mesquite

PERENNIAL HERBS, shrubs, or trees.

LEAVES twice compound; pinnae 1 to several pairs; leaflets few to numerous, mostly with raised veins.

FLOWERS 2 to numerous in globose heads, white, pink, or red; stamens elongate, numerous, united at the base by their filaments, often brightly colored.

PODS thick, flattened, the sides sharply recurved after dehiscence.

BASIC chromosome number, as determined by counts on 2 species, $x = 8$ (D. & W.).

A large genus with about 130 species, mainly distributed in tropical America, a few species extending into the southwestern portions of the United States. The species have little or no agronomic use, though *C. conferta* has been reported as a browse plant of some importance in trans-Pecos Texas.

KEY TO SPECIES

1. Leaves predominantly with 2–7 pairs of pinnae; stems herbaceous.
    2. Flowers terminal on peduncles 1–5 cm. long or more (flowers in bud often sessile, but the peduncle becoming pronounced at maturity); leaves copiously pubescent; pinnae 3–7 pairs . . . . **1.** *C. herbacea*
    2. Flowering heads axillary, not on a conspicuous peduncle; leaves moderately puberulent to nearly glabrate; pinnae 2–4 pairs . . . . **2.** *C. humilis*
1. Leaves predominantly with 1 pair of pinnae (very rarely, 2 pairs, but these few on each plant); stems woody.
    3. Flowers 2 on each peduncle, never more; legume 8–10 mm. wide . . . . **3.** *C. biflora*
    3. Flowers 3–15 on each peduncle; legume 5–7 mm. wide . . . . **4.** *C. conferta*

1. *Calliandra herbacea* Engelm. *ex* Gray, Amer. Acad. Arts & Sci. Mem., ser. 2, 4:1849

   Anneslia herbacea (Engelm.) Britt. & Rose

   Higher elevations of trans-Pecos Texas and New Mexico, usually in rocky, igneous soils (Map 3). June–August. This species is closely related to the species below and perhaps should be considered no more than a variety of it. Except for the peduncle, the characters which separate the two taxa seem to intergrade.

   Chromosome number not determined.

2. *Calliandra humilis* (Schlecht.) Benson, Amer. Jour. Bot. 30:630. 1943

   Anneslia humilis (Schlecht.) Britt. & Rose

   Grasslands at higher elevations of trans-Pecos Texas, usually in rocky, igneous soils (Map 3). June–August. A widespread, variable species occurring in Mexico, New

Mexico, and Arizona. Found in Texas at somewhat lower elevations than the above species to which it is apparently closely related. The typical variety of *C. humilis* occurs in central Mexico. Northward, this taxon is replaced by var. *reticulata* (Gray) Benson.

Chromosome number not determined.

3. *Calliandra biflora* Tharp, Rhodora 56:132. 1954

Restricted endemic from southern Texas, where it occurs in deep, sandy soils (Map 4). May–July.

Chromosome number not determined.

4. *Calliandra conferta* Benth. *ex* Gray, Pl. Wright. 1:63. 1852

Southern, central, and trans-Pecos areas of Texas, usually in rocky, limestone soils, at an elevation of 4,000 feet or less (Map 4). April–July. This species has often passed for *C. eriophylla* Benth., a variable, widespread species of Mexico, New Mexico, and Arizona. *C. conferta*, as noted by Gray in his original description, differs from typical *C. eriophylla* in having only 1 pair of pinnae and generally smaller, more pubescent flowers. *C. conferta*, in its typical form, has short peduncles (10 mm. or less) and occurs in central and southern Texas. In trans-Pecos Texas this typical form is replaced by populations with much longer peduncles which are perhaps worthy of varietal rank.

Chromosome number not determined.

4. ACACIA   Acacia

TREES, shrubs, or, rarely, suffruticose herbs, usually armed with straight spines or recurved prickles.

LEAVES twice compound (rarely, simple in Australian species); pinnae 1 to several pairs; leaflets mostly small, few to numerous; petiolar gland usually present.

FLOWERS in globose or spicate heads, yellow or white, often

very fragrant; stamens numerous (20 or more), separate to the base.

FRUIT variable, an indehiscent or dehiscent, woody or turgid, mostly linear legume.

BASIC chromosome number, as determined from counts on approximately 60 species, $x = 13$ (D. & W.).

A very large genus with about 600 species widely distributed in the tropics and dry regions of both hemispheres. It is especially abundant in Australia where some 300 species occur. Several species extend from Mexico into the southwestern desert regions. Some of the shrubs are important browse plants, especially in the dry areas of central Texas and trans-Pecos Texas. *A. farnesiana* is extensively cultivated as an ornamental because of the exquisite fragrance of its flowers.

KEY TO SPECIES

1. Flowers, when open, in definite spikes, two to six times as long as wide.
   2. Legume somewhat woody, 7 mm. wide or less; spines straight, paired at each node . . . . . . 1. *A. rigidula*
   2. Legume fleshy, 12 mm. wide or more; spines recurved or absent, infrastipular, not paired at the nodes.
      3. Leaflets mostly 6–12 mm. long; pods not contorting (twisting); seeds narrowly obovate to ovate . . 2. *A. wrightii*
      3. Leaflets mostly 3–6 mm. long; mature pods often contorting; seeds nearly orbicular . . . . 3. *A. greggii*
1. Flowers, when open, in globose heads or very short spikes one and one half times as long as wide or less.
   4. Stipules spinose, straight, usually long (rarely, absent or much reduced).
      5. Bracts borne at summit of peduncle; plants of central and southern Texas (*A. farnesiana* often introduced elsewhere).
         6. Fruit glabrous, less than 7 cm. long; petiolar gland borne near middle of petiole or absent . . 4. *A. farnesiana*
         6. Fruit densely pubescent, 7 cm. long or more; petiolar gland borne between the two lowest pinnae . .
            . . . . 5. *A. tortuosa*

    5. Bracts borne near middle of peduncle, plants of western
       Texas.
       7. Pinnae 1–2(3) pairs.
          8. Leaflets linear, almost filiform, alternate, spaced 1 mm.
            or more apart; legume conspicuously brown or black
            glandular-dotted .   .   .   .   .   6. *A. schottii*
          8. Leaflets ovate, flattened, inconspicuously alternate,
            spaced 0.8 mm. apart or less; legume not conspicu-
            ously black-glandular .   .   .   .   7. *A. vernicosa*
       7. Pinnae 4–7 pairs   .   .   .   .   .   8. *A. constricta*
  4. Stipules not spinose; spines (prickles) recurved, infrastipular
    (not paired at the nodes) or absent.
      9. Low, suffrutescent plants, 2–4 feet tall; flowers white, pedi-
        cellate; petiolar gland absent.
        10. Pinnae 3–8(10) pairs; stem glabrous; plants of southern
          and western Texas   .   .   .   .   9. *A. texensis*
        10. Pinnae 7 to many pairs; stem glabrous or with wide-
          spreading hairs   .   .   .   10. *A. angustissima*
      9. Shrubs or trees, usually 4 feet tall or more; flowers yellow
        or whitish; petiolar gland present.
        11. Leaflets numerous (20–50 pairs); pinnae 3 to many pairs
          .   .   .   .   11. *A. berlandieri*
        11. Leaflets 4–15 pairs; pinnae 1–4(5) pairs.
          12. Leaflets 3–10 mm. long.
            13. Leaves rather evenly pubescent throughout   .
              .   .   .   .   .   .   12. *A. malacophylla*
            13. Leaves completely glabrate or nearly so   .   .
              .   .   .   .   .   .   13. *A. roemeriana*
          12. Leaflets 3 mm. long or less   .   .   8. *A. constricta*

  1. *Acacia rigidula* Benth., Lond. Jour. Bot. 1:504. 1842.
BLACK-BRUSH
    Acaciopsis rigidula (Benth.) Britt. & Rose
    Southern Texas and trans-Pecos Texas, usually in
rocky limestone soils (Map 5). February–July. Texas and
adjacent Mexico. A small tree or shrub common in southern Texas. The species is often included with *A. amentacea*
DC., a closely related species from central Mexico which
differs from *A. rigidula* in having a more pubescent
petiole, and pinnae with only 2 pairs of leaflets.

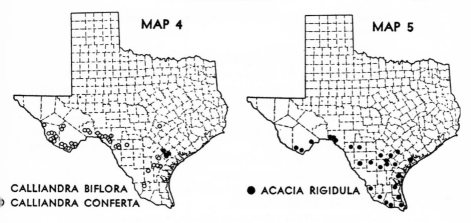

MAP 4

MAP 5

CALLIANDRA BIFLORA
CALLIANDRA CONFERTA

● ACACIA RIGIDULA

Chromosome number, $2n = 26$ (Turner and Fearing, unpublished).

2. *Acacia wrightii* Benth. *ex* Gray, Pl. Wright. 1:64. 1852. WRIGHT ACACIA

Senegalia wrightii (Benth.) Britt. & Rose

Central, southern, and trans-Pecos areas of Texas, in mostly limestone soils, particularly along dry stream beds (Map 6). March–August. Southwestern United States and Mexico. In southernmost Texas, specimens are found having very pubescent leaves and flowers; elsewhere in Texas the leaves and flowers are essentially glabrous. *A. wrightii* is closely related to *A. greggii* (see below) and the two are sometimes separated with difficulty, especially when good fruiting material is lacking. The ranges of the two overlap, and it may be that occasional hybridization obscures specific delimitation. Further field work is needed to clarify the problem.

Chromosome number not determined.

3. *Acacia greggii* Gray, Pl. Wright. 1:65. 1852. CATS-CLAW

Senegalia greggii (Gray) Britt. & Rose

Southern, central, and trans-Pecos areas of Texas, mostly

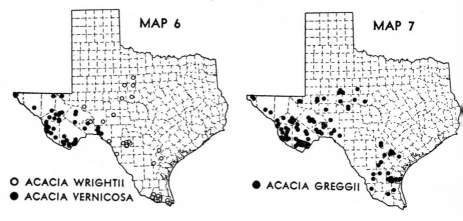

in dry, rocky, limestone soils (Map 7). March–July. Southwestern United States and northern Mexico. In trans-Pecos Texas plants may be found with very pubescent leaves and flowers. *A. greggii* is closely related to *A. wrightii* and is often separated with difficulty from that species.

Chromosome number not determined.

4. *Acacia farnesiana* (L.) Willd., Sp. Pl. 4:1083. 1806. HUISACHE

    Vachellia farnesiana (L.) Wright & Arn.

    Acacia densiflora (Alexander) Cory

    Southern Texas in sandy or heavy clay soils (Map 8); occasionally introduced elsewhere, particularly as an ornamental or shade tree in yards and along the highways in central and western Texas. February–May. A widely distributed species in tropical and subtropical regions of both hemispheres. The leaves and tender branches are reportedly browsed by cattle, especially during winter months. In southern Europe the flowers are used for making perfumes.

    Chromosome number, $2n = 52$ (D. & W.).

5. *Acacia tortuosa* (L.) Willd., Sp. Pl. 4:1083. 1805

    Poponax tortuosa (L.) Raf.

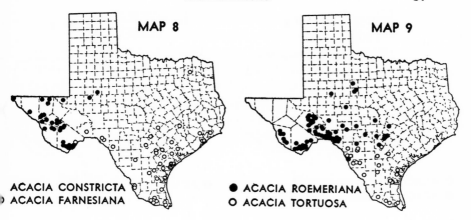

MAP 8

MAP 9

ACACIA CONSTRICTA
○ ACACIA FARNESIANA

● ACACIA ROEMERIANA
O ACACIA TORTUOSA

Southern Texas mostly in limestone soils (Map 9). March–April. Various islands of the West Indies, Texas, and adjacent Mexico. *A. tortuosa* is closely related to *A. schaffneri* (Wats.) Hermann, a species of central Mexico which has much stouter branches and larger pods. Britton and Rose (1928) apparently confused the Texas material with the latter species.

Chromosome number, $2n = 26$ (D. & W.).

6. *Acacia schottii* Torr., Bot. Mex. Bound. Surv. 62. 1859. SCHOTT ACACIA

Acaciopsis schottii (Torr.) Britt. & Rose

Brewster County, Texas, and probably adjacent Mexico, at altitudes of 3,000–4,000 feet; a localized species, apparently confined to the desert washes along the Rio Grande (Map 10). May–September. This species most closely resembles *A. vernicosa*, from which it may be distinguished by the characters used in the key. The species is locally abundant, often dominating the community in which it occurs.

Chromosome number not determined.

7. *Acacia vernicosa* Standl., Contr. U. S. Nat. Herb. 20:187. 1919

Acaciopsis vernicosa (Standl.) Britt. & Rose

Acacia constricta var. *vernicosa* (Standl.) Benson

Frequent throughout trans-Pecos Texas in almost all soils, at altitudes of 2,000–5,000 feet (Map 6). April–July. Western Texas to Arizona and Mexico. Closely related to *A. constricta* and sometimes treated as a variety of that species (see remarks below).

Chromosome number, $2n = 26$ (Turner and Fearing, unpublished).

8. *Acacia constricta* Benth. *ex* Gray, Pl. Wright. 1:66. 1852.
MESCAT ACACIA

Acaciopsis constricta (Benth. *ex* Gray) Britt. & Rose

Western Texas in almost all soil types, 2,000–5,000 feet (Map 8). May–September. Southwestern United States and adjacent Mexico. A form without thorns has been segregated as a different variety (var. *paucispina* W. & S.). *A. constricta* is frequently associated with *A. vernicosa*, but observation has shown, in Texas at least, that the former blooms one to two weeks earlier than the latter.

Chromosome number, $2n = 52$ (Turner and Fearing, unpublished).

9. *Acacia texensis* Torr. & Gray, Fl. N. Am. 1:404. 1840.
TEXAS ACACIA

Acacia cuspidata Schl. [of authors] (as indicated by Britton and Rose, 1928, the type description of this species does not fit the Texas material, particularly concerning the "glandular petiole"; it seems best to retain the name *texensis* for our material until Schlechtendal's type can be clearly applied.)

Acacia filicioides var. *texensis* (Torr. & Gray) Small

Acaciella texensis (Torr. & Gray) Britt. & Rose

Southern and western Texas in limestone or igneous soils (Map 11). May–August. Texas to Arizona and Mexico. The species is closely related to *A. angustissima* (below) and is perhaps better treated as a variety of that

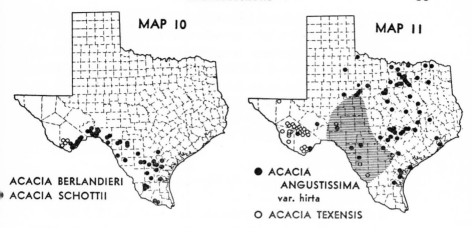

MAP 10

ACACIA BERLANDIERI
ACACIA SCHOTTII

MAP 11

● ACACIA
ANGUSTISSIMA
var. hirta

O ACACIA TEXENSIS

species. *A. texensis* intergrades with *A. angustissima* in west-central Texas; elsewhere the taxa are easily separated by the characters used in the key.

Chromosome number, $2n = 26$ (Turner and Fearing, unpublished).

10. *Acacia angustissima* (Mill.) Kuntze, Rev. Gen. Pl. 3:47. 1898. FERN ACACIA

Acacia hirta Nutt. *ex* Torr. & Gray

Acacia suffrutescens Rose

Acacia filicioides [of Small]

Principally central Texas in limestone soils or less frequently in gravels or sands (Map 11). May–September. Southwestern, south-central, and coastal regions of the eastern United States, Mexico, and Central America. This species is represented in Texas by the variety *hirta* (Nutt. *ex* Torr. & Gray) Robinson. Benson (1943) and Wiggins (1942) also credit to Texas the typical variety of the species (var. *angustissima*) which is a shrub 3–15 feet tall. Wiggins cites a specimen from Travis County collected by B. C. Tharp as var. *angustissima*, but this is apparently a glabrate individual of var. *hirta*, which is represented in Texas by two forms, one type with glabrate stems and the other having stems with wide-spreading, long, tawny hairs. Both forms may occur in the same population. *A. angustissima* does not form a small shrub or tree in Texas but is a low (2–3 feet or less) suffrutescent plant, forming localized clones by the production of long rhizomes.

Chromosome number not determined.

11. *Acacia berlandieri* Benth., Lond. Jour. Bot. 1:522. 1842.
    GUAJILLO
    Acacia emoryana Benth.
    Senegalia berlandieri (Benth.) Britt. & Rose
    Southern Texas to Brewster County along the Rio Grande on mostly dry limestone ridges (Map 10). March–December. Texas and northeastern Mexico. A very common shrub, especially between Langtry and Laredo where it dominates vast stretches of low, shrubby vegetation.

    A. emoryana was described from material collected at Socale Creek, Texas. It was separated from *A. berlandieri* on the basis of its short spicate inflorescence (typical *A. berlandieri* has globose heads). As interpreted by the present writer, *A. berlandieri* is a highly variable species with few to many pinnae, glabrous to puberulent leaves and globose or short-spicate flowering heads (1–2 cm. long, scarcely more than twice as long as wide). These characters are found throughout the range of the present species; attempts to correlate the shortly spicate heads, etc., with any given region failed.

    Chromosome number, $2n = 26$ (Turner and Fearing, unpublished).

12. *Acacia malacophylla* Benth. *ex* Gray, Pl. Wright. 1:64.
    1852
    Senegalia malacophylla (Benth. *ex* Gray) Britt. & Rose
    Reported for Texas and maintained as a good species by Standley (1922) and Britton and Rose (1928). The type locality is given as "Uplands of the Leona, Western Texas." Field work in the vicinity of the type locality (Uvalde

County) has failed to reveal any specimens of *Acacia* that match the type material. However, *A. roemeriana*, which greatly resembles the proposed species except for pubescence, is common in this area, and it may be that *A. malacophylla* is merely a pubescent form of this species. Cory and Parks (1937) list *A. malacophylla* var. *glabrata* Benth. from Texas; this is obviously an error for *Mimosa malacophylla* var. *glabrata* Benth. Infraspecific taxa of *A. malacophylla* have not been proposed.

Chromosome number not determined.

13. *Acacia roemeriana* Scheele, Linnaea 21:456. 1848. ROEMER ACACIA

Senegalia roemeriana (Scheele) Britt. & Rose

Central Texas and the trans-Pecos area of Texas in mostly dry, rocky, limestone soils (Map 9). March–June. Texas and adjacent Mexico. Becoming a tree in wet areas, with a trunk to 16 inches in diameter, but more often a shrub with somewhat straggling stems.

Chromosome number not determined.

5. LEUCAENA   Lead-tree

SHRUBS or small trees, unarmed.

LEAVES twice compound with 1 to several pairs of pinnae; leaflets few and large, or numerous and small; petiolar gland usually present.

FLOWERS in dense globose heads, white or bright yellow.

FRUIT a linear, broad, flat legume with usually 10 or more seeds, the margins not breaking from the valves at maturity.

BASIC chromosome number, as determined from counts on a single species, $x = 13$ (D. & W.).

A small genus with about 20 species in tropical and subtropical regions of North America, South America, and Poly-

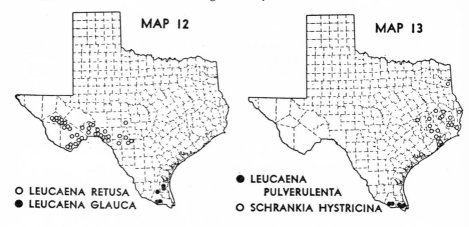

nesia. The Texas species are of little economic importance, though some of them are planted as ornamentals in various parts of the state. According to Standley (1922), some of the South American species are used to stupefy fish.

KEY TO SPECIES

1. Leaflets 4–9 pairs on each pinna; flower heads bright yellow
  .   .   .   .   1. *L. retusa*
1. Leaflets 10 to many pairs on each pinna.
  2. Leaflets 8 mm. long or less.
    3. Leaves with 10–20 pairs of pinnae; calyx tube densely pubescent; legume acute or with a beak 1 cm. long or less
    .   .   .   .   2. *L. pulverulenta*
    3. Leaves with 5–9 pairs of pinnae; calyx tube glabrous; legume with a beak 1.5–5 cm. long   .   .   .   3. *L. greggii*
  2. Leaflets, most of them, 8–20 mm. long   .   .   4. *L. glauca*

1. *Leucaena retusa* Benth. *ex* Gray, Pl. Wright. 1:64. 1852
    Caudoleuceana retusa (Benth. *ex* Gray) Britt. & Rose
    Central Texas and the trans-Pecos area of Texas in mostly rocky limestone soils (Map 12). April–July. Endemic to Texas and adjacent Mexico. The flowers are bright yellow, not white as has been reported several times in the litera-

ture. A very attractive small tree that should do well in cultivation.

Chromosome number not determined.

2. *Leucaena pulverulenta* (Schl.) Benth., Hook. Jour. Bot. 4:417. 1842. TEPEGUAJE

Southernmost Texas and adjacent Mexico (Map 13). March–June. A tree to 15 meters tall. Occasionally grown as an ornamental elsewhere.

Chromosome number not determined.

3. *Leucaena greggii* Wats., Proc. Am. Acad. 23:272. 1888. GREGG LEAD-TREE

Rhyncholeucaena greggii (Wats.) Britt. & Rose

A species of northeastern Mexico and reported for southern Texas by several workers (Cory and Parks, 1937; Britton and Rose, 1928); the present writer has not seen specimens from Texas.

Chromosome number not determined.

4. *Leucaena glauca* (L.) Benth., Hook. Jour. Bot. 4:416. 1842. WHITE POPINAC

Southernmost Texas in sandy soils (Map 12). May–June. Widely distributed in tropical and subtropical regions of both hemispheres. The plant is commonly grown as an ornamental or shade tree in parts of central and southern Texas.

Chromosome number, $2n = 104$ (D. & W.).

6. SCHRANKIA   Sensitive Briar

SEMIERECT to prostrate, perennial briars, the stems weak, not at all woody, 3–12 feet long, armed with numerous recurved spines or prickles (very rarely, unarmed).

LEAVES twice compound with 2 to several pinnae, the rachis and rachillas armed with prickles; leaflets 4 to numerous, glabrous, smooth or with raised reticulate veins.

FLOWERS in dense globose heads, pinkish-red to pinkish-white; peduncles armed with recurved prickles.

FRUIT a flattened or tetragonal, mostly prickly pod, the margin separating from the valves at maturity as in the genus *Mimosa.*

BASIC chromosome number, as determined by counts on 5 species, $x = 8$, 13 (Turner and Beaman, 1953; Turner and Fearing, unpublished).

A small genus of subtropical and temperate America with possibly 20 species; most of the species are centered in the southeastern United States and Mexico, a few extending to Argentina. The plants have sensitive leaves, but not so spectacular as those of the better-known sensitive plant, *Mimosa pudica*, which is not known to occur as a native or an escapee in the United States (earlier reports in the literature are apparently erroneous). *Schrankia* is closely related to the genus *Mimosa* from which it is classically distinguished by its tetragonal pod. In Texas, species are found which have very definite flattened pods much as in *Mimosa*. The generic name *Schrankia* is conserved over those of *Morongia* and *Leptoglottis.*

KEY TO SPECIES

1. Leaflets with raised reticulate veins beneath.
   2. Legume 1–4 cm. long, rounded at apex; peduncles 4–12 cm. long; flower heads in early bud with protruding bracts .
   .   .   .   .   1. *S. hystricina*
   2. Legume 4–12 cm. long, acute or beaked at apex; peduncle 2–7(10) cm. long; flower heads in early bud with bracts completely hidden .   .   .   .   2. *S. uncinata*
1. Leaflets smooth, or the midvein prominent only.
   3. Lower portion of stem distinctly 4- or 5-sided, glabrous; stipules small, 1–3(4) mm. long; pod 4-sided, scarcely flattened at maturity; plants of southern Texas .   3. *S. latidens*
   3. Lower portion of stem rounded, not distinctly 4- or 5-sided; stipules 3–6 mm. long; pod various.

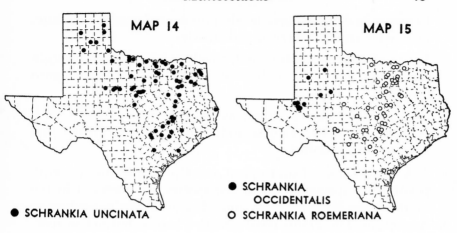

MAP 14

● SCHRANKIA UNCINATA

MAP 15

● SCHRANKIA
OCCIDENTALIS
○ SCHRANKIA ROEMERIANA

4. Mature legume 4–7 (8) cm. long, flattened, the valves three
to six times as wide as the thickened margin; pinnae
2–5(6) pairs; leaflets mostly obtuse at apex; plants of
central and north-central Texas . . 4. *S. roemeriana*
4. Mature legume 6–12 cm. long, tetragonal, not conspicuously flattened, or if so the valves less than two times as
wide as the margin; pinnae (3)4–8 pairs; leaflets mostly
acute at apex (rarely, obtuse throughout); plants of
easternmost or westernmost Texas.
5. Stems, ovary and pod puberulent; plants of western
Texas . . . . 5. *S. occidentalis*
5. Stems, ovary and pod completely glabrous; plants of
eastern Texas . . . . . 6. *S. microphylla*

1. *Schrankia hystricina* (Small *ex* Britt. & Rose) Standl.,
Public. Field Mus. Nat. Hist., Chicago, Bot. Ser. 8:13. 1930
Leptoglottis hystricina Small *ex* Britt. & Rose

Southeast Texas and southern Louisiana in deep sandy
soil of pine or oak woods and heavy clay soils of the upper
Gulf Coast (Map 13). February–May. This species is
closely related to *S. uncinata*, replacing that species in
southeast Texas.

Chromosome number, $2n = 26$ (Turner and Fearing,
unpublished).

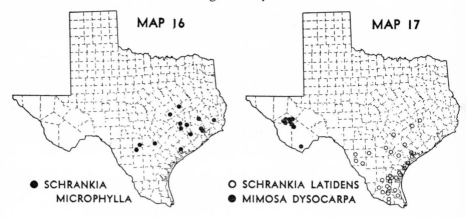

2. *Schrankia uncinata* Willd., Sp. Pl. 4:1043. 1806. CATS-CLAW SCHRANKIA

Morongia uncinata (Willd.) Britt.

Schrankia nuttallii (DC.) Standl.

Leptoglottis mimosoides Small

Central and northeastern Texas in open sandy soils of oak and pine woods and heavy clay soils of native grasslands (Map 14). April–June. Widely distributed in the central and southeastern United States.

Chromosome number, $2n = 26$ (Turner and Fearing, unpublished).

3. *Schrankia latidens* (Small) Schum., Bot. Jahresb. 29:540. 1903

Morongia latidens Small

Leptoglottis berlandieri Britt.

Southern Texas in mostly sandy or gravelly soils (Map 17). April–September. This species is closely related to *S. microphylla* and apparently replaces this species in southern Texas. Specimens seemingly intermediate between the two species have been seen where their ranges meet in south-central Texas.

Chromosome number not determined.

4. *Schrankia roemeriana* (Scheele) Blankenship, Rept. Mo. Bot. Gard. 18:168. 1907. ROEMER SCHRANKIA

Morongia roemeriana (Scheele) Heller

Schrankia platycarpa Gray

Leptoglottis reverchonii Britt. & Rose

North-central and central Texas mostly in limestone soils or gravels (Map 15). April–July. The flattened pod of this species distinguishes it from the other Texas species, though it is difficult to distinguish from *S. microphylla* or *S. occidentalis* when in flower.

Chromosome number, $2n = 26$ (Turner and Fearing, unpublished).

5. *Schrankia occidentalis* (W. & S.) Standl., Public. Field Mus. Nat. Hist., Chicago, Bot. Ser. 8:13. 1930

Deep sandy soils of the lower Panhandle of Texas, extending into Texas from New Mexico (Map 15). May–July. The species is closely related to *S. microphylla* and is perhaps best treated as a variety of that species.

Chromosome number, $2n = 26$ (Turner and Fearing, 1953).

6. *Schrankia microphylla* (Dryand.) Standl., Public. Field Mus. Nat. Hist., Chicago, Bot. Ser. 8:13. 1930. LITTLE-LEAF SCHRANKIA

Morongia angustata (Torr. & Gray) Britt.

Schrankia halliana (Britt. & Rose) Standl.

Eastern Texas in sandy or gravelly soils of open woods (Map 16). August–September. Widespread species of the central and southeastern United States. The name *S. halliana* has been applied to forms of this species which lack prickles on their pods. Pods without prickles are also found in occasional collections of *S. latidens* (specimens deposited University of Texas Herbarium).

Chromosome number, $2n = 16$ (D. & W., as *S. angustata*).

7. MIMOSA   Mimosa

SHRUBS, trees, or, rarely, perennial herbs, usually armed with recurved spines or prickles.

LEAVES twice compound with 1 to numerous pinnae; leaflets usually small and numerous.

FLOWERS in globose or rarely spicate heads, white, pink to reddish; stamens 10 or fewer, usually colored.

FRUIT a legume whose margins separate from the valves at maturity, the valves often breaking transversely.

BASIC chromosome number, as determined from counts on 8 species, $x = 13$ (14?) (D. & W.; Turner and Fearing, unpublished).

A large genus with about 400 species in tropical and subtropical regions, principally in North and South America, but a few species also occurring in Africa and Asia. The widespread, tropical, sensitive plant (*M. pudica* L.) is listed for Texas by Cory and Parks (1937), but this writer has not seen specimens.

KEY TO SPECIES

1. Plants with herbaceous, prostrate stems   .   .   1. *M. strigillosa*
1. Plants with woody, erect, or clambering stems, never prostrate.
  2. Stems clambering or straggling, briarlike; leaflets, the larger ones, ovate, 10 mm. long or more   .   .   2. *M. malacophylla*
  2. Stems stiffly erect, ascending or recurved, but never straggling and briarlike; leaflets linear to nearly orbicular, 2–8 mm. long.
    3. Leaves, at least some of them, with 8–14 pairs of pinnae; flower heads cylindric, spikelike   .   .   3. *M. dysocarpa*
    3. Leaves with 1–8 pairs of pinnae (rarely, more in *M. pigra*); flower heads globose.
      4. Pinnae, at least some of them, with 20 or more leaflets; spines flattened, white at base, scarcely, if at all, recurved; valves of legume breaking at maturity into 8 or

more transverse segments . . . . . . 4. *M. pigra*

4. Pinnae with 3–20 leaflets; spines, when present, flattened to nearly conical, brown to white at base, usually recurved; valves of legume breaking at maturity into 7 or fewer segments or remaining intact.

  5. Leaves, at least some of them, with 4–8 pairs of pinnae; valves of legume straight, separating entire from the margin at maturity.

    6. Spines conical, not conspicuously flattened near base, nor recurved; pods short-villous with straight spines along the margin; leaflets very small, not exceeding 1.5 mm.; branches flexuous . . . . . 5. *M. warnockii*

    6. Spines not conical, flattened near the base, usually recurved; pods glabrate, not at all villous, margins with short recurved spines or spines lacking; leaflets 2 mm. long or more; branches straight to somewhat flexuous . .
    . . . . 6. *M. biuncifera*

  5. Leaves with 1–3 pairs of pinnae.

    7. Valves of the pod densely covered with short yellow prickles; leaflets densely sericeous . . 7. *M. emoryana*

    7. Valves of the pod glabrous or merely scattered puberulent; leaflets glabrous to sparsely pubescent.

      8. Leaves with 1 pair of pinnae; leaflets 1 or 2 pairs to each pinna; petioles conspicuously flattened, broadened at the apex . . . . 10. *M. zygophylla*

      8. Leaves with (1)2–3 pairs of pinnae; leaflets (2)3–8 pairs to each pinna; petioles not flattened or, rarely, flattened.

        9. Petals separate to the base or nearly so; legume often shiny and light-colored (yellowish), constricting and twisting between the seeds at maturity or the valves contorting and breaking into 1-seeded segments; stems essentially straight, not zigzag . . 8. *M. borealis*

        9. Petals united for one half their length or more; legume dark brown, straight with nearly parallel valves, not contorting or breaking into segments at maturity; stems usually zigzag.

          10. Flower heads in bud 4–5 mm. wide; leaflets 1.5–3 mm. long; plants of southernmost Texas . .
          . . . . 9. *M. wherryana*

          10. Flower heads in bud 5–8 mm. wide; leaflets 3–6 mm. long; plants of central and west Texas .
          . . . . 6. *M. biuncifera* (var. *lindheimeri*)

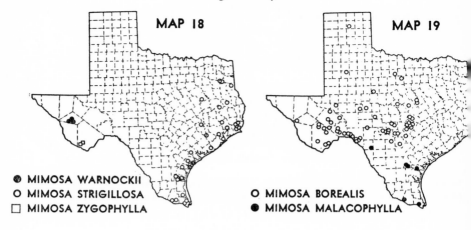

MAP 18

MAP 19

● MIMOSA WARNOCKII
O MIMOSA STRIGILLOSA
□ MIMOSA ZYGOPHYLLA

O MIMOSA BOREALIS
● MIMOSA MALACOPHYLLA

1. *Mimosa strigillosa* Torr. & Gray, Fl. N. Am. 1:399. 1840

Eastern and southern Texas in sandy or heavy clay soils (Map 18). May–October. A widespread, variable species of the southeastern United States and Mexico with a secondary center of distribution in South America (Paraguay and Argentina).

Chromosome number not determined.

2. *Mimosa malacophylla* Gray, Jour. Bost. Soc. Nat. Hist. 6:182. 1850. RASPILLA

Southern Texas and northeastern Mexico mostly in limestone soils (Map 19). June–July. Most of the Texas material belongs to var. *glabrata* Benth. (= *M. wootonii* Standl.). Var. *glabrata* can be separated from the typical variety (var. *malacophylla*) in being nearly glabrate throughout instead of densely short-pubescent.

Chromosome number not determined.

3. *Mimosa dysocarpa* Benth. *ex* Gray, Pl. Wright. 1:62. 1852. GATUÑO

Trans-Pecos Texas mostly in igneous soils, at altitudes of 5,000–6,000 feet (Map 17). June–July. Texas to Arizona and northern Mexico. A very handsome species with long

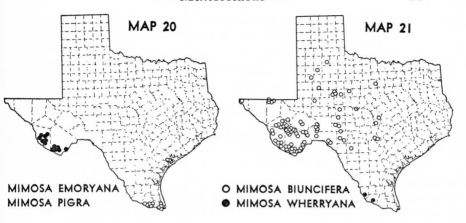

MAP 20

MAP 21

MIMOSA EMORYANA
MIMOSA PIGRA

O MIMOSA BIUNCIFERA
● MIMOSA WHERRYANA

spikes of purplish-pink flowers. The typical variety of the species (var. *dysocarpa*) occurs in Texas. Var. *wrightii* (Gray) K. & P., with less pubescence and greener foliage, occurs in Arizona and adjacent Mexico.

Chromosome number not determined.

4. *Mimosa pigra* L., Cent. Pl. 1:13. 1755. ZARZA

Southern Texas mostly in wet sandy soils (Map 20). March–November. Widely distributed in the tropics and subtropics of both the Old and New Worlds. In Texas *M. pigra* is represented by the var. *berlandieri* (Gray) Turner, which has fewer setose prickles on the pod than the typical variety (var. *pigra*).

Chromosome number not determined.

5. *Mimosa warnockii* Turner, Field & Lab. 24:15. 1956

Mimosa flexuosa Benth. *ex* Gray; not *Mimosa flexuosa* Poir.

Mimosopsis flexuosa (Benth.) Britt. & Rose

Mimosa biuncifera var. *flexuosa* (Benth.) Robinson

Trans-Pecos Texas, known only from Jeff Davis County where it occurs in rocky igneous soils (Map 18). May–August. The species is common in the grasslands at lower elevations (4,500–5,500 feet) in the Jeff Davis Mountains.

It forms low, dense clumps 2–3 feet across and scarcely more than 1–2 feet tall. Related to *M. biuncifera* with which it is sometimes included (Robinson, 1898).

Chromosome number, $2n = 26$ (Turner and Fearing, unpublished).

6. *Mimosa biuncifera* Benth., Pl. Hartw. 12. 1839. CATS-CLAW MIMOSA

Mimosopsis biuncifera (Benth.) Britt. & Rose

Central Texas and lower Panhandle and trans-Pecos areas of Texas mostly in rocky, limestone, or igneous soils (Map 21). April–September. A widespread, variable species occurring from Texas to Arizona and northern Mexico. Two varieties of the species found in Texas are: (1) var. *lindheimeri* (Gray) Robinson ($= M.$ *lindheimeri* Gray) with fewer pinnae (1–3 pairs) and broad, nearly glabrate leaflets and (2) var. *biuncifera* with more pinnae (3–8 pairs) and pubescent, linear leaflets. The latter variety is the more common of the two, often forming extensive stands along stream bottoms. The two varieties are not well marked and grade into each other. In addition, *M. biuncifera* var. *lindheimeri* appears to intergrade with *M. borealis* in trans-Pecos Texas.

Chromosome number, $2n = 52$ (D. & W.).

7. *Mimosa emoryana* Benth., Trans. Linn. Soc. 30:426. 1875. EMORY MIMOSA

Endemic to trans-Pecos Texas in Brewster and Presidio counties, where it occurs in gravelly, limestone soils, at altitudes of 2,000–4,000 feet (Map 20). May–July. A small shrub easily recognized by its distinctive, yellow-setose legume and very pubescent foliage.

Chromosome number, $2n = 52$ (Turner and Fearing, unpublished).

8. *Mimosa borealis* Gray., Mem. Amer. Acad. II. 4:39. 1849. PINK MIMOSA

Mimosa fragrans Gray

Mimosa borealis var. *texana* Gray

Mimosa texana (Gray) Small

Central, Panhandle, and trans-Pecos areas of Texas in gravelly or rocky limestone soils (Map 19). April–July. Oklahoma to New Mexico and probably adjacent Mexico. A highly variable species whose extremes are sometimes recognized as separate species. Material segregated as *M. fragrans* has longer pinnae, more linear, wider-spaced leaflets than is typical for the species, but there is complete intergradation of these characters even within the same population. In addition, when *M. borealis* grows in shady, moist areas the vegetative characters assume the aspect of material segregated as *M. fragrans*. In parts of its range *M. borealis* appears to intergrade with *M. biuncifera* (see remarks under that species).

Chromosome number not determined.

9. *Mimosa wherryana* (Britt.) Standl., Trop. Woods 34:40. 1933

Mimosopsis wherryana Britt.

Southernmost Texas usually along stream bottoms (Map 21). May–September. Texas and northeastern Mexico. Closely related to *M. biuncifera* from which it can be distinguished by the characters used in the key.

Chromosome number not determined.

10. *Mimosa zygophylla* Benth. *ex* Gray, Pl. Wright. 1:61. 1852

Mimosopsis zygophylla (Benth.) Britt. & Rose

Known to Texas by only a few collections from limestone soils in southern Brewster County of trans-Pecos Texas (Map 18). August. Apparently closely related to *M. biuncifera* var. *lindheimeri*, but superficially resembling *M. borealis*. Texas material of this species often has 2 pairs of leaflets to each pinna instead of 1, as is given in the type description of *M. zygophylla;* otherwise their descriptions match. The extremely reduced, glabrate leaf

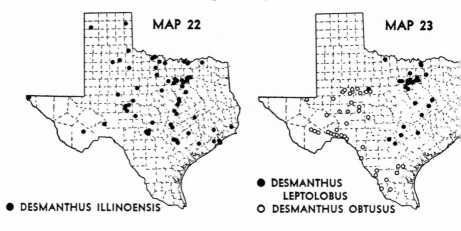

of *M. zygophylla* is often approached on specimens of *M. borealis*. However, the former taxon has nearly sessile flowers with its petals united for two thirds its length or more, while the latter has pedicellate flowers and petals separate to the base or nearly so. *M. zygophylla* is morphologically similar to *M. pringlei* Wats.; this latter taxon is cited for Texas by Robinson (1898) and Standley (1922), apparently in error for *M. biuncifera* var. *lindheimeri*.

Chromosome number not determined.

8. DESMANTHUS   Desmanthus

UNARMED SHRUBS or perennial herbs.

LEAVES twice compound, usually with several to numerous leaflets per pinna.

FLOWERS few to numerous in loose or compact heads, usually white or whitish; stamens 5 or 10, separate, some of the lower flowers in each head with sterile stamens.

FRUIT a flattened, dry, 1- to many-seeded, dehiscent legume.

Basic chromosome number, as determined from counts on 5 species, $x = 14$ (Turner and Beaman, 1953).

A genus with about 40 species, mainly distributed in the warmer regions of North and South America (Turner, 1950a), but a few taxa (of the *Desmanthus virgatus* complex) are pan-tropical, occurring along the coastlines of several continents. Mexico is exceptionally rich in species, fully half of the world's recognized taxa occurring in that country (Turner, 1950b).

Key to Species

1. Legume falcate, two to five times as long as wide; stems erect
. . . . 1. *D. illinoensis*
1 Legume linear, at least seven times longer than wide; stems decumbent to erect.
   2. Leaflets with raised, somewhat reticulate veins (upper surface sometimes smooth); legumes at maturity on peduncles 3–15 cm. long.
      3. Mature fruiting peduncles 8–15 cm. long; legume tapering to a point; the larger leaves with petioles 1 cm. or more long; leaflets glabrous or sparcely pubescent along the margins only . . . . . . 2. *D. reticulatus*
      3. Mature fruiting peduncles 3–8 cm. long; legumes obtuse or abruptly mucronate, never tapering to a point; leaves with petioles 1(1.5) cm. long or less; leaflets pubescent over the lower surface . . . . 3. *D. obtusus*
   2. Leaflets without raised reticulate veins; legumes on peduncles 0.4–6 cm. long.
      4. Stem densely short villous throughout (rarely, glabrate); petiolar glands orbicular, minute, 0.4 mm. long or less .
. . . . 4. *D. velutinus*
      4. Stems glabrous or sparingly pubescent along the angles, never evenly pubescent throughout; petiolar glands 0.3–3 mm. long.
         5. Stipules small or wanting, less than 2 mm. in length; peduncles 2 cm. long or less (exceptionally, 3 cm.) .
. . . . 5. *D. cooleyi*
         5. Stipules longer, setiform, 2–8 mm. long (sometimes ap-

pearing less when the tips are broken off); peduncles 0.4–6 cm. long.

6. Seeds placed lengthwise in pod, elliptic, 4.5–5 mm. long; legumes somewhat constricted along the margin between the seeds; pinnae 4–10 pairs; stamens 5 . 6. *D. leptolobus*

6. Seeds placed obliquely in pod (most noticeable in immature fruit), variously shaped, but less than 3 mm. in length; legume margins straight; pinnae 1–7 pairs; stamens 10.

   7. Stipules conspicuously pubescent; stems prostrate, arising from a deep tuberous taproot; petiolar gland 0.7–1.5 mm. long . . . . . . 7. *D. acuminatus*

   7. Stipules glabrous (rarely, with 5 or 6 scattered hairs); petiolar gland 0.7 mm. long or less *if* stems prostrate, 0.7–3 mm. long *if* stems erect.

      8. Fruiting peduncles 2–6 mm. long; pinnae 1–2 pairs only . . . . 8. *D. brevipes*

      8. Fruiting peduncles 10 mm. long or more; pinnae 2–7 pairs.

         9. Stipules with a conspicuous auricle at base; petiolar gland at base of lower pinnae only, 0.7 mm. long or less; stems prostrate, rarely ascending; plants of central Texas and Gulf Coast plain . . . . 9. *D. virgatus* var. *depressus*

         9. Stipules not conspicuously auricled at base; petiolar glands 1–4 between at least some of the pinnae, 0.7–2.5 mm. long; stems erect or ascending; plants of western Texas . . 9. *D. virgatus* var. *glandulosus*

1. *Desmanthus illinoensis* (Michx.) MacM., Metasp. Minn. Valley 308. 1892. ILLINOIS DESMANTHUS

   Acuan illinoense (Michx.) Kuntze

   Widely distributed in central and northern Texas, mostly in deep, silty-clay soils of ditches, road shoulders, and low fields (Map 22). June–September. A widespread, variable species occurring from north-central United States to the Mexican border.

   Chromosome number, $2n = 28$ (Turner and Beaman, 1953).

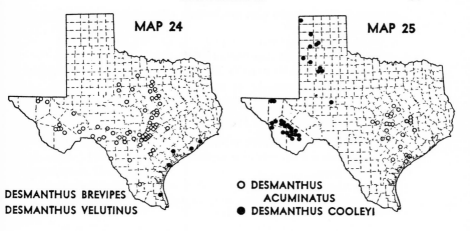

MAP 24

DESMANTHUS BREVIPES
DESMANTHUS VELUTINUS

MAP 25

O DESMANTHUS
ACUMINATUS
● DESMANTHUS COOLEYI

2. *Desmanthus reticulatus* Benth., Hook. Jour. Bot. 4:357.
1842

Acuan reticulatum (Benth.) Kuntze

Central and southern Texas in open grasslands or fields
(Map 27). March–April. A rare endemic, easily distinguished from other species of the genus by the extreme
length of its fruiting peduncle.

Chromosome number not determined.

3. *Desmanthus obtusus* S. Wats., Proc. Amer. Acad. 17:371.
1882

Acuan fallax Small

Western and southern Texas, mostly on limestone or caliche outcrops; rarely, in sandy soils (Map 23). April–
August. Texas, eastern New Mexico, and adjacent Mexico.

Chromosome number not determined.

4. *Desmanthus velutinus* Scheele, Linnaea 21:455. 1848

Acuan velutinum (Scheele) Kuntze

Trans-Pecos, central, and southern areas of Texas, mostly
in rocky limestone or caliche outcrops, rarely elsewhere
(Map 24). April–June. Texas, southeastern New Mexico,
and adjacent Mexico.

Chromosome number, $2n = 28$ (Turner and Beaman, 1953).

5. *Desmanthus cooleyi* (Eaton) Trel., Rep. Ark. Geol. Surv. 1888, 4:178. 1891. COOLEY DESMANTHUS

   Acuan jamesii (Torr. & Gray) Kuntze

   Desmanthus jamesii Torr. & Gray

   Mountainous areas of trans-Pecos Texas and in the high plains of the Panhandle (Map 25). June–August. Southwestern United States and adjacent Mexico.

   Chromosome number, $2n = 28$ (Turner and Beaman, 1953).

6. *Desmanthus leptolobus* Torr. & Gray, Fl. N. Am. 1:402. 1840

   Acuan leptolobum (Torr. & Gray) Kuntze

   North-central and central Texas, mostly in deep calcareous soils (Map 23). May–September. Central and southwestern United States.

   Chromosome number, $2n = 28$ (Turner and Beaman, 1953).

7. *Desmanthus acuminatus* Benth., Hook. Jour. Bot. 4:357. 1842

   Acuan acuminatum (Benth.) Kuntze

   Central Texas, mostly in sandy or silty-clay soils (Map 25). April–May. Known only from Texas, but apparently very closely related types occur also in Argentina (Turner, 1950).

   Chromosome number, $2n = 28$ (Turner and Beaman, 1953).

8. *Desmanthus brevipes* Turner, Field & Lab. 18:60. 1950

   Coastal Texas in sandy or heavy clay soils (Map 24). May–September. Apparently bicentric in distribution, occurring also in South America (Argentina). Burkart (1952) has described closely related forms of this species from Argentina as *D. chacoenis*, apparently at the time unaware of the present author's study of the species.

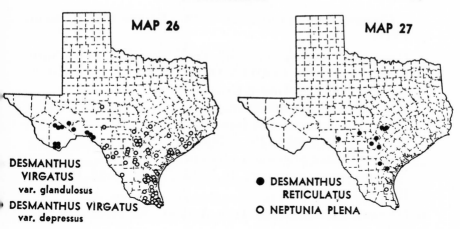

MAP 26

DESMANTHUS
VIRGATUS
var. glandulosus
● DESMANTHUS VIRGATUS
var. depressus

MAP 27

● DESMANTHUS
RETICULATUS
O NEPTUNIA PLENA

Chromosome number, $2n = 28$ (Turner and Beaman, 1953).

9. *Desmanthus virgatus* (L.) Willd., Sp. Pl. 4:1047. 1806
   Acuan tracyi Britt. & Rose
   Acuan texanum Britt. & Rose

Southern, central, and trans-Pecos areas of Texas in nearly all soil types (Map 26). April–November. A widely distributed, highly variable species, occurring in the tropical and subtropical areas of both hemispheres. The species in Texas is represented by two varieties: (1) var. *depressus* (H. & B.) Turner (= *D. depressus* H. & B.), with prostrate or semi-prostrate stems, occurring in central and southern Texas, and (2) var. *glandulosus* Turner, with erect stems, and glands between the upper pairs of pinnae, occurring in rocky, limestone soils of Val Verde County and trans-Pecos Texas. As indicated by the key to species, the two varieties are quite marked and do not seem to intergrade. The typical form of the species (var. *virgatus*) does not occur in Texas, but is common southward in Mexico and in the West Indies (Turner, 1950).

Chromosome number, $2n = 28$ (for var. *depressus*; Turner and Beaman, 1953).

9. NEPTUNIA   Neptunia

PERENNIAL HERBS with prostrate or erect stems, arising from tough, orange-colored roots.

LEAVES twice pinnate, with numerous small leaflets; stipules membranous, obliquely cordate to broadly lanceolate.

FLOWERS in dense capitate, ovoid, or subcylindric spikes, the upper flowers with anther-bearing stamens, the lower with sterile, petaloid stamens (except *N. lutea*); anthers bearing a small gland at the apex between the cells.

FRUIT a variable, flattened, 1- to many-seeded legume.

BASIC chromosome number, as determined from counts on 7 species, $x = 14$ (Turner and Beaman, 1953; Turner and Fearing, unpublished).

A small genus with about 10 species in the tropical and subtropical regions of both hemispheres. Some of the species such as *Neptunia prostrata* (Lam.) Baillon, a widespread tropical plant sometimes used as a vegetable in salads, are adapted to aquatic habitats. The species native to Texas have little, if any, significance.

KEY TO SPECIES

1. Petiole glandular; flowering peduncles bearing 2 large cordate bracts 4–8 mm. long, 3–5 mm. wide; leaflets without raised reticulate veins; plants aquatic or terrestrial   .   .   1. *N. plena*
1. Petiole eglandular; flowering peduncles bearing 1 or 2 subulate bracts 1–3 mm. long, 1–2 mm. wide, or bracts absent; leaflets with raised reticulate veins; plants terrestrial.
    2. Flowers in head with stamens all alike, anther-bearing; flower heads when in bud with 30–60 flowers, subcylindric; stipe of pod 4–15 mm. long; leaflets 8–18 pairs; calyx 1–2 mm. long (including lobes)   .   .   .   .   .   2. *N. lutea*
    2. Flowers in upper part of head with anther-bearing stamens, those in lower part smaller and with yellow (drying orange) petaloid staminodes; flower heads in bud with 20–30 flowers,

ovoid; stipe of pod 0–4 mm. long (rarely, 5 mm.); leaflets 10–35 pairs; calyx 2.0–2.7 mm. long (including lobes).

3. Pod oblong, 6–10 mm. wide; stipe 2–4 mm. long; pinnae 2–6 pairs; plants of Gulf Coast region, south Texas to Florida . . . . 3. *N. pubescens*

3. Pod broadly oblong, 10–16 mm. wide; stipe 0–2 mm. long; pinnae 2–3 (rarely, 4) pairs only; plants of central and south-central Texas . . . . . 4. *N. palmeri*

1. *Neptunia plena* (L.) Benth., Hook. Jour. Bot. 4:355. 1842

Known to Texas (and the United States) by a single collection from Kenedy County, south of Armstrong (Turner, 1951) (Map 27). October. *N. plena* normally grows in wet places, the stems and leaves floating in quiet waters. Mexico and the West Indies to the tropical and subtropical areas of South America.

Chromosome number, about $2n = 72$ (D. & W.).

2. *Neptunia lutea* (Leavenw.) Benth., Hook. Jour. Bot. 4:356. 1842

N. lutea var. *multipinnata* Turner

Throughout eastern and central Texas in nearly all soil types (Map 29). April–October. Alabama to Oklahoma, south along Gulf Coast areas of the United States. *N. lutea* var. *multipinnata* is a form of the species with larger leaves and more numerous pinnae.

Chromosome number, $2n = 28$ (Turner and Beaman, 1953).

3. *Neptunia pubescens* Benth., Hook. Jour. Bot. 4:356. 1842

Gulf Coast plain in sandy or clay soils (Map 28). May–October. Gulf Coast areas of the United States from Florida to Texas, Mexico, and the West Indies to tropical and subtropical South America.

Two intergrading varieties of this species are recognized for Texas (Turner, 1951): var. *lindheimeri* (B. L. Robinson) Turner (= *N. lindheimeri* Robinson) of southern Texas and var. *floridana* (Small) Turner (= *N. floridana*

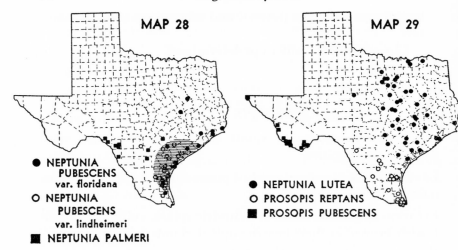

Small) of a more northeastern distribution. The following
key allows for the identification of the more typical individuals:

1. Leaflets conspicuously ciliate, most of the cilia 0.2–0.7 mm. long,
   the under surface near apex conspicuously so; fruiting peduncles 2.5–7 cm. long; calyx lobes pubescent (10–20 cilia on
   each lobe); petals ciliate at apex   .   .   .   .   .   .
   .   .   .   .   3. *N. pubescens* var. *lindheimeri*
1. Leaflets glabrous or sparsely ciliate, the cilia scarcely 0.2 mm.
   long, the under surface completely glabrous or ciliate along
   the margin only; fruiting peduncles 6–11 cm. long; calyx
   glabrous or with but 4–5 hairs along the lobes; petals glabrous
   .   .   .   .   3. *N. pubescens* var. *floridana*

Chromosome number $2n = 28$ (Turner and Beaman,
1953; for var. *floridana* and var. *lindheimeri*).

4. *Neptunia palmeri* Britt. & Rose, N. Amer. Fl. 23:182. 1928
    South-central Texas, mostly in rocky or silty calcareous
soils (Map 28). May–July. Endemic to Texas and adjacent
Mexico. Closely related to *N. pubescens*, but differing in its

broader pods, fewer pinnae, and adaptation to drier habitats.

Chromosome number not determined.

10. PROSOPIS   Mesquite

Low, WOODY SHRUBS or small trees, usually armed with straight, stout spines.

LEAVES with 1 to several pairs of pinnae and mostly numerous, narrow leaflets.

FLOWERS in globose heads or cylindric spikes, yellowish or yellowish-brown; anthers bearing apical glands.

FRUIT a straight or tightly coiled indehiscent pod.

BASIC chromosome number, as determined from counts on 11 species, $x = 14$ (D. & W.).

A genus with about 40 species occurring in the drier, subtropical regions of North America, South America, Africa, and Asia. Some of the species, such as mesquite *(P. juliflora)*, are important browse plants in many of the desert areas of North America. Mesquite readily reproduces by seed and has spread in recent years over large areas of overgrazed rangelands (see additional comments under *P. juliflora*, below).

KEY TO SPECIES

1. Flowers in globose heads; pinnae 2.5 cm. long or less; legume tightly coiled; plants of southern Texas   .   .   .   1. *P. reptans*
1. Flowers in elongate spikes; pinnae 2.5 cm. long or longer; legume straight or tightly coiled; widespread species.
   2. Legume tightly coiled (springlike); leaflets 4–8 pairs per pinna; plants of trans-Pecos Texas   .   .   2. *P. pubescens*
   2. Legume not coiled; leaflets 10 to many pairs per pinna; widely distributed   .   .   .   .   .   .   3. *P. juliflora*

1. *Prosopis reptans* Benth., Hook. Jour. Bot. 4:352. 1842.
CREEPING MESQUITE

    Strombocarpa cinerascens Gray

    Prosopis cinerascens (Gray) Benth.

    Southern Texas and adjacent Mexico in sandy or silty clay soils (Map 29); also occurring in Argentina. April–September. In Texas the species is represented by the variety *cinerascens* (Gray) Burkart, which is separated from the typical variety (var. *reptans*) by having more pubescent foliage and by its distribution (var. *reptans* is confined to Argentina).

    Chromosome number not determined.

2. *Prosopis pubescens* Benth., *in* Hook. Lond. Jour. Bot. 5:82 1846. SCREW-BEAN

    Prosopis odorata Torr.

    Strombocarpa odorata (Torr.) Gray *ex* Britt. & Rose

    Trans-Pecos Texas in mostly silty, alluvial, limestone soils (Map 29). April–September. Texas to southern California and adjacent Mexico. This and the above species belong to the section Strombocarpa of *Prosopis* which is sometimes elevated to generic rank (Benson, 1941).

    Chromosome number not determined.

3. *Prosopis juliflora* (Swartz) DC., Prodr. 2:447. 1825.
MESQUITE

    Neltuma juliflora (Swartz) Raf.

    Widespread in nearly all parts of the state and in nearly all soil types, but most common in the drier areas of southern, central, and west Texas (Maps 30 and 31). April–September. South-central and southwestern United States to Central America and the West Indies. A number of articles have been written about this species concerning its distribution (Young *et al.*, 1948), economic importance (Forbes, 1895; Standley, 1922; Walton, 1923), and taxonomy (Benson, 1941). Several intergrading varieties have been recognized for Texas: var. *velutina* (Woot.) Sarg. (= *Prosopis*

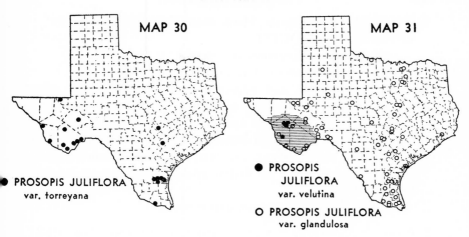

MAP 30

● PROSOPIS JULIFLORA
var. torreyana

MAP 31

● PROSOPIS
JULIFLORA
var. velutina

○ PROSOPIS JULIFLORA
var. glandulosa

velutina Woot.), a small-leaved form with densely pubescent leaflets (three to four times as long as broad) occurring in trans-Pecos Texas; var. *torreyana* Benson, a form
with glabrate leaves and narrow, somewhat longer leaflets
(seven to nine times as long as broad) in trans-Pecos and
central Texas; and var. *glandulosa* (Torr.) Cockerell (=
Prosopis glandulosa Torr.) with glabrate leaves and elongate leaflets (nine to twelve times as long as broad) occurring throughout the state, except perhaps in eastern Texas.
Intergrades between these various extremes occur.

The name *P. chilensis* has passed for *P. juliflora* in much
of the American taxonomic literature, but Benson (1941)
has indicated that *P. chilensis* is restricted to South America
and is very different from the North American plant.

Chromosome number, $2n = 56$ (Atchison, 1951; var.
velutina, $2n = 28$, Turner and Fearing, unpublished).

Subfamily Caesalpinioideae

TREES, SHRUBS, perennial herbs, or, less often, annuals. Leaves twice pinnate or once pinnate, or less often simple. Flowers mostly yellow or whitish (rarely, pinkish or reddish); petals 5 (rarely, less by reduction), only slightly irregular, not forming a distinct banner, wings, and keel (except in *Cercis*); uppermost petal internal in the bud, the petals never valvate; sepals usually separate to the base or nearly so; stamens 3–12 (rarely, numerous), mostly free.

The subfamily, if treated conservatively, contains about 1,500 species distributed in approximately 120 genera. Most of the species are endemic to tropical or semitropical areas, and are of little importance as rangeland legumes, either as grassland constituents or browse plants. The subfamily is often treated as a distinct family, Caesalpinaceae.

11. CERCIS   Redbud

UNARMED, deciduous, small trees, the flowers appearing before the leaves.

LEAVES simple, cordate to somewhat kidney-shaped; stipules not persistent.

FLOWERS rose or pink-purplish in umbel-like clusters along the preceding year's growth; corolla appearing papilionaceous; petals 5, separate; stamens 10, separate.

FRUIT an oblong, flat, dry, several- to many-seeded legume.

BASIC chromosome number, as determined from counts on 3 species, $x = 7$ (D. & W.; Turner, 1958).

A small genus with 5 species in the temperate regions of North America, Asia, and Europe. The species are of no agronomic importance, but some are widely cultivated as ornamentals in parks and gardens. *Cercis occidentalis* Torr. is listed by Cory and Parks (1937) for Texas, but this is a species of Arizona and California and is not native to Texas.

Cercis canadensis L., Sp. Pl. 1:374. 1753. REDBUD

Widespread throughout most of Texas in nearly all soil types (Map 32). March–May. Eastern United States and Mexico. A variable species, especially in Texas where a number of intergrading varieties are found. The following key to varieties is adopted with some modification from Hopkins (1942):

1. Mature leaves thinnish, dull green on both surfaces, generally cordate in outline, generally acute at apex; plants of sandy soils in east Texas or, rarely, cultivated on calcareous soils elsewhere
.   .   .   .   var. *canadensis*
1. Mature leaves thickened (coriaceous), rich, deep green, shiny, distinctly glaucous above, reniform to cordate-reniform in outline, obtuse to emarginate at apex, often merely rounded; plants of calcareous soils in central and west Texas.

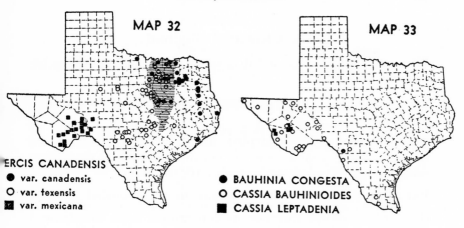

MAP 32

MAP 33

ERCIS CANADENSIS
- ● var. canadensis
- ○ var. texensis
- ▨ var. mexicana

- ● BAUHINIA CONGESTA
- ○ CASSIA BAUHINIOIDES
- ■ CASSIA LEPTADENIA

2. Petioles and young branchlets quite glabrous or nearly so; plants of the Edwards Plateau of central and north-central Texas . . . . var. *texensis*
2. Petioles and young branchlets densely woolly-tomentose, both in youth and maturity; plants of trans-Pecos Texas and adjacent counties . . . . . . var. *mexicana*

Hopkins cites several collections of *C. canadensis* var. *mexicana* (Rose) Hopkins from north-central Texas, far out of range of the normal habitat of the species. The present writer interprets these collections as var. *texensis* (Wats.) Rose. The somewhat pubescent twigs and petioles apparently are due to "gene flow" from var. *mexicana*. Anderson (1953) recognizes *C. c.* var. *texensis* as a distinct species (= *C. reniformis* Engelm.) and interprets its intergradation with *C. c. canadensis* as due to introgression or gene flow between the taxa. He apparently has included *C. c.* var. *mexicana* with his *C. reniformis*, though the two entities are as different from each other as *C. c.* var. *canadensis* and *C. c.* var. *texensis*. Collections of *C. c.* var. *texensis* from southern Texas, which Anderson has shown on his dot map, are probably cultivated in this area.

Chromosome number, $2n = 14$ (Baldwin, 1939; for var. *canadensis*).

12. BAUHINIA   Bauhinia

TREES or shrubs (rarely, woody vines), often armed with spines.

LEAVES simple or bifoliate with mostly raised palmate veins.

FLOWERS white, yellow, red, or purple, large and showy in few-flowered racemes; sepals 5; corolla of 5 similar petals.

FRUIT a linear, flattened, several-seeded, mostly dehiscent legume.

BASIC chromosome number, as determined from counts on 13 species, $x = 14$ (D. & W.; Turner, 1956b).

A large genus with about 250 species in the tropical regions of both the Old and New Worlds. The genus, so far as known, is represented in Texas by the single native species, *B. congesta*. Another species, *B. divaricata* L., has been reported for Texas by Britton and Rose (1930). However, native collections of this widespread species have not been seen from Texas by this writer, and it is believed that the collections referred to by Britton and Rose are from cultivated plants of *B. divaricata* (commonly referred to in Texas as Orchid-tree). Several species of *Bauhinia* are cultivated as yard ornamentals in southern Texas.

Bauhinia congesta (Britt. & Rose) Lundell, Phytologia 1:214. 1937. TEXAS BAUHINIA

    Casparea congesta Britt. & Rose

    Casparea jermyana Britt.

Known in Texas only from the Anacacho Hills in Kinney County where it occurs on dry, limestone soils, apparently extending into the area from adjacent Mexico (Map 33). March–May. The type locality of *C. jermyana* is given by Britton and Rose (1930) as "Enchanted Rock, Gillespie County." Recent field work has failed to reveal a *Bauhinia* in

this area. The main character they use to separate this specimen from *B. congesta* is the longer peduncles (8–12 mm.) in
B. congesta. Under critical examination this character does
not stand up, there being complete intergradation between
these lengths even on twigs from the same tree.

B. congesta is an attractive shrub in cultivation, assuming
a height of about 4 meters. There is a transplanted specimen
growing on the University of Texas campus, and from the
quality of its growth, abundance of large white flowers, and
ability to withstand frost, it should make an excellent ornamental for much of central Texas.

Chromosome number, $n = 14$ (Turner, 1956b).

13. CASSIA   Senna

PLANTS ANNUAL, perennial, or shrubby (commonly, trees in
tropical regions).

LEAVES once compound with 2 to numerous leaflets; petiolar
gland present or absent.

FLOWERS usually conspicuous, yellow, in short or elongate racemes (rarely solitary); stamens 5 to 10, often unlike, some of
them abortive.

FRUIT a several- to many-seeded, dehiscent or indehiscent,
flattened or rounded, often somewhat woody pod.

BASIC chromosome number, as determined from counts on 70
species, $x = 7, 8, 11, 12$ (Irwin and Turner, unpublished).

A very large genus with about 400 species in mostly tropical and subtropical regions of both hemispheres. Several species extend into the southwestern and eastern United States.
The section Chamaecrista, a group of annual or perennial
herbs with small, glanduliferous leaves, is sometimes elevated
to generic rank, as are various other segregate taxa.

KEY TO SPECIES

1. Leaves with 2 leaflets only.
  2. Peduncles with a single terminal flower; fruit subglobose
    .   .   .   .   1. *C. pumilia*
  2. Peduncles with 2 or more flowers; fruit linear, flattened.
    3. Leaflets three times as long as wide or less, ovate-lanceolate.
    ovate to nearly orbiculate.
      4. Leaflets mostly two and one half to three times as long as
      wide, densely short-pubescent; pubescence of upper stem
      and peduncles with hairs 2 mm. long or less   .   .
      .   .   .   .   2. *C. bauhinioides*
      4. Leaflets not more than twice as long as wide, densely
      long-pubescent; pubescence of upper stems and peduncles
      with some of the hairs 3–5 mm. long   .   3. *C. durangensis*
    3. Leaflets five times longer than wide, lanceolate   .   .
    . .   .   .   4. *C. roemeriana*
1. Leaves with 3 or more leaflets.
  5. Leaflets 2 cm. long or more.
    6. Leaflets 4 or 6, glabrous above and below   .   .   5. *C. tora*
    6. Leaflets 8 or more on most of the leaves, glabrous to densely
    pubescent.
      7. Leaflets glabrous or nearly so; plants of east Texas.
        8. Leaflets 6–12; legume brown at maturity with lighter
        margin, 5–8 mm. wide; flowers 1–3 in short clusters
        . .   .   .   6. *C. occidentalis*
        8. Leaflets 10–16; legume black at maturity, 8–10 mm.
        wide; flowers 4 or more in short racemes   .   .
        . .   .   .   7. *C. marilandica*
      7. Leaflets copiously pubescent; plants of central and west
      Texas.
        9. Fruit at maturity 6–10 cm. long; leaflets with a scat-
        tered, appressed pubescence, not at all velvety and
        soft to the touch; stems essentially glabrate except
        for occasional long hairs   .   .   .   8. *C. orcuttii*
        9. Fruit 6 cm. long or less; leaflets densely velvety pubes-
        cent, soft to the touch; stems densely pubescent
        throughout   .   .   .   .   9. *C. lindheimeriana*
  5. Leaflets less than 2 cm. long.
    10. Woody shrubs.
      11. Shrubs 1–3 m. high; petioles without glands; trans-
      Pecos Texas   .   .   .   .   .   10. *C. Wizlizenii*

11. Shrubs 0.1–0.5 m. high; petioles glandular; southern
    Texas . . . . 11. *C. greggii*
10. Perennial or annual herbs, not at all woody.
  12. Pedicel of flower and/or fruit 1–5 mm. long; petals 4–8
      mm. long; stamens 5.
    13. Stipules 3–6(8) mm. long; leaflets conspicuously cili-
        ate, cilia 0.6–1.0 mm. long; plants of mountains in
        trans-Pecos Texas . . . . 12. *C. leptadenia*
    13. Stipules (5)6–10 mm. long; leaflets without cilia or
        nearly so; plants of central and east Texas . .
        . . . . 13. *C. nictitans*
  12. Pedicel of flower and/or fruit 5–40 mm. long (rarely, less,
      but if so the petals 10 mm. long or more); petals 10–25 mm.
      long; stamens 10.
    14. Mature flowering and fruiting peduncles (2)2.5–5 cm.
        long; plants perennial . . . . 14. *C. texana*
    14. Flowering and fruiting peduncles 2 cm. long or less.
      15. Plants perennial; stems procumbent, pubescent with
          both short incurved hairs 1 mm. long or less, and
          longer, spreading hairs 2–3 mm. long; endemic
          species of southern Texas . . 15. *C. aristellata*
      15. Plant annual (rarely, short-lived perennials); stems
          erect, ascending, or semiprostrate, glabrate to
          densely pubescent, but not mixed pubescent as
          above; widespread species . . 16. *C. fasciculata*

1. *Cassia pumilio* Gray, Bost. Jour. Nat. Hist. 6:180. 1850.
DWARF SENNA
  Tharpia pumilio (Gray) Britt. & Rose
  Central and western Texas to northeastern Mexico,
mostly in limestone soils (Map 34). March–August.
  Chromosome number, $n = 14$ (Irwin, unpublished).

2. *Cassia bauhinioides* Gray, Bost. Jour. Nat. Hist. 6:180.
1850. BAUHINIA SENNA
  Earleocassia bauhinioides (Gray) Britt.
  Trans-Pecos and southern areas of Texas along the Rio
Grande in nearly all soil types (Map 33). May–July.
Texas to Arizona and Mexico.
  Chromosome number, $n = 14$ (Irwin, unpublished).

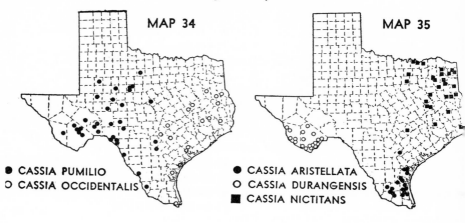

MAP 34

MAP 35

● CASSIA PUMILIO
○ CASSIA OCCIDENTALIS

● CASSIA ARISTELLATA
○ CASSIA DURANGENSIS
■ CASSIA NICTITANS

3. *Cassia durangensis* Rose, Contr. U. S. Nat. Herb. 10:98. 1906

　　Earleocassia durangensis (Rose) Britt.

　　Cassia bauhinioides var. *pilosior* Robinson *ex* Macbride
　　Trans-Pecos Texas in dry, rocky, mostly limestone soils, at altitudes of 1,500–3,500 feet (Map 35). May–October. Texas and adjacent Mexico. Closely related to *C. bauhinioides*, but differing in being a larger plant with broader leaflets and having a much longer pubescence on the stem and foliage. Macbride (1919) described the species as a variety of *C. bauhinioides*, apparently unaware of its earlier name. *C. durangensis* occurs in pure populations. It is usually found at lower elevations than *C. bauhinioides* where the ranges of these two species overlap.

　　Chromosome number, $n = 14$ (Turner, 1956b).

4. *Cassia roemeriana* Scheele, Linnaea 21:457. 1848. TWO-LEAVED SENNA

　　Earleocassia roemeriana (Scheele) Britt.

　　Central and trans-Pecos areas of Texas mostly in limestone soils (Map 36). April–August. Texas to New Mexico and northeastern Mexico.

　　Chromosome number, $n = 14$ (Turner, 1956b).

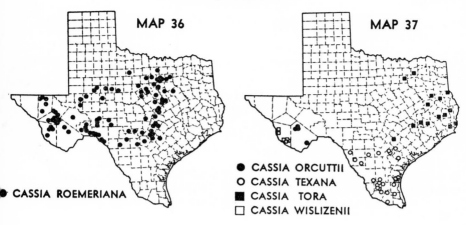

MAP 36

CASSIA ROEMERIANA

MAP 37

● CASSIA ORCUTTII
O CASSIA TEXANA
■ CASSIA TORA
□ CASSIA WISLIZENII

5. *Cassia tora* L., Sp. Pl. 376. 1753. SICKLE-POD
   Emelista tora (L.) Britt. & Rose *ex* Britt. & Wilson
   An introduced weed mostly in disturbed sandy soils of east Texas (Map 37). September–October. Widely distributed in the tropical and subtropical regions of both hemispheres. Brenan (1958) has correctly called the material treated here *C. obtusifolia* L.
   Chromosome number, $2n = 26, 28$ (D. & W.).

6. *Cassia occidentalis* L., Sp. Pl. 377. 1753. COFFEE SENNA
   Ditremexa occidentalis (L.) Britt. & Rose *ex* Britt. & Wilson
   An introduced tall, annual weed in disturbed areas of eastern, central, and southern Texas (Map 34). August–December. Widely distributed in the tropics and subtropics of both hemispheres.
   Chromosome number, $2n = 26, 28$ (D. & W.).

7. *Cassia marilandica* L., Sp. Pl. 378. 1753. WILD SENNA
   Ditremexa marilandica (L.) Britt. & Rose
   Eastern Texas mostly in sandy soils of moist woods or along stream banks (Map 38). August–October. Central and northeastern United States.
   Chromosome number, $n = 14$ (Irwin, unpublished).

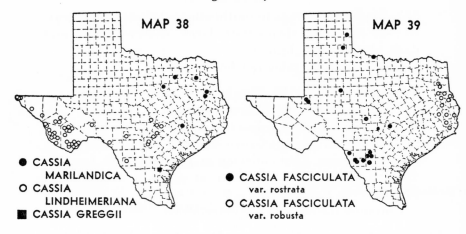

MAP 38

MAP 39

● CASSIA
   MARILANDICA
○ CASSIA
   LINDHEIMERIANA
■ CASSIA GREGGII

● CASSIA FASCICULATA
   var. rostrata
○ CASSIA FASCICULATA
   var. robusta

8. *Cassia orcuttii* (Britt. & Rose) Turner, Field & Lab. 18: 144. 1949

Peiranisia orcuttii Britt. & Rose

Brewster and Terrell counties in limestone soils, at altitudes of 3,000–5,000 feet; known only from trans-Pecos Texas and adjacent Mexico (Map 37). July–August. Much resembling *C. lindheimeriana*, but differing in being a smaller plant with smaller, glaucus leaflets and longer pods.

Chromosome number not determined.

9. *Cassia lindheimeriana* Scheele, Linnaea 21:457. 1848. LINDHEIMER SENNA

Earleocassia lindheimeriana (Scheele) Britt.

Central and trans-Pecos areas of Texas usually in limestone soils (Map 38). August–November. Texas to southeastern Arizona and Mexico.

Chromosome number, $n = 14$ (Irwin, unpublished).

10. *Cassia wislizenii* Gray, Pl. Wright. 1:60. 1852

Palmerocassia wislizenii (Gray) Britt.

Southern trans-Pecos Texas and adjacent Mexico in rocky, igneous soils, at altitudes of 3,000–4,000 feet (Map

37). May–July. Texas to southeastern Arizona and Mexico. An attractive shrub with large, showy flowers and dark, almost black, branches.

Chromosome number not determined.

11. *Cassia greggii* Gray, Pl. Wright 1:59. 1852

   Chamaecrista greggii (Gray) Pollard

   Known to Texas by only a few collections from rocky caliche hills near Orange Grove in Jim Wells County (Map 38). May–June. First collected in Texas by F. B. Jones in 1959. The species is common in parts of northeastern Mexico.

   Chromosome number not determined.

12. *Cassia leptadenia* Greenman, Proc. Amer. Acad. 41:238. 1905

   Chamaecrista leptadenia (Greenman) Cockerell

   Mountainous areas of trans-Pecos Texas mostly in igneous soils, at altitudes of 3,500–6,000 feet (Map 33). July–September. Texas to Arizona and Mexico. Closely related to *C. nictitans* (below), a species of the eastern United States.

   Chromosome number not determined.

13. *Cassia nictitans* L., Sp. Pl. 380. 1753. WILD SENSITIVE PLANT

   Chamaecrista procumbens (L.) Greene

   Eastern Texas in sandy soils, becoming an abundant weed in fallow fields (Map 35). September–October. A variable species widely distributed over the central and eastern parts of the United States. In Texas the species is represented by the typical variety (var. *nictitans*).

   Chromosome number, $n = 8$ (Senn, 1938b).

14. *Cassia texana* Buckl., Proc. Acad. Phila. 1861:452. 1862. TEXAS SENNA

   Chamaecrista texana (Buckl.) Pennell

   Endemic to southern Texas in sandy soils (Map 37).

March–September. A distinct species, easily recognized by its perennial habit and zigzag (flexuous) branches. Chromosome number, $n = 8$ (Irwin, unpublished).

15. *Cassia aristellata* (Pennell) Cory & Parks, Bull. Texas Agric. Exper. Sta. 550:56. 1937
    Chamaecrista aristellata Pennell
    Endemic to southern Texas and adjacent Mexico, mostly in sandy soils, apparently rare (Map 35). July–August. Chromosome number, $n = 8$ (Irwin, unpublished).

16. *Cassia fasciculata* Michx., Fl. Bor. Am. 1:262. 1803. PARTRIDGE PEA
    Chamaecrista fasciculata (Michx.) Greene
    Southern, eastern, central, and Panhandle areas of Texas, mostly in sandy soils (Maps 39 and 40). March–October. A common, highly variable species, widely distributed in the central and eastern portions of the United States. In Texas the species is represented by at least 5 varieties (Turner, 1955). The characters which separate these infraspecific taxa intergrade (sometimes considerably), especially where ranges merge or overlap.

    Typical specimens of the named varieties may be identified by the following key (numerous intermediate types excepted):

1. Stems stiffly erect, mostly unbranched below, the upper portion pubescent with spreading hairs 2–3 mm. long; face of leaflets glabrate; plants of easternmost Texas in cleared pine and oak woodlands   .   .   .   .   .   var. *robusta* (Poll.) Macbride
1. Stems stiffly erect to nearly prostrate, simple or diffusely branched, but without spreading hairs 2–3 mm. long, the pubescence mostly shorter or appressed; widespread taxa.
    2. Face of leaflets glabrate (intergrades with varieties *puberula* and *ferrisiae* occur).
        3. Petiolar gland 0.5 mm. wide or less; anthers purple; leaves with mostly 6–10 pairs of leaflets; plants of central Texas and northwestward to New Mexico (intergrades with var. *fasciculata*)   .   .   .   .   var. *rostrata* (W. & S.) Turner

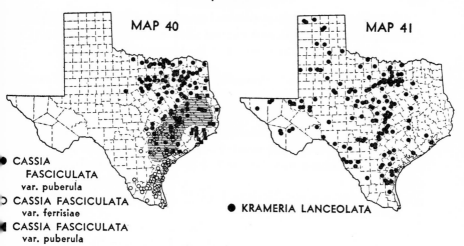

● CASSIA
  FASCICULATA
  var. puberula
◗ CASSIA FASCICULATA
  var. ferrisiae
◖ CASSIA FASCICULATA
  var. puberula

● KRAMERIA LANCEOLATA

3. Petiolar gland 0.5–1.5 mm. wide; anthers yellow, occasionally purple or mottled; leaves mostly with (9)10–15 pairs of leaflets; plants of central Texas and eastward (intergrades completely with varieties *ferrisiae* and/or *puberula*) .
   . . . . var. *fasciculata*
2. Face of leaflets densely pubescent with incurved hairs.
   4. Stems stiffly erect, mostly unbranched in the lower portion; legumes 5–6 mm. wide; petiolar gland sessile or nearly so; plants of upper Texas Gulf Coast and inland (intergrades completely with varieties *fasciculata* and/or *ferrisiae*) .
      . . . . var. *puberula* (Greene) Macbride
   4. Stems branched from the base and widely spreading; legumes 3–4.5(5) mm. wide; petiolar gland distinctly stalked; plants of lower Gulf Coast and inland (intergrades completely with varieties *fasciculata* and/or *puberula*) . .
      . . . . var. *ferrisiae* (Britt.) Turner

There appears to be complete intergradation of three of these varieties in south-central Texas (indicated by the lined area, Map 40). Some of the varietal dots on the distributional map of this species represent intermediates of the five basic taxa recognized above.

Chromosome number, $n = 8$ (Turner, 1956b, for varieties *fasciculata* and *ferrisiae*; var. *rostrata*, Irwin, unpublished).

Cultivated Species

Cassia alata L. WINGED CASSIA (locally called "Emperor's Candlesticks").

A very handsome ornamental with dark green foliage and bright yellow, erect racemes. Prior to 1953 this species was only occasionally observed in Texas, but during the last five years it has become a favorite with home gardeners and now is commonly seen in cultivation throughout south and central Texas.

Chromosome number, $2n = 24$ (D. & W.).

Cassia corymbosa Lam. CORYMBOSE CASSIA.

Introduced as a shrubby garden ornamental in recent years and now widespread in home gardens throughout south and central Texas. The plant is not so striking as the species above, the flowers and leaves being smaller and the whole plant more densely branched.

Chromosome number, $2n = 24$ (D. & W.).

14. KRAMERIA   Ratany

PERENNIAL HERBS or low woody shrubs, the stems often short and thornlike.

LEAVES (in most species) simple and without stipules, alternate, usually linear and grayish-pubescent.

FLOWERS purplish, solitary in leaf axils or racemose; sepals 4 or 5; petals 5, the upper three pronounced and long-clawed, the lower two reduced to small fleshy glands; stamens 3 or 4.

FRUIT a nearly globose, 1-seeded, indehiscent pod, armed with straight, sharp prickles.

BASIC chromosome number, as determined by counts on 3 spe-

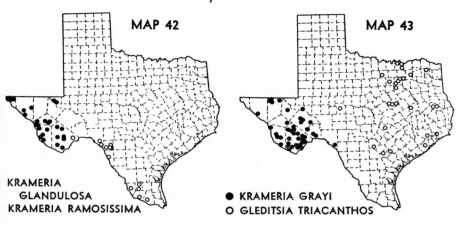

MAP 42

KRAMERIA
   GLANDULOSA
KRAMERIA RAMOSISSIMA

MAP 43

● KRAMERIA GRAYI
O GLEDITSIA TRIACANTHOS

cies, $x = 6$ (Turner, 1958). The meiotic chromosomes are remarkable for their large size, being among the largest known in the dicots.

A wholly American genus of about 20 species, mainly centered in the desert areas of Mexico, but with a few species south to Argentina. *K. lanceolata*, a widespread variable species, occurs in the United States as far north as Kansas. The species are of no significant economic importance, but several of the shrubby members are abundant in the drier areas of trans-Pecos Texas and perhaps serve as browse plants, especially during times of drought.

There is considerable controversy as to the correct phyletic position of this genus. Taubert (1894) treated the genus as a subdivision of the Caesalpinioideae within the Leguminosae. Hutchinson (1926) treated the group as a genus in the family Polygalaceae, quite removed from the Leguminosae proper. Others have elevated the genus to family rank (Krameriaceae). Recent cytological and anatomical studies (Turner, 1958) seem to indicate that the genus is worthy of family rank, though much additional study is needed before phyletic position can be established.

KEY TO SPECIES

1. Stems decumbent, completely herbaceous above ground; widespread throughout Texas .   .   .   .   .   1. *K. lanceolata*
1. Stems erect or ascending, woody shrubs or subshrubs; plants of south-central and trans-Pecos areas of Texas.
      2. Pedicels densely glandular (very rarely, not glandular, but if so, then the prickles of the fruit with scattered barbs near the apex as opposed to barbless prickles or whorled barbs at the apex of the prickles in the species below) .   .   .
      .   .   .   .   *2. K. glandulosa*
      2. Pedicels without glands.
            3. Leaves 2–6 mm. long; prickles of the fruit 2 mm. long or less at maturity, without barbs; petals 6–8 mm. long .
            .   .   .   .   *3. K. ramosissima*
            3. Leaves 5–25 mm. long, at least some of them 10 mm. long; prickles of the fruit 2–6 mm. long at maturity, with a whorl of barbs at the apex; petals 8–12 mm. long .   .   .
            .   .   .   .   *4. K. grayi*

1. *Krameria lanceolata* Torr., Ann. Lyc. N. Y. 2:168. 1827
   Krameria secundiflora of authors, not of DC.

   Widespread throughout Texas except for sandy areas of east Texas, occurring on all soil types but predominantly in tight clay (Map 41). Texas to Kansas, Arkansas, New Mexico, Arizona, and Mexico. April–June, flowering again in September with fall rains. Populations growing along the Gulf Coast have more succulent leaves than is typical for the species as it grows in drier areas.

   Chromosome number determined as $n = 6$ (Turner, 1958).

2. *Krameria glandulosa* Rose & Painter, Contr. U. S. Nat. Herb. 10:108. 1906. RANGE RATANY

   Trans-Pecos Texas in dry sandy, limestone, or igneous soils (Map 42), at altitudes of 3,000–5,000 feet. New Mexico, Arizona, and Mexico. April–July. The stiff, slender, acicular, ultimate branchlets give the plant a spinescent appearance. This taxon is perhaps better treated as a variety of *K. parvifolia* Benth., a species of Arizona, California, and Mexico. *K. glandulosa* can be distinguished from this species by the presence of stipitate glands on the pedicels; *K. parvifolia* in its typical form is eglandular. As noted in the key, occasional specimens of *K. glandulosa* without glands may be found in Texas.

Chromosome number not determined.

3. *Krameria ramosissima* (Gray) Wats., Proc. Amer. Acad. 17:326. 1882

South-central and southern Texas and adjacent Mexico in limestone or gravelly soils along the Rio Grande (Map 42). May–June. Associated with *Cercidium texanum* and other low thorny shrubs; common about Del Rio, Texas.

Chromosome number, $n = 6$ (Turner, 1958).

4. *Krameria grayi* Rose & Painter, Contr. U. S. Nat. Herb. 10:108. 1906. WHITE RATANY

Trans-Pecos Texas in dry sandy, limestone, or igneous soils, at altitudes of 3,000–5,000 feet (Map 43). June–September. Southwestern United States and northern Mexico. This species and *K. glandulosa* are common members of the drier shrubby communities in trans-Pecos Texas.

Chromosome number, $n = 6$ (Turner, 1958).

15. GLEDITSIA   Honey Locust

TREES or tall shrubs, often armed with stout, branched thorns.

LEAVES once compound or twice compound, even on the same tree; leaflets usually 10 or more pairs on each pinna.

FLOWERS in spikelike racemes, yellowish or greenish-yellow; stamens 3–10, separate.

FRUIT on oval to elongate, flattened, mostly indehiscent pod.

BASIC chromosome number, as determined from counts on 7 species, $x = 14$ (D. & W.).

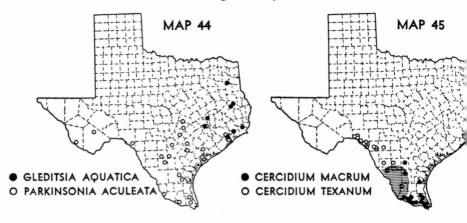

A genus with about 11 woody species occurring in North America, South America, Asia, and Africa. The genus is sometimes spelled *Gleditschia*.

KEY TO SPECIES

1. Pods linear-oblong, elongate, many-seeded, indehiscent; ovary pubescent . . . . 1. *G. triacanthos*
1. Pods oval, oblique, 1- to 3-seeded, tardily dehiscent; ovary glabrous . . . . 2. *G. aquatica*

1. *Gleditsia triacanthos* L., Sp. Pl. 1056. 1753. HONEY LO-CUST

Central and east Texas and the Panhandle, in damp, sandy, or low, alluvial soils (Map 43). April–May. Widespread species occurring from eastern Canada to Florida. The species is commonly cultivated in various parts of the state as a shade tree and sometimes becomes established as an escapee in disturbed areas. In Brazoria County, Texas, specimens of what appear to be forms of this species with smaller, fewer-seeded pods have been described as *G. texana* Marsh. According to some authorities (Sargent, 1933), *G. texana* would best be considered a hybrid between *G. triacanthos* and *G. aquatica* (below).

Chromosome number, $2n = 28$ (D. & W.).

2. *Gleditsia aquatica* Marsh., Arbust. Am. 54. 1785. WATER LOCUST

Asacara aquatica (Marsh.) Raf.

East Texas in swamps and low, alluvial woods (Map 44). May–June. Central United States to Florida. The species reportedly hybridizes with *G. triacanthos* in various parts of its range (see above).

Chromosome number, $2n = 28$ (D. & W.).

16. GYMNOCLADUS   Coffee-tree

UNARMED TREES to 30 meters tall, with stout twigs and red pith.

LEAVES large, twice compound with 7 or more leaflets to each pinna (rarely, some of the leaves with only 1 leaflet on the lower pinnae).

FLOWERS whitish, in terminal racemes; petals 5, all alike; stamens 10, separate.

FRUIT an oblong, flattened, pulpy, dark red pod.

BASIC chromosome number, as determined from counts on a single species, $x = 14$ (D. & W.).

A genus with only 2 species, in the temperate regions of the eastern United States and China.

Gymnocladus dioica (L.) Koch, Dendr. 1:5. 1869. KENTUCKY COFFEE-TREE

Reported for Texas by Fassett (1939). His dot map (p. 21), indicates a collection from the Texas Panhandle, near the Oklahoma border. The present writer has not seen specimens from Texas.

Chromosome number, $2n = 28$ (D. & W.).

17. PARKINSONIA   Retama (Jerusalem-thorn)

SPINY, LARGE SHRUBS or small trees to 15 meters tall with a trunk to 30 cm. in diameter; bark smooth, yellowish-green.

LEAVES twice compound with 2 very elongate pinnae (to 50 cm.) and a very short petiole (the whole leaf often appearing as 2 once-compound leaves); leaflets numerous, small, deciduous from the flattened axis of the pinna.

FLOWERS conspicuous, bright yellow, slightly irregular, mostly in elongate racemes.

FRUIT a linear, semiturgid, nearly terete, torulose pod.

BASIC chromosome number, as determined from counts on a single species, $x = 7$ (D. & W.).

A genus with 3 or 4 species in the tropics and subtropics of North America, South America, and semidesert areas of South Africa; possibly adventive in other areas. The leaves and young stems of some of the species are reportedly eaten by stock (Standley, 1922).

Parkinsonia aculeata L., Sp. Pl. 375. 1753. RETAMA (also known locally as "Paloverde").

Southern and trans-Pecos Texas; probably introduced elsewhere (Map 44). March–September. Florida; southern Texas to Arizona, Mexico, and South America. The species is widely cultivated as an ornamental in various parts of Texas. It grows rapidly and produces an abundance of attractive yellow flowers. In some areas of central Texas it has apparently escaped cultivation and become a troublesome weed in recently disturbed fields.

Chromosome number, $2n = 14$ (D. & W.).

18. CERCIDIUM   Paloverde

TREES or shrubs, branches usually crooked, smooth, green, and armed with short, straight spines.

LEAVES twice compound with 1–2 pairs of pinnae; leaflets smooth, few; petiolar gland absent.

FLOWERS bright yellow, in short axillary racemes; petals 5, slightly unequal; stamens 10, separate, all alike.

FRUIT a flat, oblong or linear, somewhat woody legume; seeds 1 to few.

BASIC chromosome number, as determined from counts on 2 species, $x = 14$ (Turner, 1956b; Turner and Fearing, unpublished).

A small genus of 8 or 9 species widely distributed in the tropical and subtropical regions of both North and South America. Most of the species are adapted to arid or semiarid habitats.

KEY TO SPECIES

1. Ovary glabrous or nearly so; base of pod glabrous; pinnae mostly (1)2 or 3 pairs   .   .   .   .   .   .   *1. C. macrum*
1. Ovary densely pubescent; base of pod appressed-pubescent; pinnae mostly 1 or, rarely, 2 pairs   .   .   .   *2. C. texanum*

1. *Cercidium macrum* Johnst., Contr. Gray Herb. 70:64. 1924. PALOVERDE

Endemic to southernmost Texas and northeastern Mexico, occurring in tight clay or sandy soils (Map 45). March–September. This species has been confused with *C. floridum* Benth. *ex* Gray, a closely related species which, according to Johnston (1924), is a plant of Arizona, California, and northwestern Mexico, having larger, thicker pods and paler foliage.

Chromosome number, $n = 14$ (Turner, unpublished).

2. *Cercidium texanum* Gray, Pl. Wright. 1:58. 1852. PALO-VERDE

> *Parkinsonia texana* (Gray) Wats.

Endemic to south-central Texas and adjacent Mexico in rocky or gravelly limestone soils (Map 45). April–August. A sparsely leaved spiny shrub, apparently of little value even as a browse plant. The species appears to intergrade with *C. macrum* where their ranges overlap in southern Texas.

Chromosome number, $n = 14$ (Turner, 1956b).

19a. HOFFMANSEGGIA   Rush-pea

UNARMED LOW SHRUBS or perennial herbs.

LEAVES twice compound (odd-pinnate), with 3 to several pinnae; leaflets mostly small, smooth, or glandular-dotted, rarely, with raised veins.

FLOWERS yellow, conspicuous, in open racemes; stamens 10, separate, all alike.

FRUIT a straight or curved legume, elastically dehiscent at maturity.

BASIC chromosome number, as determined from counts on 4 species, $x = 12$ (D. & W.; Turner, 1956b).

A genus of about 30 species mostly in dry areas of subtropical North America, South America, and South Africa. Several species extend into the southwestern United States from adjacent Mexico. The genus is of little economic importance. *H. densiflora* reportedly has edible tuberous roots, which were roasted and eaten by southwestern aboriginals. This species has also been listed as a valuable soil binder by Kearney and Peebles (1942).

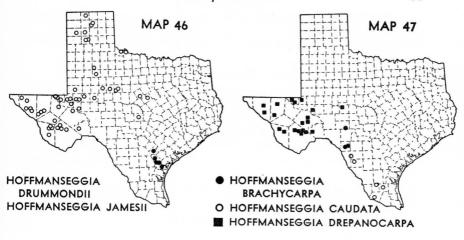

MAP 46

MAP 47

HOFFMANSEGGIA
DRUMMONDII
HOFFMANSEGGIA JAMESII

● HOFFMANSEGGIA
    BRACHYCARPA
○ HOFFMANSEGGIA CAUDATA
▨ HOFFMANSEGGIA DREPANOCARPA

KEY TO SPECIES

1. Mature leaves with predominantly 3 pinnae (rarely, 5), 1–4
cm. long; plants of southern Texas . . 1. *H. drummondii*
1. Mature leaves with (3)5 or more pinnae, 5–15 cm. long.
    2. Leaflets with conspicuous raised reticulate veins beneath;
    plants of southern Texas.
        3. Leaflets, the larger ones, ovate, 4–10 mm. wide, glandular-
        dotted beneath . . . . . . 2. *H. caudata*
        3. Leaflets oblong, 2–3 mm. wide, without glands beneath
        . . . . 3. *H. tenella*
    2. Leaflets smooth, without raised veins beneath, except for the
    midvein.
        4. Leaflets dotted beneath with visible dark sessile glands.
            5. Leaflets 2–5 pairs to each pinna.
                6. Plants glabrous or minutely pubescent; stems herba-
                ceous; pod 20 mm. long or less . 4. *H. brachycarpa*
                6. Plants conspicuously pubescent with villous hairs;
                stems suffrutescent; pod 23 mm. long or more.
                    7. Leaflets 2–4 mm. long, 1–2.5 mm. wide; pinnae with
                    3–5 leaflets; plants of southern Texas . . .
                    . . . . 5. *H. melanosticta*
                    7. Leaflets 4–10 mm. long, 2.5–5 mm. wide; pinnae
                    with 2–3 leaflets; plants of trans-Pecos Texas .
                    . . . . 6. *H. parryi*

5. Leaflets 5–10 pairs to each pinna . . . 7. *H. jamesii*
4. Leaflets without obvious dark sessile glands beneath.
  8. Branches of raceme and calyx with pedicellate glands.
    9. Petals conspicuously clawed (the claw 4–6 mm. long),
      densely glandular; filaments with pedicellate glands;
      widespread species . . . . . 8. *H. densiflora*
    9. Petals short-clawed (the claw 2 mm. long or less), not
      glandular (rarely, 1–5 glands present); filaments with
      bristle-like hairs, but not glandular . . 9. *H. oxycarpa*
  8. Branches of raceme and calyx without pedicellate glands
. . . . 10. *H. drepanocarpa*

1. *Hoffmanseggia drummondii* Torr. & Gray, Fl. N. Am. 1:
393. 1840. DRUMMOND RUSH-PEA
    Larrea drummondii (Torr. & Gray) Britt.
    Hoffmanseggia texensis Fisher
    Known only from Karnes, Goliad, and Bee counties in
sandy-clay soils (Map 46). May–July. Endemic to Texas.
A rare but very distinct species. The name *H. texensis* has
been applied to forms of this species with pubescent stems.
    Chromosome number not determined.

2. *Hoffmanseggia caudata* Gray, Bost. Jour. Nat. Hist. 6:179.
1850
    Schrammia caudata (Gray) Britt. & Rose
    Southern Texas in loose sandy soils (Map 47). March–
June. Endemic to Texas. The species was split from *Hoffmanseggia* by Britton and Rose and a new, monotypic
genus, *Schrammia*, established.
    Chromosome number not determined.

3. *Hoffmanseggia tenella* Tharp & Williams, Ann. Mo. Bot.
Gard. 23:451. 1936.
    Known only from Nueces County in southern Texas,
the type locality (Map 48). Endemic to Texas. A very distinct species, but superficially resembling *H. drepanocarpa*.
    Chromosome number not determined.

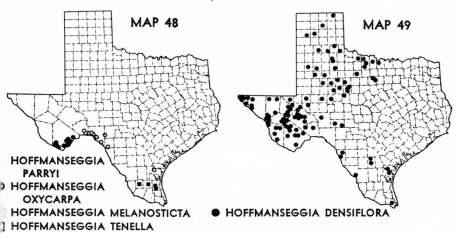

MAP 48   MAP 49

HOFFMANSEGGIA
PARRYI
HOFFMANSEGGIA
OXYCARPA
HOFFMANSEGGIA MELANOSTICTA   ● HOFFMANSEGGIA DENSIFLORA
HOFFMANSEGGIA TENELLA

4. *Hoffmanseggia brachycarpa* Gray, Pl. Wright. 1:55. 1852
   Larrea brachycarpa (Gray) Britt.
   Restricted endemic of south-central Texas in gravelly
   or rocky limestone soils (Map 47). May. Only a few col-
   lections known to this writer.
   Chromosome number not determined.

5. *Hoffmanseggia melanosticta* (Schauer) Gray, Pl. Wright.
   1:54. 1852
   Larrea melanosticta (Schauer) Britt.
   Sandy or rocky soils of the Rio Grande plain in southernmost Texas (Map 48). March–June. A widespread, variable species of Mexico.
   Chromosome number not determined.

6. *Hoffmanseggia parryi* (Fisher) Turner, Field & Lab.
   18:47. 1950
   Larrea parryi (Fisher) Britt.
   Known only by a few collections from rocky, limestone
   soils in southern Brewster County (Map 48). June. Locally endemic to Texas and adjacent Mexico. According
   to Fisher (1892), closely related to *H. melanosticta* and

treated by him as a variety of that species (*H. m.* var. *parryi* Fisher).

Chromosome number not determined.

7. *Hoffmanseggia jamesii* Torr. & Gray, Fl. N. Am. 1:393. 1840. JAMES RUSH-PEA

Larrea jamesii (Torr. & Gray) Britt.

Western Texas mostly in dry, sandy, or alluvial soils (Map 46). May–September. Central and southwestern United States.

Chromosome number not determined.

8. *Hoffmanseggia densiflora* Benth. *ex* Gray, Pl. Wright. 1:55. 1852. INDIAN RUSH-PEA

Larrea densiflora (Benth. *ex* Gray) Britt.

Widespread species of southern and western Texas in nearly all soil types (Map 49). March–September. Central and southwestern United States to central Mexico. Common along roadsides in western Texas, forming large colonies. The roots of this species form underground tubers which are reportedly good hog feed. They were also roasted and used for food by the Indians. Fisher (1892) reduced the species to synonymy under *H. falcaria* Cav., a closely related, highly variable species from Central and South America.

Chromosome number, $n = 12$ (Turner, 1956b).

9. *Hoffmanseggia oxycarpa* Benth. *ex* Gray, Pl. Wright. 1:55. 1852

Larrea oxycarpa (Benth.) Britt.

Terrell and Val Verde counties in rocky, limestone soils (Map 48). March–May. This species is easily distinguished in the field by its conspicuous, red-glandular inflorescence.

Chromosome number, $2n = 24$ (Turner and Fearing, unpublished).

10. *Hoffmanseggia drepanocarpa* Gray, Pl. Wright. 1:58. 1852. SICKLE-POD RUSH-PEA

Larrea drepanocarpa (Gray) Britt.

Western Texas in sandy or limestone soils, at altitudes of 2,000–4,500 feet (Map 47). April–July. Southwestern United States and north-central Mexico.

Chromosome number, $2n = 24$ (Turner and Fearing, unpublished).

19b. CAESALPINIA   Caesalpinia

SHRUBS or trees, mostly unarmed (rarely, spiny).

LEAVES twice compound (rarely, once compound); leaflets mostly small and numerous.

FLOWERS yellow or red, large and showy in mostly elongate racemes; stamens often very elongate, reddish.

FRUIT variable, but mostly flattened and dehiscent.

BASIC chromosome number, as determined from counts on 15 species, $x = 12$ (11?) (D. & W.).

A genus, if treated broadly (including *Poinciana*), with about 60 species, widely distributed in the tropical and subtropical regions of both hemispheres. The species are of little economic importance, though some of them are cultivated as ornamentals. Tannins are also extracted from the pods of certain Mexican species.

KEY TO SPECIES

1. Leaflets 2–6 pairs on each pinna; stamens 1–2 cm. long; native species of southernmost Texas.
   2. Leaflets 10–25 mm. long; shrubs or small trees 1.5 meters tall or more   .   .   .   .   1. *C. mexicana*
   2. Leaflets 3–7 mm. long; small shrublets 50 cm. high or less
   .   .   .   .   2. *C. phyllanthoides*
1. Leaflets 7–15 pairs on each pinna; stamens 4–6 cm. long; introduced species of central and western Texas   .   .   3. *C. gilliesii*

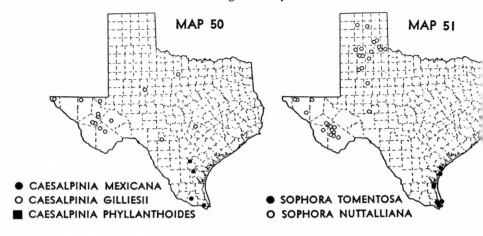

MAP 50

MAP 51

● CAESALPINIA MEXICANA
O CAESALPINIA GILLIESII
■ CAESALPINIA PHYLLANTHOIDES

● SOPHORA TOMENTOSA
O SOPHORA NUTTALLIANA

1. *Caesalpinia mexicana* Gray, Proc. Amer. Acad. 5:157. 1862. MEXICAN CAESALPINIA
  Poinciana mexicana (Gray) Rose
  Poinsianella mexicana (Gray) Britt. & Rose
  A rare species of southernmost Texas, usually occurring on sandy uplands (Map 50). February–July. A widespread Mexican species distributed from Tamaulipas to Sinaloa and south to Guerrero. The species is sometimes grown as an ornamental in southern Texas.
  Chromosome number, $2n = 24$ (D. & W.).

2. *Caesalpinia phyllanthoides* Standl., Contr. U. S. Nat. Herb. 28:425. 1922
  Poincianella phyllanthoides (Standl.) Britt. & Rose
  Only two collections are known from Texas by the present writer (Map 50), one from Three Rivers (Live Oak County) and the other from six miles north of Orange Grove (Jim Wells County), where it reportedly grows in rock crevices. March. Endemic to Texas and the adjacent state of Tamaulipas, Mexico.
  Chromosome number not determined.

3. *Caesalpinia gilliesii* Wall. *ex* Hook., Bot. Misc. Hook. 1:129. 1830. BIRD-OF-PARADISE (Paradise Poinciana)

Poinciana gilliesii Hook.

Erythrostemon gilliesii (Hook.) Link, K. & O.

An introduced species, more commonly found in central and western Texas where it is well adapted to dry habitats (Map 50). May–September. Native to South America, but widely cultivated for its showy flowers. The highway department has planted the shrub along roadways of central and western Texas where it has become well established, often spreading into adjacent fields.

Chromosome number, $2n = 24$ (D. & W.).

Cultivated Species

Caesalpinia pulcherrima (L.) Swartz
BARBADOS FLOWER

This species is cultivated as a yard ornamental in parts of central and southern Texas. It resembles *C. gilliesii* but lacks the sticky, viscid inflorescence of that species.

Chromosome number, $2n = 24$ (D. & W.).

Subfamily Papilionoideae

TREES, SHRUBS, HERBS, or twining vines, usually without spines. Leaves once pinnate to simple, never twice pinnate. Flowers irregular, of various colors in spikes, racemes, panicles, or solitary; petals usually separate, at least at the base, imbricate in bud with the banner (upper petal) external, the two lateral petals (wings) clawed and the two lower petals modified into a distinct keel (except in *Petalostemum* and *Eysenhardtia*, or when absent by reduction); sepals united, forming a distinct calyx tube; stamens 10 or fewer, usually united (not so in *Sophora* and *Baptisia* in Texas genera). A very large group with about 9,000 species distributed into approximately 400 genera. The species of this subfamily are found throughout the world, and they are next to the grass family in economic importance. Most of the agronomic species are cultivated in areas where rainfall or irrigation makes growth possible. Considerable research has been done concerning the development of appropriate cultivated strains under these conditions, and consequently a voluminous literature has accumulated on these plant types. Native rangeland legumes have been least studied and their part in the maintenance of natural grass stands has not yet been fully ascertained.

The subfamily Papilionoideae is often treated as a distinct family, the Fabaceae or Papilionaceae.

20. SOPHORA   Sophora

UNARMED DECIDUOUS or evergreen trees, shrubs, or perennial herbs.

LEAVES once compound, odd-pinnate with several to numerous leaflets; stipules minute, deciduous.

FLOWERS in handsome terminal or axillary racemes, yellow, white to purplish; stamens separate.

FRUIT a constricted, indehiscent, woody or fleshy, several- to many-seeded pod (rarely, 1- or 2-seeded by abortion).

BASIC chromosome numbers, as determined from counts on 9 species, $x = 9, 14$ (D. & W.).

A genus with about 70 species in the warmer regions of both hemispheres. Except for their ornamental value the species are of little economic importance.

KEY TO SPECIES

1. Plants herbaceous, 60 cm. tall or less   .   .   1. *S. nuttalliana*
1. Plants woody shrubs or small trees.
  2. Leaves glabrous or slightly pubescent at maturity; flowers white to purplish.
    3. Leaves with 5–11(13) leaflets; flowers violet-blue to purplish; leaflets coriaceous, thickened; fruit grayish to brown, 11 mm. thick or more; leaves persisting through the winter (evergreen).
      4. Leaflets 1.7 cm. wide or more, glabrous above; inflorescence 5–15 cm. long   .   .   .   .   2. *S. secundiflora*
      4. Leaflets 1–1.5 cm. wide, upper surface somewhat pubescent; known only from Guadalupe Mountains in Texas
      .   .   .   .   3. *S. formosa*
    3. Leaves (well-developed ones) with 13–17 leaflets; flowers white (rarely, faintly tinged with purple); fruit black at maturity, 8 mm. thick or less; leaves deciduous   .   .
    .   .   .   .   4. *S. affinis*
  2. Leaves densely and conspicuously pubescent; flowers bright yellow; plants of southernmost Texas   .   .   5. *S. tomentosa*

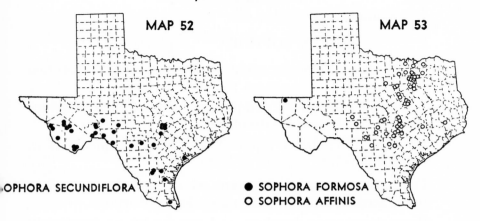

MAP 52

MAP 53

OPHORA SECUNDIFLORA

● SOPHORA FORMOSA
O SOPHORA AFFINIS

1. *Sophora nuttalliana* Turner, Field & Lab. 24: 15. 1956. WHITE LOCO

S. sericea Nutt.; not *S. sericea* Andrews

Western Texas, mostly in igneous or calcareous alluvial soils (Map 51). April–May. South Dakota to Arizona, New Mexico, and Texas. A low plant forming colonies from underground rhizomes. Vegetatively, *S. nuttalliana* resembles species of *Astragalus*, but when in flower or fruit it is readily distinguished from members of that genus.

Chromosome number not determined.

2. *Sophora secundiflora* (Ort.) Lag. *ex* DC., Cat. Hort. Monsp. 148. 1813. TEXAS MOUNTAIN LAUREL

Central, southern, and trans-Pecos areas of Texas in rocky limestone, igneous or, less often, sandy soils (Map 52). March–May (September). Texas to New Mexico and adjacent Mexico. The seeds and flowers of this species are reportedly extremely poisonous; one seed is often sufficient to cause the death of a human being (Standley, 1922). Cases of illness in children after eating the flowers have been reported from time to time in the Texas newspapers. Because of its attractive evergreen leaves and handsome flowers, the species is commonly cultivated as an ornamental in yards.

Chromosome number, $2n = 18$ (D. & W.).

3. *Sophora formosa* K. & P., Wash. Acad. Sci. Jour. 29:482. 1939

Known by a single, sterile collection from the Guadalupe Mountains of trans-Pecos Texas (deposited, Sul Ross State College Herbarium, Alpine, Texas) (Map 53). A rare plant previously known from only a few localities in New Mexico and Arizona. The Texas plant is tentatively referred here; the collection was made by Barton H. Warnock of Sul Ross State College. It is possible that the Texas material represents an undescribed species.

Chromosome number not determined.

4. *Sophora affinis* Torr. & Gray, Fl. N. Am. 1:390. 1838. EVE'S NECKLACE

Central Texas, mostly in rocky limestone soils on the Edwards Plateau or along creek bottoms in silty, alluvial soils (Map 53). March–May. Oklahoma, Arkansas, Louisiana, and Texas. The seeds of this species are reportedly poisonous.

Chromosome number not determined.

5. *Sophora tomentosa* L., Sp. Pl. 373. 1753. YELLOW SOPHORA

Southern Texas, mostly in loose sand along the Gulf Coast (Map 51). March–October. Widely distributed along the seashores in the tropics of both hemispheres.

Chromosome number, $2n = 18$ (D. & W.).

21. BAPTISIA   Wild Indigo

UNARMED, PERENNIAL HERBS, the stems arising from thick, tough rhizomes.

LEAVES 3-foliate to simple; stipules broad and leaflike to absent.

FLOWERS white to bright yellow or blue, in long or short

terminal racemes or, rarely, 1 to several in the upper leaf axils; stamens 10, separate to their base.

FRUIT an inflated, somewhat papery or woody, mostly indehiscent pod with 2 to numerous seeds.

BASIC chromosome number, as determined from counts on 7 species, $x = 9$ (D. & W.; Turner, 1956b).

A genus with about 30 species. Eastern and southeastern United States. The species are of little economic importance, though some of them are common "weeds" on overgrazed coastal pastures in Texas. *B. laevicaulis* and *B. viridis* form extensive hybrid swarms along the Gulf Coast grassland, especially where areas have become excessively disturbed (see remarks below). Certain species of the genus have been reported as poisonous to livestock in the southeastern states.

In spite of Larisey's rather recent monograph (1940) the genus is in much need of re-evaluation, especially from the standpoint of field work and population study.

KEY TO SPECIES

1. Flower pedicels at maturity, 15–35 mm. long; bracts of the inflorescence persisting.
   2. Leaflets predominantly narrow-spatulate, obtuse, rounded or gradually narrowed into an acute apex, mostly 10–35 mm. wide (intergrades with *B. laevicaulis*) . . 2. *B. leucophaea*
   2. Leaflets predominantly obovate-rhombic to obovate-cuneate, broadly acute or abruptly obtuse at the apex, mostly 20–25 mm. wide . . . . 1. *B. laevicaulis*
1. Flower pedicels 10 mm. long or less; bracts of the inflorescence early deciduous.
   3. Flowers blue; stipules broad and conspicuous, most of them persisting, 10 mm. long or more . . . 3. *B. australis*
   3. Flowers yellow or white; stipules lanceolate, deciduous or much reduced, 0.5–5 mm. long.
      4. Petioles (of mature leaves) slender, 5–12 mm. long; flowers white . . . . 4. *B. leucantha*
      4. Petioles short and thick, 0.5–5 mm. long; flowers yellow.
         5. Stems glabrous; flowers in terminal racemes.

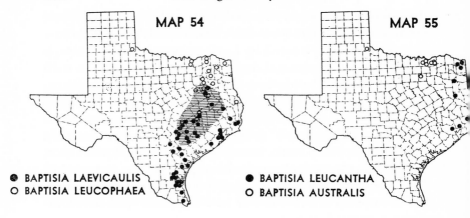

6. Leaves with 3 leaflets only; leaflets mostly 4.5–8 cm.
    long   .   .   .   .   5. *B. sphaerocarpa*
6. Leaves with 1 or 2 leaflets on the upper portions of the
    stems; leaflets mostly 2.5–5 cm. long   .   .   6. *B. viridis*
5. Stems densely short-pubescent; flowers either all axillary
    or both axillary and terminal   .   .   7. *B. nuttalliana*

1. *Baptisia laevicaulis* (Gray) Small, Bull. Torr. Bot. Club
25:134. 1895
    Baptisia bushii Small
    Baptisia cuneata Small
    Texas Gulf coast on sandy or clay soils, and inland on
sandy soils to Bastrop and Houston counties (Map 54).
March–May. Texas and Louisiana. The species is easily
recognized throughout most of its range, but northward it
grades into *B. leucophaea* with which it is closely related.
(Larisey, 1940, cites several collections of *B. laevicaulis*
from southern Texas as *B. leucophaea*, though they are not
mapped as such.) However, in the coastal area of Texas
extensive hybrid swarms are formed between *B. laevicaulis*
and *B. viridis*, especially in overgrazed fields (Turner, unpublished). These two species, morphologically, are very
distinct, yet whenever they occur together, hybrids or their

derivatives have been detected. This hybridization and re-combination of gene types has caused much taxonomic con-fusion. *B. bushii*, treated by Larisey as a "good" species, is apparently an occasional recombination type found in such hybrid swarms. Populations of *B. laevicaulis* from southern-most Texas, with nearly glabrate leaves, have been called *B. cuneata*, but extensive field work has indicated that these slightly differentiated geographical races are scarcely worthy of specific rank; intergrades with the typical form occur, and, except for marginal leaf pubescence, there seems to be no other character to mark them. In addition, *B. laevi-caulis* appears to hybridize on rare occasions with *B. nuttal-liana* in parts of its range.

Chromosome number, $n = 9$ (Turner, 1956b).

2. *Baptisia leucophaea* Nutt., Gen. N. Amer. Pl. 1:282. 1818. PLAINS WILD INDIGO

North-central and northeastern Texas, mostly in sandy or gravelly soils (Map 54). March–April. North-central United States to Texas. Two varieties of this species have been recognized for Texas: (1) var. *leucophaea*, with con-spicuously pubescent leaves and stems and (2) var. *gla-brescens* Larisey, with less pubescent leaves and glabrous stems. This latter variety is probably no more than a form of the species showing introgressant characters of *B. laevi-caulis*. Pubescent forms of *B. laevicaulis* are also known (see remarks above).

Chromosome number not determined.

3. *Baptisia australis* (L.) R. Br., Ait. Hort. Kew., ed. 2, 3:6. 1811. BLUE WILD INDIGO

North-central Texas in sandy or gravelly soils (Map 55). April–May. South-central and northeastern United States. In Texas the species is represented by var. *minor* (Lehm.) Fernald, which has shorter petioles and thicker leaves than the typical variety of the species. Hybrids between this species and *B. leucophaea* have been reported from adjacent

Oklahoma and elsewhere and are to be expected in north-central Texas where the ranges of these two taxa overlap. The described hybrids are quite striking and are known as *B.* × *bicolor* Greenm. & Larisey.

Chromosome number, $2n = 18$ (D. & W.).

4. *Baptisia leucantha* Torr. & Gray, Fl. N. Am. 1:385. 1840

Eastern Texas on sandy soils of pine and oak woodlands; also on clay in Harris, Liberty, and Jefferson counties (Map 55). April–June. Central United States from Minnesota and Wisconsin to Louisiana. A widespread variable species, especially in the southern part of its range where it hybridizes with several overlapping species. *B.* × *fragilis* Larisey is one such hybrid type described from Jefferson County, Texas, and adjacent Louisiana, and is the result of a natural cross between *B. leucantha* and *B. viridis* (Larisey, 1940). Hybrid swarms between the species are abundant along the railroad tracks between Dayton and Crosby, Texas (Turner, unpublished).

Chromosome number, $2n = 18$ (D. & W.; Turner, 1956b).

5. *Baptisia sphaerocarpa* Nutt., Jour. Acad. Nat. Sci. Phila. 7:97. 1834

Not collected in Texas as yet, but to be expected in the northeastern portion since collections are known from adjacent Oklahoma and Arkansas. The species reportedly hybridizes with *B. leucantha* and *B. leucophaea* in the latter states. *B. sphaerocarpa* is closely related to *B. viridis*, but has larger leaves and thinner pods than this latter species.

Chromosome number, $n = 9$ (Turner, unpublished).

6. *Baptisia viridis* Larisey, Ann. Mo. Bot. Gard. 27:196. 1940

Mostly eastern Texas in sandy, gravelly, or silty-clay soils of pine and oak woodlands or clay soils of coastal grassland (Map 56). April–May. South-central United States from Missouri to Louisiana. The species forms extensive hybrid swarms with *B. laevicaulis* on the southeastern

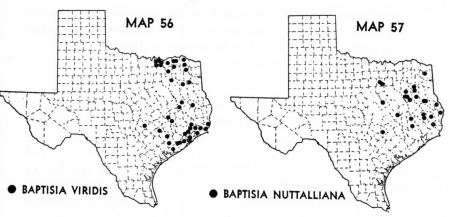

MAP 56 ● BAPTISIA VIRIDIS

MAP 57 ● BAPTISIA NUTTALLIANA

coastal plain (see comments under the latter species). In addition, hybrids between this species and *B. leucantha* (*B. × fragilis* Larisey) and between *B. leucophaea* (*B. × intermedia* Larisey) have been reported for Texas (in this latter case specimens cited by Larisey as hybrids from southeastern Texas are probably *B. viridis* × *B. laevicaulis*).

Chromosome number, $n = 9$ (Turner, 1956b).

7. *Baptisia nuttalliana* Small, Fl. Southeast. U. S., ed. 1. 599. 1903. NUTTALL WILD INDIGO

Eastern Texas, mostly in sandy or silty alluvial soils of pine and oak woodlands (Map 57). March–May. South-central United States from Missouri to Louisiana. Apparently this species occasionally hybridizes with *B. laevicaulis* and *B. leucophaea*.

Chromosome number, $n = 9$ (Turner, unpublished).

22. CROTALARIA   Crotalaria (Rattle-pod)

SHRUBS, PERENNIAL HERBS, or annuals.

LEAVES simple or trifoliate; stipules absent or pronounced, often decurrent along the stem.

FLOWERS few to numerous in terminal racemes or 1 to several in the axils of leaves; yellow, purplish, pink to nearly white; stamens 10, monadelphous (at least below the middle).

FRUIT a subglobose to cylindric, inflated pod with 2 to numerous seeds.

BASIC chromosome number, as determined from counts on approximately 41 species, $x = 7, 8$ (D. & W.).

A very large genus with about 300 species in the tropical and subtropical regions of both hemispheres, but particularly abundant in Africa. A few of the species extend into the temperate regions of North America as far as Vermont. Introduced species are sometimes used as cover crops in parts of the southeastern United States.

KEY TO SPECIES

1. Leaves trifoliate.
    2. Legume densely tomentose with spreading hairs; petioles with wide-spreading hairs 1–3 mm. long   .   .   1. *C. incana*
    2. Legume appressed-pubescent to nearly glabrate; petioles glabrate or with appressed hairs 1 mm. long or less   .   .
    .   .   .   .   2. *C. pumila*
1. Leaves simple.
    3. Leaves, the larger ones, 2 cm. wide or more; cultivated species.
        4. Stipules minute, setaceous or absent; inflorescence without bracts or the bracts small, subulate   .   .   .   3. *C. retusa*
        4. Stipules broad, ovate, conspicuous; inflorescence with conspicuous ovate bracts   .   .   .   .   .   4. *C. spectabilis*
    3. Leaves 1.5 cm. wide or less; native species.
        5. Pubescence on calyx and stem mostly of spreading hairs, 1–2 mm. long   .   .   .   .   .   .   5. *C. sagittalis*
        5. Pubescence of appressed hairs, 0.3–1 mm. long   .   .
        .   .   .   .   6. *C. purshii*

1. *Crotalaria incana* L., Sp. Pl. 716. 1753

    Southernmost Texas in deep sandy soils (Map 58).

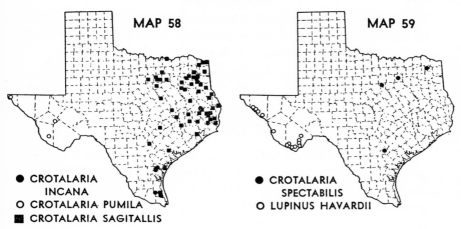

MAP 58

MAP 59

● CROTALARIA
INCANA
O CROTALARIA PUMILA
■ CROTALARIA SAGITALLIS

● CROTALARIA
SPECTABILIS
O LUPINUS HAVARDII

March–September. Florida peninsula through tropical America; also in Africa.

Chromosome number, $2n = 14$ (D. & W.).

2. *Crotalaria pumila* Ort., Hort. Bot. Matrit. Dec. 2:23. 1797
Crotalaria lupulina H.B.K.

Known in Texas only from the trans-Pecos area where it occurs in igneous or silty-clay soils (Map 58). August–September. Florida peninsula and tropical America.

Chromosome number, $2n = 32$ (D. & W.; Turner, 1956b).

3. *Crotalaria retusa* L., Sp. Pl. 715. 1753

An introduced species, native to the Old World tropics, occasionally escaping cultivation (Senn, 1939, cites a collection from Fort Worth, Texas).

Chromosome number, $2n = 16$ (D. & W.).

4. *Crotalaria spectabilis* Roth., Nov. Pl. Sp. 341. 1821. SHOWY CROTALARIA

An introduced species, native to the Old World tropics, occasionally escaping cultivation (Map 59). Similar to the above but distinguishable by the characters used in the key to species.

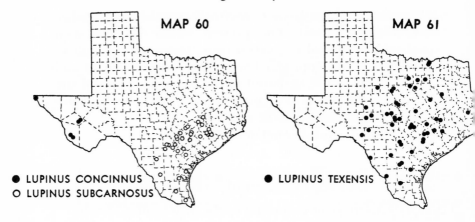

MAP 60

MAP 61

● LUPINUS CONCINNUS
○ LUPINUS SUBCARNOSUS

● LUPINUS TEXENSIS

Chromosome number not determined.

5. *Crotalaria sagittalis* L., Sp. Pl. 714. 1753. ARROW CROTA-
LARIA

Eastern Texas, mostly in sandy soils (Map 58). April–
September. Eastern, central, and southwestern United
States to Central America. Two varieties are listed for Texas
by Senn (1939): (1) var. *fruticosa* (Mill.) Fawc. & Rendl.,
with suffruticose stems, but otherwise differing in few de-
tails from (2) var. *sagittalis*, the predominant form of the
species in Texas, with herbaceous stems. Numerous intergrades between such extreme forms can be found in much
of the Texas material, and it is doubted that var. *fruticosa*,
as a biologic entity, occurs in the state.

Chromosome number, $2n = 32$ (Turner and Fearing, unpublished).

6. *Crotalaria purshii* DC., Prod. 2:124. 1825. PURSH CROTA-
LARIA

Reported for eastern Texas in sandy soils (Fernald, 1950;
Cory and Parks, 1937). Southeastern United States. Very
similar to *C. sagittalis* (above) and perhaps should be considered no more than a regional variety of that species. *C.
purshii* is reportedly a perennial, and *C. sagittalis* an annual

(Gleason, 1952). In Texas *C. sagittalis* may be an annual or short-lived perennial. The present writer has not seen specimens of typical *C. purshii* from Texas, though collections from Mississippi and Louisiana have been noted and the species may yet be found in the eastern portion of the state. The specimens of *C. purshii* cited for Texas by Senn (1939) are here treated as *C. sagittalis*.

Chromosome number not determined.

23. LUPINUS   Lupine (Bluebonnet)

UNARMED ANNUAL or perennial herbs, or less often shrubs.

LEAVES palmately compound with (1)2 to many leaflets; stipules adnate to the base of the petiole.

FLOWERS showy, mostly white, blue, or purplish (rarely, yellow), in rather large terminal racemes or spikes; stamens monadelphous, anthers of two kinds.

FRUIT a dry, oblong, or linear, somewhat flattened, dehiscent legume with several to numerous, hard, "pebble-like" seeds.

BASIC chromosome number, as determined from counts on approximately 20 species, $x = 12$ (D. & W.; Turner, 1957; Senn, 1938a, reports a probable base number of $x = 6$, the species with aberrant numbers being interpreted as derived aneuploids.)

A large, complex genus with perhaps 200 species in the temperate regions of North America, South America, and the Mediterranean area of Europe and western Asia. The genus seems to have a center of distribution in the western portion of the United States. Some of the members are important agricultural species, being used as cover crops for soil improvement. Most of the cultivated species are annuals, originally native to Europe but widely introduced elsewhere (Africa, Asia, Australia, and South America). *L. albus*, a white-flowered species, is commonly cultivated in Argentina, where it reportedly does well on fertile, neutral soils. Its introduction in Texas might prove profitable since the climates in parts of Texas and Argentina are quite similar. The Texas Bluebonnets (*L. subcarnosus* and *L. texensis*) are members of this genus and perhaps are worthy of extensive experimental study since the species are so common in the springtime on central Texas rangelands. A number of the western North American species of this genus are poisonous to livestock.

KEY TO SPECIES[2]

1. Pubescence of stem and petioles spreading at right angles; leaflets long-hairy on both surfaces; plants 15 cm. high or less
. . . . 1. *L. concinnus*
1. Pubescence of stem and petioles predominantly ascending or appressed; leaflets sparsely hairy or glabrous on upper surface.
  2. Racemes (including peduncle) 18–45 cm. long; wing petals 10–12 mm. long, 5–7 mm. wide; banner with creamy or yellowish eye; plants of trans-Pecos Texas . . 2. *L. havardii*
  2. Racemes 6–25 cm. long; wing petals 7–10 mm. long (often 12 mm. in *L. plattensis*); banner with bright white eye; plants of Panhandle, central, and eastern areas of Texas (perhaps *L. texensis* cultivated or occasionally introduced along roadsides in trans-Pecos Texas).
    3. Leaves with predominantly 7–10 (very rarely, 6 or 5) leaflets; plants perennial . . . . . 3. *L. plattensis*
    3. Leaves with predominantly 5–6 (very rarely, 7) leaflets; winter annuals or biennials.
      4. Wing petals on fresh flowers inflated, cheeklike in front view, light blue; pubescence of flower buds and mature pod yellowish-gray or brown; tip of incompletely expanded raceme rounded, not very conspicuous from a distance; leaflets mostly obtuse or rounded at apex; plants occurring in sandy or sandy-clay soils of oak and pine areas . . . . 4. *L. subcarnosus*
      4. Wing petals on fresh flowers not inflated, nearly straight in front view, dark blue (except for occasional albinos); pubescence of flower buds and mature pod silvery or

---

[2] Partially adapted from that of Shinners (1953).

white; tip of incompletely expanded raceme white, pointed or acute, conspicuous from a distance; leaflets mostly acute to obtuse at apex; plants occurring in calcareous, gravelly, or sandy-clay soils, but often growing in sand along roadways . .
. . . . 5. *L. texensis*

1. *Lupinus concinnus* Agardh., Syn. Gen. Lup. 6:1835.
ANNUAL LUPINE
Trans-Pecos Texas at mid-elevations of the Davis and Chinati mountains (Map 60). April. Southwestern United States and adjacent Mexico. A widespread, variable species, only a few collections known from Texas.
Chromosome number not determined.

2. *Lupinus havardii* S. Wats., Proc. Amer. Acad. 17:369.
CHISOS BLUEBONNET
Trans-Pecos Texas, mostly along dry, sandy, or gravelly washes of the Rio Grande (Map 59). February–April. Endemic to Texas and undoubtedly to adjacent Mexico.
Chromosome number not determined.

3. *Lupinus plattensis* S. Wats., Proc. Amer. Acad. 17:369. 1882
Not collected in Texas as yet, but to be expected in the Panhandle region since it is found in adjacent Cimarron County, Oklahoma (Shinners, 1953). West-central United States.
Chromosome number not determined.

4. *Lupinus subcarnosus* Hook., Bot. Mag. 63; t.3467. 1836.
TEXAS BLUEBONNET
Lupinus perennis var. *austrinus* Shinners
South-central and southern Texas, mostly in sandy soils of pine and oak woodlands (Map 60). March–April. Endemic to Texas, but often introduced elsewhere as an ornamental. Shinners described, from specimens collected in deep southeast Texas, what appeared to be a variety of *L. perennis*, a species with 7–11 leaflets, larger flowers and with a more northern and eastern distribution than *L. subcarnosus*. Close examination of Shinners' designated type

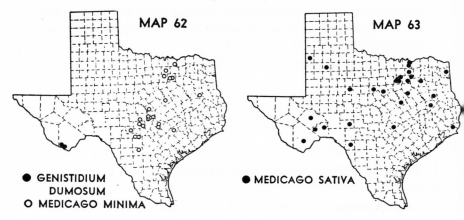

MAP 62

MAP 63

● GENISTIDIUM
   DUMOSUM
O MEDICAGO MINIMA

● MEDICAGO SATIVA

(deposited in University of Texas Herbarium) shows the plant to be typical *L. subcarnosus*, with small flowers, 5 leaflets, and general aspect of the species (it does not appear to be perennial, as suspected by Shinners).

L. subcarnosus, by act of the legislature, has been designated the official state flower of Texas, but the layman rarely makes any distinction between this species and *L. texensis* (below) and, hence, recognizes either of these as the state flower.

Chromosome number, $n = 18$ (Turner, 1957).

5. *Lupinus texensis* Hook., Bot. Mag. 63; t.3492. 1836. TEXAS BLUEBONNET

Central Texas, mostly on calcareous soils of the Blackland and Grand prairies and rocky soils of the Edwards Plateau (Map 61). March–May. Endemic to Texas, but often cultivated elsewhere. This species has been introduced along roadsides throughout much of the state. It is sometimes found in sandy soils in such localities, but under normal circumstances occurs in clay soils; *L. subcarnosus* occurs in sandy soils (Turner, 1957). Hybrids between these species have not been detected in the field, though the two appear closely related and often grow side by side where sandy and calcareous outcrops meet. Erbe (1957) was not able to hybridize the species artificially. See additional comments under *L. subcarnosus*, above.

Chromosome number, $n = 18$ (Turner, 1957).

24. GENISTIDIUM

UNARMED, SMALL, slender-stemmed shrub.

LEAVES pinnately 3-foliate; stipules subulate, less than 2 mm. long.

FLOWERS reddish or yellow; style subulate, bearded; stamens diadelphous, the vexillar stamen free.

FRUIT a dry, dehiscent, flattened legume.

BASIC chromosome number not determined.

A genus with a single species restricted to the Chihuahuan desert of Mexico and adjacent Texas.

Genistidium dumosum Johnston, Jour. Arn. Arb. 22:113. 1941

Known in Texas only from Brewster County on Reed Plateau near Terlingua, where it occurs in rocky limestone soil (Map 62). June–August. Discovery of this plant in the summer of 1941 by B. H. Warnock was the first record for the United States (specimen in the Sul Ross State College Herbarium; previously known only from the state of Coahuila, Mexico).

Chromosome number not determined.

25. MEDICAGO   Bur Clover

ANNUAL or perennial herbs or, very rarely, shrubs.

LEAVES trifoliate, the terminal leaflet stalked; leaflets with nerves ending in teeth; stipules partially fused to the petiole.

FLOWERS purple, bluish (rarely, white) or yellow in few- to many-flowered, often congested, racemes; stamens diadelphous.

FRUIT mostly a spirally, curved or coiled, often spiny, 1- to many-seeded, indehiscent pod.

BASIC chromosome number, as determined from counts on approximately 40 species, $x = 8(7?)$ (D. & W.).

A genus with about 120 species native to the temperate regions of Europe, Asia, and Africa, but widely introduced elsewhere. A voluminous literature has been built up on this genus, mainly as a result of agronomic research on the important agricultural species, *M. sativa* (alfalfa). Reference should be made to Whyte *et al.* (1953) for a concise account of the economic importance of this plant group. All of the species occurring in Texas have been introduced.

KEY TO SPECIES[3]

1. Flowers 6–11 mm. long, violet or bluish (rarely, white); plant perennial . . . . 1. *M. sativa*
1. Flowers 2–5 mm. long, yellow; plant annual or biennial.
  2. Stipules acuminate, slightly dentate to entire along the margin; leaves, stems, stipules, and calyxes more or less pubescent.
    3. Fruit a spineless or nearly spineless, black or dark brown pod at maturity; flowers 1.5–2 mm. long . . .
    . . . . 2. *M. lupulina*
    3. Fruit a spiny, coiled pod (bur) at maturity; flowers 2.5–4 mm. long . . . . 3. *M. minima*
  2. Stipules deeply divided, very conspicuously lacerate; plant essentially glabrous except for occasional stem pubescence.
    4. Fruit a tightly coiled, spineless, flattened pod, 10–15 mm. in diameter at maturity; flower pedicels 2–3 mm. long; stipules divided to the base . . . 4. *M. orbicularis*
    4. Fruit a loosely curled, barrel-shaped pod, 4–7 mm. in diameter; flower pedicels 0.5–2 mm. long; stipules deeply divided, but arising from a distinct membranous base.

---

[3] Partially adapted from that of Wagner (1948).

5. Stipules mostly divided deeply beyond the middle (individual stipule lacerations mostly 2–6 mm. long); leaflets mostly longer than wide, without a central spot . .
. . . . 5. *M. hispida*
5. Stipules not divided beyond the middle (individual stipule lacerations mostly 0.5–2 mm. long); leaflets as broad as long or broader, usually with a central purple spot .
. . . . 6. *M. arabica*

1. *Medicago sativa* L., Sp. Pl. 778. 1753. ALFALFA
  A widespread "weed" along roadways and in abandoned fields throughout Texas (Map 63). April–July. Native to western Asia, but now distributed over much of the temperate world. Alfalfa is a popular forage crop; it has been cultivated for at least 2,500 years, but only during the last few hundred years has it assumed world-wide use in agriculture. It is the most important forage crop in the United States, both as to total acreage sown and hay tonnage produced. A recent, concise account of this species may be found in Isely's treatment of the genus (1951).
  Chromosome number, $2n = 16, 32, 64$ (D. & W.).

2. *Medicago lupulina* L., Sp. Pl. 779. 1753. BLACK MEDICK
  Central and eastern Texas in silty or sandy soils along road-shoulders or in disturbed fields (Map 64). April–May (or later). Native to Eurasia, but now introduced and naturalized in temperate regions throughout much of the world.
  Chromosome number, $2n = 16, 32$ (D. & W.).

3. *Medicago minima* (L.) L., Amoen. Acad. 4:105. 1759. SMALL MEDICK
  Central and north-central Texas, mostly in calcareous or silty-sandy soils along roadways and in disturbed fields (Map 62). March–April (rarely, later). Native to Eurasia, but widely introduced in warm, temperate regions where it has become established in waste places. The species seems to grow best in the southeastern United States.

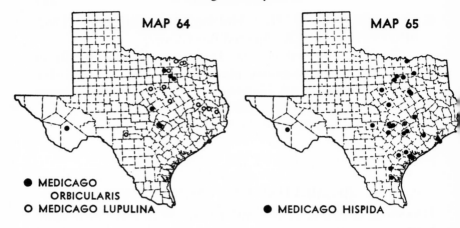

Chromosome number, $2n = 16$ (D. & W.).

4. *Medicago orbicularis* (L.) Bartalina, Cat. Piante . . . Citta di Siena, p. 60. 1776. BUTTON CLOVER

Sparingly distributed in central and north-central Texas on calcareous or silty-clay soils in lawns and along roadsides (Map 64). May. Native to Europe and northern Asia, but now introduced in much of the temperate world.

Chromosome number, $2n = 16$ (D. & W.).

5. *Medicago hispida* Gaertn., Fruct. et Semin Pl. 2:349. 1791. BUR CLOVER

Widely distributed throughout most of Texas in nearly all soil types (Map 65). March–April. Native to eastern and southern England; reportedly introduced and naturalized elsewhere (Clapham *et al.*, 1952). A form of the species with greatly reduced spines on the fruit has been called var. *apiculata* (Willd.) Burnat. It has been collected in relatively few localities in Texas. Bur Clover is used as a spring pasture legume on rangelands and as a hay or cover crop in cultivated areas. According to Shinners (1956), the correct name for this species is *M. polymorpha* L.

Chromosome number, $2n = 14, 16$ (D. & W.).

6. *Medicago arabica* (L.) Hudson, Fl. Ang. 288. 1762. SPOTTED MEDICK (Spotted Bur Clover)

Central and north-central Texas, mostly on gravelly or silty-sandy soils in grassy places and waste ground (Map 66). February–April. Native to the Mediterranean region of Europe and Asia, but widely introduced elsewhere. Chromosome number, $2n = 16$ (D. & W.).

26. MELILOTUS   Sweet Clover

UNARMED, ANNUAL or perennial herbs with erect or decumbent stems.

LEAVES trifoliate, the terminal leaflets stalked and with denticulate margins; stipules fused to the base of the petiole.

FLOWERS numerous in elongate, often spikelike, axillary racemes, yellow or white; stamens diadelphous.

FRUIT a small, globose or ovate, 1- to 2-seeded pod.

BASIC chromosome number, as determined from counts on approximately 14 species, $x = 8$ (D. & W.).

A genus with about 22 species native to the Mediterranean area of Europe, Africa, and western Asia. Some of the species are important crop plants and have become widely naturalized throughout the world. In the southeastern United States they play important roles, both as weedy and cultivated plants, being common in the pioneer stage of plant succession on fallow, impoverished soils and as a source of hay in planned pasture improvement programs.

KEY TO SPECIES

1. Flowers white; pod reticulate-veined, dark brown to black at maturity . . . . 1. *M. albus*
1. Flowers yellow; pod appearing cross-ribbed or smooth, gray, light brown to tan at maturity.

The Legumes of Texas

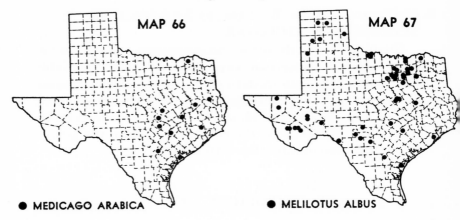

MAP 66

MAP 67

● MEDICAGO ARABICA

● MELILOTUS ALBUS

2. Flowers 1–3 mm. long; pod globose; stipules widened below
with scarious margins; annuals   .   .   .   *2. M. indicus*
2. Flowers 3–5 mm. long; pod ovoid (longer than broad);
stipules not widened below with scarious margins; biennials
.   .   .   .   *3. M. officinalis*

1. *Melilotus albus* Desr., *in* Lam. Encyc. 4:63. 1797. WHITE
SWEET CLOVER

Widely planted in Texas as a pasture legume and commonly escaping cultivation (Map 67). This species is reportedly native to western Asia, but has been introduced
throughout much of Europe, Asia, Australia, and temperate South and North America. A number of strains are
grown in Texas, but the annual strain, Hubam, is perhaps
the most common.

Chromosome number, $2n = 16, 24, 32$ (D. & W.).

2. *Melilotus indicus* (L.) All., Fl. Pedem. 1:308. 1785. SOUR
CLOVER

Cultivated in Texas, but commonly escaping and becoming a weed along roadsides and in abandoned fields (Map
68). Native to the Mediterranean area of western Asia, but
widely introduced elsewhere.

Chromosome number, $2n = 16$ (D. & W.).

3. *Melilotus officinalis* (L.) Lam., Fl. Fr. 2:594. 1778.
YELLOW SWEET CLOVER

Often cultivated in Texas and sometimes escaping to become a weed along roadways and in abandoned fields (Map 69). Native to western Asia, but widely introduced elsewhere. In flower this species is likely to be confused with the more common *M. indicus*, but the species can be readily distinguished by the characters used in the key.

Chromosome number, $2n = 16$ (D. & W.).

27. TRIFOLIUM   Clover

UNARMED, ANNUAL, biennial, or perennial herbs with rounded stems.

LEAVES palmately trifoliate or, rarely, pinnately trifoliate; stipules mostly ovate, entire, fused to the petiole for about half their length.

FLOWERS in capitate or dense subcapitate spikes, the petals white to reddish or yellow; stamens diadelphous.

FRUIT a small, 1- to 4-seeded pod, enclosed in the persistent calyx and corolla at maturity.

BASIC chromosome number, as determined from counts on approximately 40 species, $x = 6, 7, 8, 9$ (D. & W.).

A large, predominantly temperate genus with some 300 species, mostly in the northern hemisphere. The genus seems to have two centers of distribution: (1) the Mediterranean region of Europe, Asia, and Africa and (2) western North America. However, a number of the agriculturally important species have been widely introduced throughout the world and have become established over much of this area as common weeds, particularly in lawns. The principal agricultural value of clover is in its use as forage, hay, and pasture crops. Texas has a few native species, but practically nothing is known about their agronomic potential.

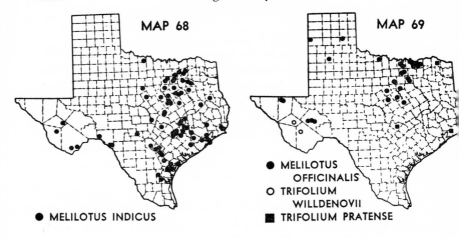

MAP 68

MAP 69

● MELILOTUS
   OFFICINALIS
○ TRIFOLIUM
   WILLDENOVII
■ TRIFOLIUM PRATENSE

● MELILOTUS INDICUS

KEY TO SPECIES[4]

1. Leaves pinnately trifoliate (the terminal leaflet with a longer stalk than the lateral ones); flowers yellow.
   2. Banner 2–4 mm. wide; flowers 20–40 in each head   . .
   .   .   .   .   1. *T. campestre*
   2. Banner 1–2 mm. wide; flowers 5–18 in each head   . .
   .   .   .   .   2. *T. dubium*
1. Leaves palmately trifoliate (all the leaflets sessile or nearly so); flowers not yellow.
   3. Leaflets more than three times as long as wide.
      4. Stem and foliage silky-pubescent; flowering heads densely pubescent, not subtended by bracts; introduced   . .
      .   .   .   .   3. *T. arvense*
      4. Stem and foliage glabrous; flowering heads glabrous, subtended by deeply divided bracts; native to mountainous areas of trans-Pecos Texas   .   .   .   4. *T. willdenovii*
   3. Leaflets rarely more than twice as long as wide, usually one to one and one half times as long as wide.
      5. Flower heads sessile or nearly so at the ends of main branches (peduncles less than 0.5 cm. long)   . .
      .   .   .   .   5. *T. pratense*
      5. Flower heads on peduncles 1 cm. long or more.
         6. Flower heads at least twice as long as wide (3 cm. long or more), spikelike   .   .   .   6. *T. incarnatum*

---

[4] Adopted with certain modifications from that of Hennen (1950).

6. Flower heads globose (umbellate or capitate), about as long as wide.

  7. Flowers sessile in the heads or nearly so (pedicels 1 mm. long or less); cultivated or rare introduced species.

    8. Petioles and stems glabrous or nearly so; fruit developing above ground.

      9. Erect or ascending annual; flower heads without bracts at the base   .   .   .   7. *T. resupinatum*

      9. Creeping perennial; flower heads with definite bracts at the base   .   .   .   .   .   8. *T. fragiferum*

    8. Petioles and stems pubescent with wide-spreading, tawny hairs; fruit subterranean   .   .   .   .

.   .   .   .   9. *T. subterraneum*

  7. Flowers distinctly pediceled (mature pedicels 1–8 mm. long); native or common introduced species.

    10. Mature flowering heads 2.5–4 cm. across; stems erect or ascending, not creeping   .   .   10. *T. reflexum*

    10. Mature flowering heads 2.5(3) cm. across or less; if somewhat more, then the stems prostrate and creeping.

      11. Flower heads short-racemose, the pedicels arising along a distance of 2–5 mm. at the end of the peduncle; calyx lobes shorter than the tube; stems creeping; flowers white   .   .   .   11. *T. repens*

      11. Flower heads umbellate, the pedicels all arising at the end of the peduncle; calyx lobes, at least some of them, as long as the tube; stems erect or ascending, if creeping, then fruits developing below the ground; flowers deep rose-red to yellowish-white.

        12. Peduncles arising from creeping stolons; stems rooting at the nodes; petals, at maturity, two to four times as long as the calyx   .   .

.   .   .   .   .   .   12. *T. amphianthum*

        12. Peduncles arising from erect or ascending stems; stems not rooting at the nodes; petals one to two times as long as the calyx.

          13. Calyx lobes, some of them, about as long as wide   .   .   .   13. *T. bejariense*

          13. Calyx lobes, all of them, two to three times as long as wide   .   .   14. *T. carolinianum*

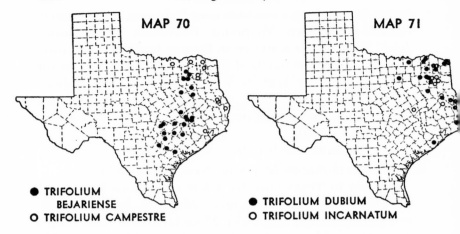

MAP 70   MAP 71

● TRIFOLIUM
    BEJARIENSE   ● TRIFOLIUM DUBIUM
○ TRIFOLIUM CAMPESTRE   ○ TRIFOLIUM INCARNATUM

1. *Trifolium campestre* Schreb., *in* Sturm, Deutschl. Fl. 16: pl. 13. 1804. LOW HOP CLOVER
   Sandy soils along roadways of pine and oak woodlands in eastern Texas (Map 70). April. A weedy plant, introduced into the United States from Europe. The species is common in northern parts of the United States. There has been much confusion over the correct name to be used for the various introduced hop clovers (Fernald, 1950; Isely, 1951). The name used here is that adopted by most European and some American workers (Herman, 1953).
   Chromosome number, $2n = 14$ (D. & W.).

2. *Trifolium dubium* Sibth., Fl. Oxon. 231. 1794. SHAMROCK (Small Hop Clover)
   Eastern Texas in sandy soils (Map 71). April–May. The species is native to Eurasia but has been widely introduced in the United States and elsewhere. A weedy plant, occasionally found along roadsides and in disturbed areas.
   Chromosome number, $2n = 14, 28, 16$ (D. & W.).

3. *Trifolium arvense* L., Sp. Pl. 769. 1753. RABBIT-FOOT CLOVER
   Known to Texas only by a single collection from a popu-

lation found along a roadside near Robinson in McLennan County (Southern Methodist University Herbarium). June. The species is native to Europe but has been introduced throughout much of the world, particularly in the cooler, temperate regions of the Northern Hemisphere. According to Isely (1951), the species grows best in light, sandy soils, frequently occurring in sterile soils where other legumes fail.

Chromosome number, $2n = 14$ (D. & W.).

4. *Trifolium willdenovii* Spreng., Syst. 3:208. 1826

Known to Texas only by a few collections from creek bottoms in the trans-Pecos area (Map 69). August. Southern Canada down the Rocky Mountains and coast ranges to northern Mexico. A widespread, variable species. The Texas and Mexican material (adjacent state of Chihuahua) is placed here with some doubt, having more linear leaves and smaller heads than is typical for the species in the far-western United States. Hennen (1950) called the Texas material *T. wormskjoldii* Lehm., which, according to Abrams (1944), is a species of Greenland. Ewan (1943) has discussed the nomenclature of this species. Chromosome number not determined.

5. *Trifolium pratense* L., Sp. Pl. 768. 1753. RED CLOVER

Occasionally escaping cultivation in Texas; known from only a few collections (Map 69). May–July. European in origin, but the species is now found in nearly all parts of the temperate world where agriculture is practiced. Isely (1951) has given a concise account of its agronomic importance.

Chromosome number, $2n = 14$ (28) (D. & W.).

6. *Trifolium incarnatum* L., Sp. Pl. 769. 1753. CRIMSON CLOVER

Cultivated in the eastern part of the state, but occasionally escaping (Map 71). April. Native to the Mediterranean area of Europe but widely introduced elsewhere as a pasture and soil improvement legume.

Chromosome number, $2n = 14$ (D. & W.).

7. *Trifolium resupinatum* L., Sp. Pl. 771. 1753. PERSIAN CLOVER

Known from cultivation and as an occasional escapee in Texas (Map 75). April–May. Native to Europe but widely introduced elsewhere.

Chromosome number, $2n = 16$ (D. & W.).

8. *Trifolium fragiferum* L., Sp. Pl. 772. 1753. STRAW-BERRY CLOVER

Not known from Texas as yet but reportedly occurring in lawns in the north-central United States and as an occasional escapee from cultivation elsewhere. Native to Eurasia and North Africa.

Chromosome number, $2n = 16$ (D. & W.).

9. *Trifolium subterraneum* L., Sp. Pl. 767. 1753. SUBTER-RANEAN CLOVER

Known to Texas only as a lawn weed from Texas A. & M. Experimental Farm, Denton, Denton County. May. Native to Eurasia.

Chromosome number, $2n = 12, 16$ (D. & W.).

10. *Trifolium reflexum* L., Sp. Pl. 766. 1753. BUFFALO CLOVER

Northeastern Texas, mostly in sandy soils of cutover pine and oak woodlands (Map 73). May–July. Widespread throughout the central and southeastern United States.

Chromosome number, $2n = 16$ (D. & W.).

11. *Trifolium repens* L., Sp. Pl. 767. 1753. WHITE CLOVER

One of the most common cultivated species in Texas, widely used as a lawn and pasture legume and frequently escaping (Map 72). March–November. Native to northern Europe but now widespread throughout the temperate

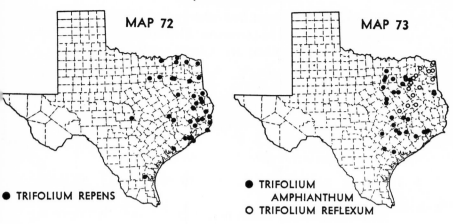

MAP 72

● TRIFOLIUM REPENS

MAP 73

● TRIFOLIUM
   AMPHIANTHUM
O TRIFOLIUM REFLEXUM

and subtropical world. A large number of cultivated strains of this species have received names in the agronomic trade.

Chromosome number, $2n = 32, 48$ (64) (D. & W.).

12. *Trifolium amphianthum* Torr. & Gray, Fl. N. Am. 1:316. 1838. PEANUT CLOVER

Eastern Texas in sandy and sandy-clay soils of open pine and oak woodlands (Map 73). March–May. Endemic to Texas and probably Louisiana. The species is called "peanut clover" because of the cleistogamous flowers which develop underground fruit, suggesting little peanuts. Nothing is known about the agronomic potential of the native Texas clovers. Most of them appear to grow readily in disturbed places, and perhaps with appropriate selection and breeding work they might prove successful cover crops in the areas of Texas where they are already edaphically and climatically adapted.

Chromosome number not determined.

13. *Trifolium bejariense* Moric., Pl. Noav. Am. 2. 1833

Eastern Texas in sandy or sandy-clay soils of open woods and prairies (Map 70). March–May. Endemic to Texas.

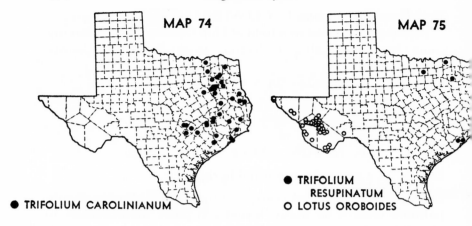

MAP 74

MAP 75

● TRIFOLIUM CAROLINIANUM

● TRIFOLIUM
RESUPINATUM
O LOTUS OROBOIDES

Chromosome number, $2n = 16$ (Turner and Fearing, unpublished).

14. *Trifolium carolinianum* Michx., Fl. Bor. Am. 2:58. 1803. CAROLINA CLOVER

Central and eastern Texas, mostly in sandy or sandy-clay soils of pine and oak woodlands. (Map 74). April–May. Southeastern United States from Kansas to Virginia and Florida.

Chromosome number not determined.

Excluded or Rarely Introduced Species

Trifolium hybridum L. ALSIKE CLOVER

This plant is reported for Texas by Cory and Parks (1937). It is a widespread weed in the northern United States, but the present writer has not seen specimens from Texas, nor was it reported by Hennen (1950) in his treatment of the Texas species. However, it is not unlikely that it might become introduced in the near future since it is reported as a lawn weed in adjacent states. *T. hybridum* resembles *T. repens*, but does not have the creeping stems of that species.

Chromosome number, $2n = 16$ (D. & W.).

Trifolium glomeratum L. CLUSTER CLOVER

Reported as a weed in a field of Hop Clover, the seed having come from Australia; collection from Freestone County (Shinners, 1954).

Chromosome number, $2n = 16$ (D. & W.).

28. LOTUS   Deer Vetch (Trefoil)

UNARMED, ANNUAL or perennial herbs.

LEAVES once compound (rarely, simple), odd-pinnate or sub-palmate with 3 to many leaflets; stipules membranous to glandlike, often appearing absent.

FLOWERS 1 to several in axillary umbels, whitish to yellowish, rose or purple; stamens diadelphous.

FRUIT a dry, straight or strongly arcuate, dehiscent or inde-hiscent, several- to many-seeded pod.

BASIC chromosome number, as determined from counts on approximately 8 species, $x = 6, 7$ (D. & W.).

A genus with about 120 species in the temperate regions of both hemispheres, but centered in the Old World about the Mediterranean Sea; in the New World the genus seems centered in western North America. Some of the species are important agricultural legumes, being used for pasturage and hay in many parts of the world. *L. corniculatus*, a deep-rooted perennial, produces good cover in poor or shallow soils and is cultivated in parts of Texas. Experimental plantings of this species at the University of Texas have shown exceptional growth and survival even during months of severe drought. Other species in this group from the drier areas of north Africa and Europe might prove successful in any introduction program. *L. oroboides*, a native of trans-Pecos Texas, appears to be an important grassland legume in rocky, igneous soils of that area.

The American species of this genus are sometimes placed in the genus *Hosackia*, the Old World species being restricted to the genus *Lotus*.

KEY TO SPECIES

1. Introduced or cultivated species; perennial; peduncles with
   (2)3 to several flowers or fruits   .   .   .   1. *L. corniculatus*
1. Native species; annual or perennial; peduncles with a single
   (rarely, 2) flower(s) or pod(s).
   2. Perennials; plants of trans-Pecos Texas   .   .   2. *L. oroboides*
   2. Annuals; plants of central and eastern Texas   .   .   .
   .   .   .   .   3. *L. purshianus*

1. *Lotus corniculatus* L., Sp. Pl. 775. 1753. BIRDS-FOOT TRE-
   FOIL

   An introduced species, occasionally escaping cultivation and becoming established along roadsides. Native to southern Europe, but widely cultivated and perhaps now established in parts of America, Asia, North Africa, and Australia. An extremely variable species with several intergrading varieties. Some of the varieties seem particularly adapted to the dry summers of central Texas and should be worthy of extensive experimental work in this area.

   Chromosome number, $2n = 12, 24$ (D. & W.).

2. *Lotus oroboides* (H.B.K.) Ottley *ex* Kearney & Peebles,
   Jour. Wash. Acad. Sci. 29:483. 1939

   Lotus puberulus (Benth.) Greene

   Trans-Pecos Texas, mostly in rocky, igneous soils at altitudes of 3,500–5,500 feet (Map 75). March–September. Southwestern United States and adjacent Mexico. A widespread, highly variable species, especially in Texas (Ottley, 1944). Ottley lists several varieties of this species which occur outside of Texas; in addition, a number of presumed hybrids with other species have been reported. *L. oroboides* appears to be in need of detailed field work and experimental garden studies.

   Chromosome number not determined.

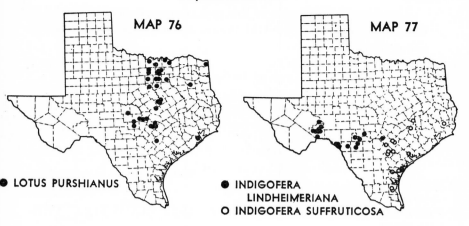

MAP 76 · LOTUS PURSHIANUS

MAP 77 · INDIGOFERA LINDHEIMERIANA · O INDIGOFERA SUFFRUTICOSA

3. *Lotus purshianus* (Benth.) Clements & Clements, Rocky Mt. Fl. p. 183. 1914. DEER VETCH

Lotus americanus (Nutt.) Bisch.; not *L. americanus* Vell.

Hosackia americana (Nutt.) Piper

North-central, central, and south-central Texas, mostly in gravelly or disturbed clay soils (Map 76). April–June. Pacific Coast states eastward into the central United States. A widespread, variable species, especially in the western part of its range.

Chromosome number not determined.

Excluded Species

Lotus wrightii (Gray) Greene

Reported for western Texas by Cory and Parks (1937). The present writer has not seen specimens from Texas. Ottley (1944) does not cite collections of the species from Texas, though it is apparently common in the mountainous areas of adjacent New Mexico and Mexico.

Lotus rigidus (Benth.) Greene

Reported for Texas by Cory and Parks (1937), apparently in error for *L. oroboides*. *L. rigidus* is a species of Arizona and westward.

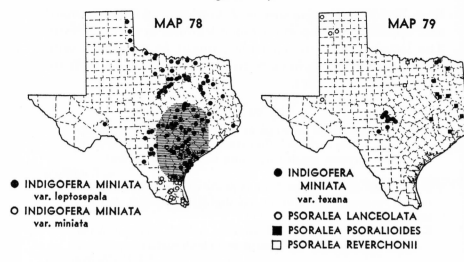

29. INDIGOFERA   Indigo

UNARMED, PERENNIAL herbs or shrubs.

LEAVES once compound, odd-pinnate or less often palmate or unifoliate; stipules herbaceous, subulate to setaceous.

FLOWERS usually in axillary racemes or loose spikes, pink, red to purple; stamens diadelphous or monadelphous.

FRUIT a 1- to many-seeded, globose to linear, dehiscent pod, the seeds usually separated by false partitions.

BASIC chromosome number, as determined from counts on 20 species, $x = 8, 7$ (6) (D. & W.; Turner, 1956b).

A large genus with about 400 species in the tropical and subtropical regions of both hemispheres. Many of the species have agricultural value as fodder, cover, and green manure. Two species, *I. suffruticosa* and *I. tinctoria*, are utilized as a source of indigo in some tropical areas. In the southeastern United States *I. hirsuta* (Hairy Indigo) is utilized as a cover and forage crop on moderately poor, sandy soils with little lime. Two of the native species, *I. miniata* and *I. lindheimeri-ana*, appear to be important range legumes in parts of Texas. The latter species, in particular, might be improved, with appropriate breeding work, with the closely related *I. suffruti-cosa* or some of its allies.

KEY TO SPECIES

1. Stems procumbent or prostrate to somewhat ascending; leaflets 5–9, never more, arranged alternately along the rachis; well-developed racemes much surpassing the subtending leaf .
. . . . 1. *I. miniata*
1. Stems stiffly erect; leaflets 7–15, opposite or nearly so along the rachis; racemes as long as, or but slightly exceeding, the sub-tending leaf.
  2. Mature pods with a small, swollen, reddish, glabrous knob at the base; leaves densely strigose on both surfaces . .
  . . . . 2. *I. lindheimeriana*
  2. Mature pod acute at base, w/o a swollen reddish knob; leaves sparsely strigose, the upper surface less densely so . .
  . . . . 3. *I. suffruticosa*

1. *Indigofera miniata* Ortega, Hort. Matr. Dec. 98. 1789. SCARLET PEA
  I. argentata Rydb.
  Mostly southern, central, and northern Texas in sandy or deep limestone soils (Maps 78 and 79). April–September. Georgia and Florida to Kansas and south to Mexico, also in Cuba. A widespread, highly variable species, showing much intergradation between the several infraspecific taxa enumerated below. In Texas the species is represented by the following varieties: (1) var. *texana* (Buckley) Turner,[5] with predominantly curled or nonappressed hairs on the stems and long stipules (5–8 mm.), occurring in the central mineral region of Texas (Mason, Llano, Gillespie, Burnet, and Kerr counties); this variety is fairly well marked; (2) var. *leptosepala* (Nutt.) Turner (= *I. leptosepala* Nutt.),

---

[5] *Indigofera miniata* var. *texana* (Buckley) Turner, comb. nov.—*I. texana* Buckley, Proc. Acad. Nat. Sci. Phila. 1861:431. 1861.

with nearly all the stem hairs appressed and with petals 8–20 mm. long, occurring mostly in northern and central Texas but intergrading completely with (3) the typical variety *miniata*, with petals 5–8 mm. long, appressed stem hairs and with stipules 3–5 mm. long. Rydberg (1923) accredits *I. brevipes* (S. Wats.) Rydb. to Texas, but this taxon seems confined to Mexico. *I. argentata* Rydb., also accredited to Texas by Rydberg, appears to be no more than densely pubescent individuals of *I. miniata*, scarcely worthy of varietal status.

Chromosome number, $n = 16$ (for var. *texana* and var. *leptosepala*; Turner, 1956b).

2. *Indigofera lindheimeriana* Scheele, Linnaea 21:464. 1848. LINDHEIMER INDIGO

Central and trans-Pecos Texas, mostly in limestone or silty, alluvial soils (Map 77). June–August. Endemic to south-central Texas and adjacent Mexico; closely related to the species below but clearly distinct.

Chromosome number, $n = 8$ (Turner, 1956b).

3. *Indigofera suffruticosa* Mill., Gard. Dict., ed. 8, no. 2. 1768. ANIL INDIGOFERA

Southeastern Texas, usually in sandy or silty, alluvial soils (Map 77). July–November. Mostly tropical and subtropical areas of both hemispheres, but native to the Americas; it has become naturalized elsewhere.

Chromosome number, $2n = 32$ (D. & W.).

Cultivated Species

Indigofera tinctoria L. CEYLON INDIGO

This species is widely cultivated and is reported for Texas by Cory and Parks (1937). It is native to southern India. The present writer has not seen specimens from Texas. It can be distinguished from all other Texas species by its linear, long-beaked pods.

Chromosome number not determined.

30. PSORALEA   Psoralea

HERBS, SHRUBS, or rarely, small trees; in Texas the species are all perennial herbs.

LEAVES palmately or pinnately compound to, rarely, simple. The leaflets usually glandular-dotted; stipules present, persistent; stipels present.

FLOWERS of various colors (except yellow) in axillary or terminal racemes; rarely, in capitate heads or single; stamens diadelphous or monadelphous.

FRUIT a dry, 1-seeded, indehiscent pod.

BASIC chromosome number, as determined from counts on 12 species, $x = 10$, 11 (D. & W.; Turner, 1956b; Ledingham, 1957).

A genus with about 120 species occurring in both the Old and New Worlds, but primarily centered in southern Africa, North America, and Australia. The species are of little economic importance, though *P. bituminosa* and *P. patens* have been reported as valuable forage plants in some areas.

KEY TO SPECIES[6]

1. Leaves pinnately 3-foliolate.
  2. Leaflets lanceolate to oblong-lanceolate, three to seven times as long as wide; flowers in elongate, spikelike racemes.
    3. Corolla deep purple, 7–10 mm. long; calyx 3.2–4 mm. long
      .   .   .   .   *1. P. simplex*
    3. Corolla lilac or lavender, 4–7 mm. long; calyx 2–3 mm. long
      .   .   .   .   *2. P. psoralioides*
  2. Leaflets rhombic-lanceolate to ovate or orbicular, about one to two (or three) times as long as wide; flowers few, in heads or very short spikes.

    4. Plant with elongate, prostrate, leafy stems; leaves membranous, upper and lower surfaces not markedly different,

---

[6] Adapted, with certain modifications, from that of Shinners (1951).

variously pubescent to nearly glabrous, without white veins
. . . . 3. *P. rhombifolia*
4. Plant scapose (stem not evident); leaves leathery, the
lower surface densely appressed-pubescent, the upper glabrous or nearly so, except for the prominent white veins
. . . . 4. *P. rydbergii*
1. Leaves palmately 3- to 7-foliolate, or the uppermost only 1- to
2-foliolate (the middle leaflets rarely stalked in aberrant forms
of *P. scaposa*).
5. Inflorescence a slender, loose raceme or slender, interrupted
spike less than 1.5 cm. thick; bracts of inflorescence 4 mm. or
less long; calyx 2–7 mm. long (enlarging in fruit).
6. Branches and under surface of leaflets glabrous and prominently resin-dotted; calyx lobes 1 mm. or less long .
. . . . 5. *P. lanceolata*
6. Branches and under surface of leaflets minutely or conspicuously pubescent, not prominently resin-dotted; calyx
lobes (1)1.5–6 mm. long.
7. Pedicels of many or all the flowers longer than the
calyxes; calyxes 2–4 mm. long (slightly enlarged in
fruit).
8. Leaflets linear to lanceolate, seven to sixteen times as
long as wide . . . . . 6. *P. linearifolia*
8. Leaflets oblanceolate to obovate, two to six times as
long as wide . . . . . 7. *P. tenuiflora*
7. Pedicels absent or shorter than the calyxes; calyxes 5–7
mm. long (conspicuously enlarged in fruit) . .
. . . . 8. *P. digitata*
5. Inflorescence a dense, spikelike raceme 2–4 cm. thick; bracts
of inflorescence 4–15 mm. or more long; calyx 8–17 mm. or
more long.
9. Plants with leafy stems, the leaves at flowering time not all
at, or very near, the base.
10. Stem glabrous or appressed pubescent.
11. Bracts ovate-orbicular, abruptly contracted to a narrow, sharp point, the body about as wide as long
. . . . 9. *P. reverchonii*
11. Bracts ovate-lanceolate or oblong-lanceolate, gradually acute or acuminate, much longer than wide.
12. Leaflets linear-lanceolate or narrowly oblong-
lanceolate, seven to fourteen times as long as
wide . . . . . . 10. *P. cyphocalyx*

12. Leaflets broadly lanceolate, rhombic, elliptic, or oboval,
two to five times as long as wide . . 11. *P. cuspidata*
10. Stem densely white tomentose or hirsute with widely
spreading hairs.
13. Stem with a dense soft, white pubescence; plants 30 cm.
tall or more at maturity, the main stem branched .
. . . . 12. *P. argophylla*
13. Stem with coarse, spreading pubescence; plants 20 cm.
tall or less, the main stem unbranched . . .
. . . . 13. *P. latestipulata*
9. Plants scapose, all the leaves at or crowded close to the base at
flowering time.
14. Peduncles and petioles with widely spreading hairs .
. . . . 14. *P. subulata*
14. Peduncles and petioles with appressed or closely ascending
hairs.
15. Peduncles (3)4–10 cm. long, slightly shorter to slightly
longer than the petioles; root a small, nearly globose
tuber . . . . 15. *P. scaposa*
15. Peduncles 1–3 cm. long, mostly less than half as long as
the petioles; root an oblong-fusiform tuber . .
. . . . 16. *P. hypogaea*

1. *Psoralea simplex* Nutt. *ex* Torr. & Gray, Fl. N. Am. 1:303.
1838
Orbexilum simplex (Nutt.) Rydb.
Eastern Texas, mostly in damp sandy soils of pine and
oak woodlands (Map 80). May. Southeastern United
States from Alabama to Oklahoma and Texas.
Chromosome number not determined.

2. *Psoralea psoralioides* (Walt.) Cory, Rhodora 38:406. 1936.
SAMPSON'S SNAKEROOT
Psoralea pedunculata (Mill.) Vail; not *Psoralea pedun-
culata* Poir.
Orbexilum pedunculatum (Mill.) Rydb.
Eastern Texas in sandy soils of pine and oak woodlands
(Map 79). April–May. Southeastern United States from
Illinois to Virginia and south to Texas and Florida. In

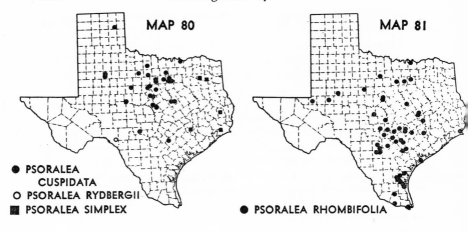

MAP 80

● PSORALEA
　CUSPIDATA
○ PSORALEA RYDBERGII
▨ PSORALEA SIMPLEX

MAP 81

● PSORALEA RHOMBIFOLIA

Texas the species is represented by the variety *eglandulosa* (Ell.) Freeman, which is distinguished from the typical variety of more eastern distribution by having eglandular floral bracts (or nearly so).

Chromosome number not determined.

3. *Psoralea rhombifolia* Torr. & Gray, Fl. N. Am. 1:303. 1838
　　Pediomelum rhombifolium (Torr. & Gray) Rydb.
　　Pediomelum coryi Tharp & Barkley
　　Southern, central, and north-central Texas, mostly in sandy or silty-clay soils (Map 81). March–July. Louisiana to Texas and adjacent Mexico. A variable taxon, but very distinct from the other species of Texas *Psoralea*.
　　Chromosome number, $n = 11$ (Turner, 1956b).

4. *Psoralea rydbergii* Cory, Rhodora 38:405. 1936
　　Pediomelum humile Rydb.
　　Psoralea humilis (Rydb.) Macbr.; not *P. humilis* Mill.
　　Known to Texas by only two collections, both from Val Verde County (San Felipe Springs; foot of Devil's Lake, about 20 miles north to northwest of Del Rio; May 9, 1947, Southern Methodist University Herbarium) (Map 80). Texas and adjacent Mexico.
　　Chromosome number not determined.

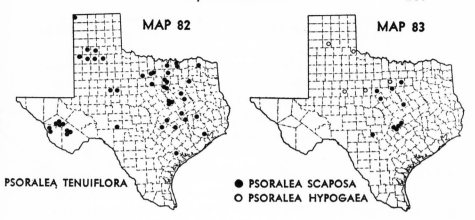

MAP 82

MAP 83

PSORALEA TENUIFLORA

● PSORALEA SCAPOSA
O PSORALEA HYPOGAEA

5. *Psoralea lanceolata* Pursh, Fl. Am. Sept. 2:475. 1814
   Psoralidium lanceolatum (Pursh) Rydb.
   Psoralea micrantha Gray
   Psoralidium micranthum (Gray) Rydb.
   Northern Panhandle of Texas, mostly in sandy soils along stream bottoms (Map 79). June. South-central Canada south to Texas and Arizona.
   Chromosome number, $n = 11$ (Ledingham, 1957).

6. *Psoralea linearifolia* Torr. & Gray, Fl. N. Am. 1:300. 1838
   Psoralidium linearifolium (Torr. & Gray) Rydb.
   North-central and Panhandle areas of Texas, mostly in rocky, calcareous soils (Map 86). May–June. Central United States from Nebraska and Wyoming south to Texas.
   Chromosome number not determined.

7. *Psoralea tenuiflora* Pursh, Fl. Am. Sept. 2:475. 1814.
   SCURVY PEA
   Psoralea floribunda Nutt. *ex* Torr. & Gray
   Psoralea obtusiloba Torr. & Gray
   Psoralidium obtusilobium (Nutt.) Rydb.
   Psoralidium tenuiflorum (Pursh) Rydb.
   Throughout most of Texas except for the extreme east-

ern and southern portions of the state (Map 82). May–July. Central United States from Illinois to Montana and south to Texas and Arizona, also adjacent Mexico. A widespread, variable species; in trans-Pecos Texas, populations with somewhat broader leaflets than is typical for the species have been called var. *bigelovii* (Rydb.) Macbride (= *Psoralea bigelovii* [Rydb.] Tidestrom). Complete intergradation between these taxa occur.

Chromosome number not determined.

8. *Psoralea digitata* Nutt. *ex* Torr. & Gray, Fl. N. Am. 1:300. 1838

Psoralidium digitatum (Nutt.) Rydb.

North-central and eastern Texas, mostly in sandy soils (Map 84). May–July. Central United States from South Dakota to Texas. Two varieties are recognized for Texas: (1) var. *digitata*, with narrowly oblong-lanceolate leaflets, those of the middle leaves 4–8 mm. wide, and (2) var. *parvifolia* Shinners, with linear leaflets, those of the middle leaves 2–4 mm. wide. The former variety is characteristic of the West and East Cross Timbers; the latter of oak and pine woodlands of northeast Texas. As viewed from herbarium material, the taxa appear to intergrade.

Chromosome number, $n = 11$ (for var. *parvifolia*, Turner, 1956b; and var. *digitata*, Turner and Fearing, unpublished).

9. *Psoralea reverchonii* Wats., Proc. Amer. Acad. 21:447. 1886

North-central Texas in rocky limestone soils (Map 79). July. Endemic to central Oklahoma and adjacent Texas.

Chromosome number not determined.

10. *Psoralea cyphocalyx* Gray, Boston Jour. Nat. Hist. 6:172. 1850

Pediomelum cyphocalyx (Gray) Rydb.

Eastern border of Edwards Plateau in central and north-

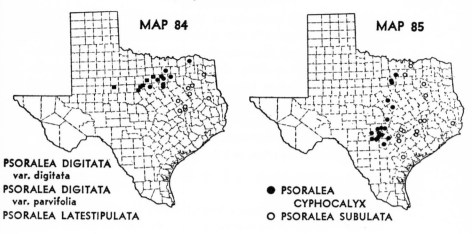

MAP 84

MAP 85

PSORALEA DIGITATA
  var. digitata
PSORALEA DIGITATA
  var. parvifolia
PSORALEA LATESTIPULATA

● PSORALEA
  CYPHOCALYX
O PSORALEA SUBULATA

central Texas on rocky limestone soils (Map 85). April–June. Endemic to Texas.

Chromosome number, $n = 11$ (Turner, 1956b).

11. *Psoralea cuspidata* Pursh, Fl. Am. Sept. 741. 1814

  Pediomelum cuspidatum (Pursh) Rydb.

  Pediomelum caudatum Rydb.

  Psoralea caudata (Rydb.) Cory

Central and northern Texas mostly in rocky limestone soils (Map 80). April–May. A widespread, variable species of the central United States, occurring from Minnesota to Montana and south to Texas. In northern Texas the species is represented by tall, branched populations with narrowly lanceolate stipules; in south-central Texas and west to Pecos County, populations occur with short, mostly unbranched stems and broad, ovate stipules.

Chromosome number, $n = 11$ (Turner and Fearing, unpublished).

12. *Psoralea argophylla* Pursh, Fl. Am. Sept. 475. 1814

Not collected in Texas as yet, but to be expected since specimens have been seen from Cimarron County, Okla-

homa, only a short distance north of the Texas border.
July–August. Southern Canada through the Great Plains
to New Mexico and Oklahoma.

Chromosome number, $n = 11$ (Ledingham, 1957).

13. *Psoralea latestipulata* Shinners, Field & Lab. 19:22. 1951

North-central Texas in rocky limestone soils (Map 84).
March–May. Endemic to Texas. Closely related to *P. cuspidata*, but smaller and less branched.

Chromosome number not determined.

14. *Psoralea subulata* Bush, Ann. Rept. Mo. Bot. Gard. 17:120.
1906

Pediomelum subulatum (Bush) Rydb.

Eastern Texas mostly in deep sandy soils of pine or oak
woodlands (Map 85). March–May. Texas and Louisiana
and possibly in adjacent Oklahoma. Forms of this species,
with smaller leaves, have been recognized as a distinct
variety (var. *minor* Shinners); however, such small-
leaved forms are found throughout the range of *P. subulata* and appear to be no more than occasional variants.

Chromosome number, $n = 11$ (Turner, unpublished).

15. *Psoralea scaposa* (Gray) Macbride, Contrib. Gray Herb.
65:15. 1922

Pediomelum scaposum (Gray) Rydb.

Pediomelum goughae Tharp & Barkley

Central and north-central Texas in rocky limestone soils
(Map 83). April–May. Endemic to Texas. Closely related
to *P. hypogaea*, and perhaps best treated as a variety of
that species, as Gray interpreted the taxa (see remarks below). *P. scaposa* and *P. hypogaea* appear to intergrade
where their ranges approach each other. The *P. hypogaea*
complex is in much need of critical field study. Shinners
has described a variety (var. *breviscapa*) of this species
which the present writer interprets as being fairly typical
P. hypogaea and so treats the taxon below.

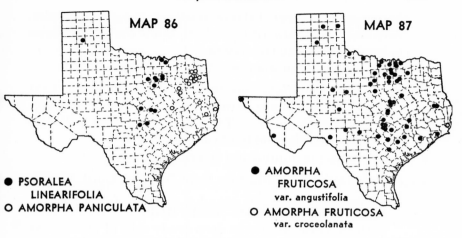

MAP 86

● PSORALEA
LINEARIFOLIA
O AMORPHA PANICULATA

MAP 87

● AMORPHA
FRUTICOSA
var. angustifolia
O AMORPHA FRUTICOSA
var. croceolanata

Chromosome number, $n = 11$ (Turner, 1956b; reported as *P. hypogaea*).

16. *Psoralea hypogaea* Nutt. *ex* Torr. & Gray, Fl. N. Am. 1:302. 1838

Pediomelum hypogaeum (Nutt.) Rydb.

Northwestern and Panhandle areas of Texas, mostly in sandy soils (Map 83). April–June. Central United States from Nebraska to Montana and south to Texas and New Mexico. Closely related to *P. scaposa* (above) and possibly intergrading with that species. Shinners (1951) treated the Texas forms of this species as *P. scaposa* var. *breviscapa*. *P. hypogaea* picks up some of the characters of *P. scaposa* in the southern part of its range; perhaps this has helped confuse their circumscription.

Chromosome number not determined.

Excluded Species

Psoralea esculenta Pursh

Reported for Texas by Small (1903) and Cory and Parks (1937).

According to Shinners (1951), the species is incorrectly reported for the state. The present writer has not seen specimens of *P. esculenta* from Texas. Most of the reports are probably misidentifications of *P. cuspidatum*.

Chromosome number, $n = 11$ (Ledingham, 1957).

31. AMORPHA   Amorpha

UNARMED SHRUBS or perennial, suffruticose herbs.

LEAVES once compound, odd-pinnate with 7 or more usually glandular-punctate leaflets; stipules slender, falling early; stipels present.

FLOWERS in spikelike racemes, the petals reduced to a single purplish, blue, or whitish banner; stamens 10, exserted.

FRUIT an indehiscent, relatively short, 1- or 2-seeded, glandular-punctate pod.

BASIC chromosome number, as determined from counts on 4 species, $x = 10$ (D. & W.).

A genus with about 20 species in the temperate regions of North America. The species are characteristically members of damp or wet habitats. They are of little economic significance, though *A. fructicosa* is sometimes grown as an ornamental.

KEY TO SPECIES

1. Leaflets (1.5)2–3 cm. wide; calyx uniformly pubescent.
    2. Leaflets with conspicuous raised veins beneath; spikes of inflorescence (mature ones) (15)20–40 cm. long   .   .   .
        .   .   .   .   1. *A. paniculata*
    2. Leaflets inconspicuously veined beneath; spikes of inflorescence 10–20 cm. long   .   .   .   .   .   .   2. *A. texana*
1. Leaflets 0.8–1.8(2.2) cm. wide; calyx glabrous to variously pubescent.
    3. Leaves sessile or subsessile, the petiole 8 mm. long or less
        .   .   .   .   3. *A. canescens*
    3. Leaves distinctly petiolate, the petioles 10 mm. long or more.

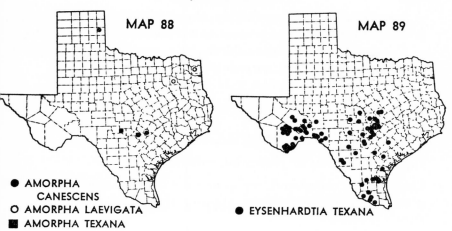

● AMORPHA
   CANESCENS
○ AMORPHA LAEVIGATA
■ AMORPHA TEXANA

● EYSENHARDTIA TEXANA

4. Stalk of the leaflet conspicuously warty with raised glands; calyx conspicuously glandular; mature flowering racemes 15–30 cm. long . . . . . . 4. *A. laevigata*
4. Stalk of the leaflet inconspicuously glandular, if at all; calyx indistinctly glandular; flowering racemes 10–15(20) cm. long . . . . 5. *A. fructicosa*

1. *Amorpha paniculata* Torr. & Gray, Fl. N. Am. 1:306. 1838
   Endemic to east Texas and adjacent Louisiana in deep woodlands and bogs (Map 86). May–June.
   Chromosome number not determined.

2. *Amorpha texana* Buckl., Proc. Acad. Phila. 1861:452. 1862. TEXAS AMORPHA
   Central Texas in limestone soils along stream bottoms (Map 88). May. Apparently a rare endemic species. Glabrate forms have been segregated as var. *glabrescens* Palmer.
   Chromosome number not determined.

3. *Amorpha canescens* (Nutt.) Pursh, Fl. Am. Sept. 467. 1814. LEAD-PLANT
   Eastern, central, and Panhandle areas of Texas in mostly sandy or gravelly soils. (Map 88). May–July. Widespread

species occurring from south-central Canada to Texas and New Mexico. Glabrate forms from eastern Texas have been segregated as var. *glabrata* Gray; in its typical form the species is densely pubescent.

Chromosome number, $2n = 20$ (D. & W.).

4. *Amorpha laevigata* Nutt. *ex* Torr. & Gray, Fl. N. Am. 1:306. 1838

The present writer has seen two Texas collections of this species (Map 88). June. It is apparently closely related to *A. texana* and perhaps is best treated as a narrow-leaved eastern variety of that species.

Chromosome number not determined.

5. *Amorpha fruticosa* L., Sp. Pl. 713. 1753. BASTARD IN-DIGO

Amorpha fragrans Sweet

Apparently throughout Texas along stream bottoms (Map 87). April–June. A widespread, highly variable species occurring from Canada to northern Mexico. Palmer (1931) credits several varieties and forms to Texas. Of these, only the following seem worthy of mention: (1) var. *fruticosa*, the typical form of the species, with broad, elliptic leaflets (uncommon and occurring only in easternmost Texas); (2) var. *angustifolia* Pursh, with narrower leaflets (the common form of the species in central and western Texas); (3) var. *croceolanata* Mouill., with densely pubescent leaves and calyxes (eastern Texas); and (4) var. *occidentalis* (Abrams) Kearney & Peebles (= *A. occidentalis* Abrams), with oval or oblong, glabrate leaflets and mostly solitary racemes (western and Panhandle areas of Texas). Except for the var. *croceolanata* from deep east Texas, the varieties appear to intergrade to a considerable degree. This species-complex is in need of critical field study.

Chromosome number, $2n = 40$ (D. & W.; Turner, 1956b, for var. *angustifolia*).

32. EYSENHARDTIA   Kidney Wood

UNARMED, or rarely, thorny, much-branched shrubs or small trees.

LEAVES once compound, odd-pinnate, with numerous, usually small, glandular-punctate leaflets; stipules narrowly subulate; stipels absent, but small apiculate pustule subtending each leaflet.

FLOWERS white in terminal, spikelike racemes; petals essentially all alike, scarcely differentiated into banner, wings, and keel; stamens 10, diadelphous.

FRUIT a small, glandular, mostly indehiscent, 2–4-seeded pod.

BASIC chromosome number, as determined from counts on a single species, $x = 20$ (Turner and Fearing, unpublished).

A small genus with about 12 species in the drier, semidesert areas of North America. The species are of little economic importance, though some of the Mexican species are used locally for medicinal purposes (Standley, 1922).

KEY TO SPECIES

1. Leaflets mostly 5–12 mm. long, 15–40 to each leaf; widespread species   .   .   .   .   1. *E. texana*
1. Leaflets 3–4 mm. long, 13–17 to each leaf; rare species of Presidio County, Texas, and adjacent Mexico   .   .   2. *E. spinosa*

1. *Eysenhardtia texana* Scheele, Linnaea 21:462. 1848. TEXAS KIDNEY WOOD
     Eysenhardtia angustifolia Pennell
     Southern, central, and trans-Pecos areas of Texas, mostly in dry, limestone soils, but occurring on sandy soils in south Texas (Map 89). April–September. Texas and adjacent Mexico. Forms of this species from the trans-Pecos area of Texas with longer leaves and leaflets were described as *E.*

angustifolia by Pennell (1919). However, examination of 80 different collections of *E. texana* in the University of Texas Herbarium from throughout the state shows extensive intergradation in the characters used by Pennell. This fact, combined with apparent lack of any geographical correlation of the larger-leaved forms, seems to indicate that *E. angustifolia* is no more than the extremes of a rather widespread, variable species.

Chromosome number, $2n = 40$ (Turner and Fearing, unpublished).

2. *Eysenhardtia spinosa* Engelm. *ex* Gray, Bost. Jour. Nat. Hist. 6:174. 1850. SPINY KIDNEY WOOD

This species was formerly known only from the state of Chihuahua, Mexico. The first collection for Texas and the United States was made by the late L. C. Hinckley in Presidio County on Capote Peak; at an altitude of 5,000 feet; August (specimen in Sul Ross State College Herbarium, Alpine, Texas).

Chromosome number not determined.

33. DALEA   Dalea

UNARMED (rarely, spinescent) annual or perennial herbs or shrubs.

LEAVES once compound (rarely, simple), odd-pinnate with glandular-dotted leaflets (glands often obscured by pubescence); stipules and stipels present.

FLOWERS in terminal racemes, often spikelike, of various colors; petals distinctly papilionaceous, forming a banner, wings, and keel, these arising from the base of the staminal tube or on its side, but not at its apex; stamens 9 or 10 (rarely, 7 or 8), monadelphous.

FRUIT a dry, indehiscent, 1- to 2-seeded pod, mostly included in the persistent calyx or but slightly exceeding it.

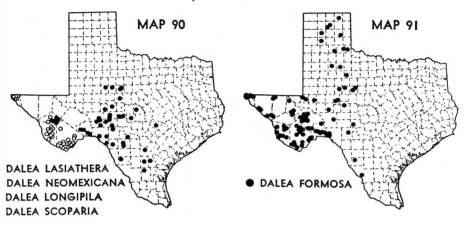

MAP 90

DALEA LASIATHERA
DALEA NEOMEXICANA
DALEA LONGIPILA
DALEA SCOPARIA

MAP 91

● DALEA FORMOSA

BASIC chromosome number, as determined from counts on 7 species, $x = 7$ (D. & W.; Turner, 1956b; Turner and Fearing, unpublished).

A large genus with about 250 species in the drier, warmer regions of North and South America. The species are of little economic importance, though some of them are frequent in rocky, grassy habitats in parts of Texas; some of the shrubs, such as *D. formosa*, have been reported as important browse plants.

KEY TO SPECIES

1. Leaves simple (rarely, 3-foliate) . . . 1. *D. scoparia*
1. Leaves never simple.
  2. Plants more or less shrubby or suffrutescent, the stems persisting to produce new branchlets each year (straggling and stoloniferous in *D. greggii*).
    3. Branches and leaves glabrous.
      4. Calyx lobes as long as the tube or longer . . .
      . . . . 2. *D. formosa*
      4. Calyx lobes much shorter than the tube . . .
      . . . . 3. *D. frutescens*
    3. Branches and leaves villous to puberulent.
      5. Plants straggling, the stems decumbent and rooting at

the nodes; calyx lobes lanceolate, 1–3 mm. long; leaves
densely sericeous . . . . . . 4. *D. greggii*
  5. Plants with stiffly erect stems; calyx lobes triangular,
  0.5–1 mm. long *or*, if longer, subulate and some of them
  recurved at tip; leaves variously pubescent but not densely
  sericeous.
    6. Calyx lobes subulate, at least some of them recurved at
    the tip; plants of extreme southern Texas . . .
    . . . . 5. *D. thyrsiflora*
    6. Calyx lobes triangular, 0.5–1 mm. long, not recurved at
    tip; plants of western Texas . . . 6. *D. argyrea*
2. Plants annual or perennial, the stems not persisting (the very
  lowest portions of the stem sometimes persisting in *D. wrightii*).
    7. Flowers short-pediceled (best seen on old spikes after the
    flowers fall), spreading at right angles or reflexed at maturity;
    spikes densely covered with long, brown or tawny hairs.
      8. Bracts ovate, 10–15 mm. long; stems stiffly erect, sparsely
      pubescent, conspicuously glandular-pustulate . . .
      . . . . 7. *D. lachynostachys*
      8. Bracts lanceolate, 8 mm. long or less; stems straggling,
      densely soft pubescent, with scattered glands, but not
      pustulate.
        9. Leaflets cuneate-obovate, truncate or retuse at apex, with
        conspicuous crenulate margins, the glands nearly all
        marginal . . . . . . 8. *D. neomexicana*
        9. Leaflets mostly elliptic, rounded at apex (rarely, retuse),
        without crenulate margins, the glands scattered, not
        conspicuously marginal . . . . 9. *D. longipila*
    7. Flowers sessile, or nearly so, ascending, never reflexed; spikes
    variously pubescent.
      10. Leaves completely glabrous.
        11. Plants annual.
          12. Plants robust at maturity, 30–80 cm. high; stem a
          central main axis arising from a stout taproot.
            13. Spikes lax, 3- to 15-flowered (rarely, more),
            the flowers 2–4 mm. apart on the axis . .
            . . . . 10. *D. enneandra*
            13. Spikes congested, 20- to many-flowered, the
            flowers 1 mm. apart or less . 11. *D. alopecuroides*
          12. Plants small, 10–30 cm. high; stems several from
          a delicate taproot; known in Texas only from the
          Davis Mountains.

14. Flowing peduncles mostly 3–9 cm. long at maturity;
    keel 2 mm. long .   .   .   .   12. *D. polygonoides*
14. Flowing peduncles mostly 1–3 cm. long at maturity;
    keel 3 mm. long .   .   .   .   13. *D. brachystachys*
11. Plants perennial.
    15. Calyx lobes subulate, six to forty times as long as wide,
        usually as long as the calyx tube or longer .   .
        .   .   .   .   14. *D. pogonathera*
    15. Calyx lobes acute to acuminate, six times as long as wide
        or less, shorter than the calyx tube .   15. *D. lasiathera*
10. Leaves variously pubescent.
    16. Stems prostrate, widely spreading; flowers red to pink.
        17. Calyx tube and lobes densely villous .   16. *D. lanata*
        17. Calyx tube glabrous, the lobes villous .   .
        .   .   .   .   17. *D. terminalis*
    16. Stems erect to suberect or decumbent, but not prostrate and
        spreading; flowers yellow.
        18. Stipules setiform, indurate, 5–9 mm. long.
            19. Leaflets 3; spikes 1.5 cm. wide .   .   18. *D. jamesii*
            19. Leaflets 5–7 (rarely, 3; if so, the spikes 2 cm. wide
                or more); spikes 1.5–2.5 cm. wide at maturity .
                .   .   .   .   .   .   19. *D. wrightii*
        18. Stipules short, subulate, scarcely indurate, 1–3 mm.
        long.
            20. Leaflets 3 .   .   .   .   .   .   20. *D. hallii*
            20. Leaflets 5–9.
                21. Stems coarse, erect, 3–5 dm. high; spikes 1.5–2.5
                    cm. wide .   .   .   .   .   21. *D. aurea*
                21. Stems slender, often decumbent, 1–4 dm. high;
                    spikes 1.3 cm. wide or less .   .   22. *D. nana*

1. *Dalea scoparia* Gray, Mem. Amer. Acad. II 4:32. 1849.
BROOM DALEA
    Psorothamnus scoparius (Gray) Rydb.
    El Paso County in trans-Pecos Texas, where it occurs in
deep, sandy soil at altitudes of 4,000–4,500 feet (Map 90).
Texas to Arizona and adjacent Mexico.
    Chromosome number not determined.

2. *Dalea formosa* Torr., Ann. Lyc. N. Y. 2:177. 1827.
FEATHER DALEA

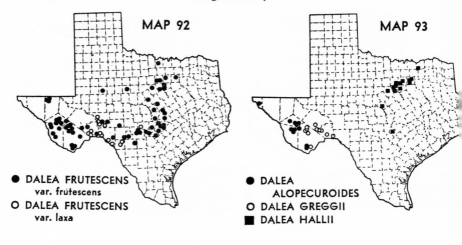

MAP 92

● DALEA FRUTESCENS
var. frutescens
○ DALEA FRUTESCENS
var. laxa

MAP 93

● DALEA
ALOPECUROIDES
○ DALEA GREGGII
■ DALEA HALLII

Parosela formosa (Torr.) Vail

Throughout western Texas, mostly in rocky limestone soils (Map 91). June–September. Southwestern United States and adjacent Mexico. A common shrub, reportedly valuable as a browse plant in trans-Pecos Texas.

Chromosome number not determined.

3. *Dalea frutescens* Gray, Bost. Jour. Nat. Hist. 6:175. 1850. BLACK DALEA

Parosela frutescens (Gray) Vail *ex* Rose

Central and trans-Pecos Texas mostly in rocky limestone and igneous soils (Map 92). July–October. Texas, New Mexico, and adjacent Mexico. Most of the Texas material is typical of the species and falls into the var. *frutescens*, having flowers in congested spikes or heads, these latter 0.5–1.5 cm. long. Specimens from south-central Texas (Val Verde to Gillespie counties) may be found with flowers in loose spikes, 1.5–6 cm. long. Such forms have been called var. *laxa* (Rydb.) Turner (= *Parosela laxa* Rydb.). Intergrades between these forms occur.

Chromosome number not determined.

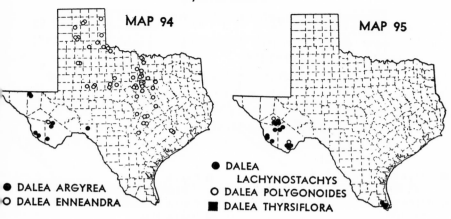

MAP 94

MAP 95

● DALEA ARGYREA
○ DALEA ENNEANDRA

● DALEA LACHYNOSTACHYS
○ DALEA POLYGONOIDES
■ DALEA THYRSIFLORA

4. *Dalea greggii* Gray, Mem. Amer. Acad. II 5:314. 1854. GREGG DALEA

Parosela greggii (Gray) Heller

Trans-Pecos Texas in rocky, limestone soils, at altitudes of 2,000–4,500 feet (Map 93). March–August. Texas to southern Mexico (Gentry, 1950).

Chromosome number not determined.

5. *Dalea thyrsiflora* Gray, Proc. Amer. Acad. 5:177. 1861

Parosela humilis (Mill.) Rydb., not *Dalea humilis* G. Don

Southernmost Texas, mostly in clay or silty, alluvial soils (Map 95). September–December. Texas to Guatemala.

Chromosome number not determined.

6. *Dalea argyrea* Gray, Pl. Wright. 1:47. 1852. SILVER DALEA

Parosela argyrea (Gray) Heller

Trans-Pecos Texas in rocky limestone soils, at altitudes of 1,500–5,000 feet (Map 94). July–September. Texas, New Mexico, and adjacent Mexico. A shrub to 3 feet tall and reportedly poisonous to stock.

Chromosome number not determined.

7. *Dalea lachynostachys* Gray, Pl. Wright. 1:46. 1852.
GLAND-LEAF DALEA
Parosela lachynostachys (Gray) Heller
Trans-Pecos Texas in limestone or igneous soils, at altitudes of 3,500–5,500 feet (Map 95). June–October. Texas to Arizona and adjacent Mexico.
Chromosome number, $2n = 14$ (Turner and Fearing, unpublished).

8. *Dalea neomexicana* (Gray) Cory, Rhodora 38:406. 1936.
NEW MEXICO DALEA
Parosela neomexicana (Gray) Heller
Trans-Pecos Texas in limestone or gypseous soils, at altitudes of 2,000–5,000 feet (Map 90). March–November. Texas, New Mexico, and adjacent Mexico. Closely related to *D. mollis Benth.*, and perhaps better treated as a variety of that species (*D. mollis* var. *neomexicana* Gray). The *D. mollis* complex is in need of critical study.
Chromosome number not determined.

9. *Dalea longipila* (B. L. Robinson) Cory, Rhodora 38.406. 1936
Parosela longipila (B. L. Robinson) Rydb.
Val Verde and Terrell counties in rocky, limestone soils (Map 90). June–October. Texas and adjacent Mexico. Closely related to *D. mollis* Benth., and the above taxon, and perhaps best treated as a variety of the former (*D. mollis* var. *longipila* B. L. Robinson *ex* Rydb.). The species-complex is in need of critical study.
Chromosome number not determined.

10. *Dalea enneandra* Nutt., Fraser Cat. 1813
Dalea laxiflora Pursh (see nomenclatural note by Shinners, 1949).
Central and Panhandle areas of Texas, mostly in silty or sandy, alluvial soils; a single population known from

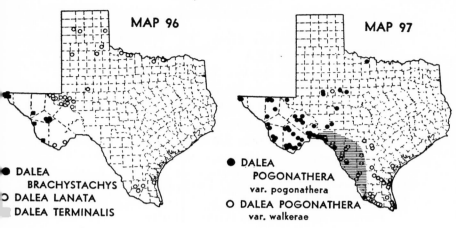

MAP 96

● DALEA
   BRACHYSTACHYS
○ DALEA LANATA
▌ DALEA TERMINALIS

MAP 97

● DALEA
   POGONATHERA
   var. pogonathera
○ DALEA POGONATHERA
   var. walkerae

trans-Pecos Texas (Map 94). June–July. North-central United States to Texas. Most of the Texas material is typical of the species and falls into the var. *laxiflora*; however, apparently dwarf populations of the species are known from Hill and Ellis counties and have been named var. *pumila* Shinners.[7]

Chromosome number not determined.

11. *Dalea alopecuroides* Willd., Sp. Pl. 3:1336. 1803. FOX-TAIL DALEA

   Parosela alopecuroides (Willd.) Rydb.
   Dalea oreophila (Cory) Cory
   Petalostemum oreophilum Cory
   Trans-Pecos Texas, mostly in igneous soils, at altitudes of 3,500–5,500 feet (Map 93). September–October. North-central United States to northernmost Mexico.
   Chromosome number, $2n = 14$ (D. & W.).

12. *Dalea polygonoides* Gray, Pl. Wright. 2:39. 1853
   Parosela polygonoides (Gray) Heller
   Known to Texas only from collections made on the high-

---

[7] *Dalea enneandra* var. *pumila* (Shinners) Turner, comb. nov.— *Dalea laxiflora* var. *pumila* Shinners, Field & Lab. 21:164. 1953.

er elevations of Mt. Livermore in Jeff Davis County (Map 95). September. Texas to Arizona and adjacent Mexico. A delicate annual, much resembling the species below, which is found at somewhat lower elevations (4,000–6,000 feet).

Chromosome number not determined.

13. *Dalea brachystachys* Gray, Pl. Wright. 2:39. 1853

Parosela brachystachys (Gray) Heller

Lower elevations of the Davis Mountains in trans-Pecos Texas, mostly in igneous soils, at altitudes of 4,000–6,000 feet (Map 96). August–September. Texas to Arizona and adjacent Mexico. Much resembling the above species but differing in flower technicalities and occurring at somewhat lower elevations.

Chromosome number, $2n = 14$ (Turner and Fearing, unpublished).

14. *Dalea pogonathera* Gray, Mem. Amer. Acad. II. 4:31. 1849. BEARDED DALEA

Parosela pogonathera (Gray) Vail

North-central, trans-Pecos, and southern areas of Texas in limestone or sandy soils (Map 97). March–September. Texas to Arizona and adjacent Mexico. Two varieties may be recognized in Texas: (1) var. *pogonathera*, the typical form of the species, having deep purple petals and a thicker, more condensed spike, occurring in western Texas, and (2) var. *walkerae* (Tharp & Barkley) Turner (= *Parosela walkerae* Tharp & Barkley), having pale purple or flesh-colored petals and a narrower, less dense spike, occurring in southern Texas. All intergrades between the two taxa are found as one examines a wide range of material collected between these two geographical regions.

Chromosome number, $2n = 14$ (Turner and Fearing, unpublished, for var. *walkerae*).

15. *Dalea lasiathera* Gray, Pl. Wright. 1:48. 1852. PURPLE DALEA

Parosela lasiathera (Gray) Heller

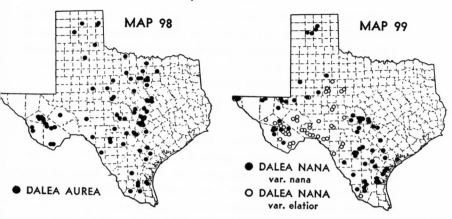

MAP 98

MAP 99

● DALEA NANA
var. nana
O DALEA NANA
var. elatior

● DALEA AUREA

Central and trans-Pecos Texas in calcareous or silty-clay soils (Map 90). March–June. Texas and adjacent Mexico. Chromosome number not determined.

16. *Dalea lanata* Spreng., Syst. Veg. 3:327. 1826. WOOLLY DALEA

Parosela lanata (Spreng.) Britt.

Western, Panhandle, north-central, and southernmost areas of Texas, usually occurring in deep sand (Map 96). June–October. South-central United States to Mexico. Closely related to the species below; at least one intergrade has been seen between the species (Southern Methodist University Herbarium).

Chromosome number, $n = 7$ (Turner, 1956b).

17. *Dalea terminalis* M. E. Jones, Contr. West. Bot. 12:8. 1908

Parosela terminalis (M. E. Jones) Heller

Trans-Pecos Texas, along the Rio Grande in deep, sandy soils (Map 96). May–September, Southwestern United States and adjacent Mexico. Much resembling the above species (see above comment).

Chromosome number not determined.

18. *Dalea jamesii* (Torr.) Torr. & Gray, Fl. N. Am. 1:308. 1838. JAMES DALEA

Parosela jamesii (Torr.) Vail

Western Texas in limestone, igneous, or sandy soils (Map 100). April–July. South-central and southwestern United States to Mexico.

Chromosome number not determined.

19. *Dalea wrightii* Gray, Pl. Wright 1:49. 1852. WRIGHT DALEA

Parosela wrightii (Gray) Vail

Parosela warnockii Tharp and Barkley

Trans-Pecos Texas in igneous or limestone soils, at altitudes of 2,000–5,000 feet (Map 101). April–September. Southwestern United States and adjacent Mexico.

Chromosome number, $2n = 14$ (Turner and Fearing, unpublished).

20. *Dalea hallii* Gray, Proc. Amer. Acad. 8:625. 1873. HALL DALEA

Parosela hallii (Gray) Heller

Central Texas on calcareous prairies or in rocky limestone soils (Map 93). May–June (occasionally later). Endemic to Texas.

Chromosome number not determined.

21. *Dalea aurea* Pursh, Fl. Am. Sept. 2:740. 1814. GOLDEN DALEA

Parosela aurea (Pursh) Britt.

Southern, central, and western Texas in nearly all soil types (Map 98). May–July. North-central United States to Mexico. One of the most common species of *Dalea* in Texas, occurring in a wide variety of habitats and showing considerable variability. In the sandy soils of southern Texas, populations are found with an extremely long pubescence on the stems and foliage; such collections from this area superficially resemble *Petalostemum obovatum*, but the two are readily distinguished when floral morphologies are compared.

Chromosome number, $n = 7$ (Turner, 1956b).

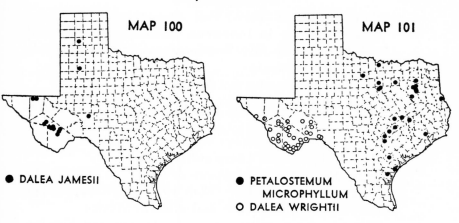

MAP 100

MAP 101

● DALEA JAMESII

● PETALOSTEMUM
MICROPHYLLUM
O DALEA WRIGHTII

22. *Dalea nana* Torr. *ex* Gray, Mem. Amer. Acad. II. 4:31. 1849. DWARF DALEA

Parosela nana (Torr. *ex* Gray) Heller

Parosela lesueuri Tharp & Barkley

Southern, central, trans-Pecos, and Panhandle areas of Texas in nearly all soil types (Map 99). June–August. South-central and southwestern United States to Mexico. A widespread, variable species often occurring with *Dalea aurea* and possibly hybridizing with that species. Two varieties may be recognized for Texas: (1) the typical variety *nana*, with thicker spikes and having ovate, abruptly acute bracts below the flowers, and (2) variety *elatior* Gray (= *Dalea rubescens* Wats.; = *Parosela whitehouseae* Tharp & Barkley), having narrower spikes with lance-ovate bracts below the flowers; the latter is the principal form of the species in south-central Texas, but intergrades occur, especially in the Davis Mountains of trans-Pecos Texas, perhaps as a result of occasional hybridization with the typical variety.

Chromosome number not determined.

34. PETALOSTEMUM   Prairie Clover

UNARMED PERENNIAL or, less often, annual herbs with glandular-dotted foliage.

LEAVES once compound, odd-pinnate with 3 to numerous leaflets; stipules linear or subulate, persistent.

FLOWERS in dense terminal heads or spikes, white, yellowish, pink, or purplish; corolla composed of a separate banner, and 4 similar petals (according to Moore, 1936, these are staminodia), these latter inserted at the mouth of a staminal tube, alternating with the 5 anthers; stamens 5, monadelphous.

FRUIT a short, obovate, or semi-orbicular, 1- to 2-seeded, mostly indehiscent, dry pod, enclosed in, or but slightly longer than, the persistent calyx.

BASIC chromosome number, as determined from counts on 7 species, $x = 7$ (Turner, 1956b; Ledingham, 1957).

A wholly North American genus with some 35 species. Most of the members are temperate grassland forbs, but some of the taxa are adapted to more mesic sites in the southeastern United States. The species are of little economic importance, though *P. pulcherrimum* and *P. multiflorum* are among the more common legumes on much of the native grassland in Texas. Shinners (1949) has included this genus with the larger, related genus, *Dalea*. The present writer does not accept such a treatment. The genus *Petalostemum* is sometimes spelled *Petalostemon* and is conserved over that of *Kuhnistera*.

KEY TO SPECIES

1. Leaflets (on well-developed leaves) 25–40; flowers white; calyx
      tube pubescent   .   .   .   .   .   .   1. *P. microphyllum*
1. Leaflets 3–25.

2. Calyx glabrous, or ciliate on the margins of the lobes only; flowers white.

   3. Flower heads (spikes) globose or subglobose, 1.2 cm. long or less . . . . 2. *P. multiflorum*

   3. Flower heads elongate, cylindric, 1.5 cm. long or more (rarely, less on late-flowering branches).

      4. Calyx tube covered with large, scattered glands; calyx strongly oblique; annuals.

         5. Leaflets 8–12(16); tips of bracts pubescent . . . . 3. *P. phleoides*

         5. Leaflets 14–25; tips of bracts glabrous . . . . 4. *P. glandulosum*

      4. Calyx tube with a ring of small glands at the top (rarely, glandless); calyx not noticeably oblique; perennial . . . . 5. *P. candidum*

2. Calyx, or at least the calyx lobes, densely pubescent; flowers yellowish, rose, or purplish.

   6. Leaves and stem both glabrous (rarely, sparingly pilose, or the stems short-pubescent and the leaves glabrous).

      7. Petals pale yellowish; bracts narrowly lanceolate, brownish-pubescent throughout . . . . 6. *P. compactum*

      7. Petals rose or purplish; bracts ovate, often abruptly acuminate; if narrowly lanceolate, then the upper portion glabrate.

         8. Leaflets 11–17 (on well-developed leaves); peduncles of well-developed heads (10)12–30 cm. long; annuals . . . . 7. *P. emarginatum*

         8. Leaflets 3–11, peduncles 1–10(15) cm. long; perennials.

           9. Bracts narrowly lanceolate; stems decumbent or weakly ascending; plants of the Gulf Coast grassland (and Oklahoma) . . . . 8. *P. decumbens*

           9. Bracts ovate to broadly lanceolate; stems stiffly erect or ascending; plants of central and northern Texas.

              10. Spikes slender, 10 mm. wide or less.

                 11. Calyx tube and lobes covered with a dense spreading, usually tawny pubescence; plants of Panhandle and northwest areas of Texas . . . . 9. *P. tenuifolium*

                 11. Calyx tube and lobes unevenly pubescent with a short, white, appressed pubescence, or else the calyx glabrate; plants of central Texas.

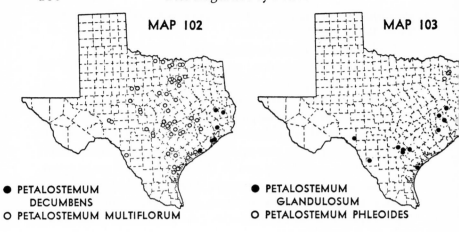

MAP 102

MAP 103

● PETALOSTEMUM
    DECUMBENS
○ PETALOSTEMUM MULTIFLORUM

● PETALOSTEMUM
    GLANDULOSUM
○ PETALOSTEMUM PHLEOIDES

12. Calyx lobes completely glabrate or merely ciliate along
the margin; south-central Texas (intergrading with the
species below) . . . . . . 10. *P. sabinale*
12. Calyx lobes conspicuously pubescent . . . .
. . . . 11. *P. stanfieldii*
10. Spikes 10 mm. wide or more.
13. Calyx densely villous throughout with spreading hairs
. . . . 12. *P. purpureum*
13. Calyx with a dense appressed pubescence, the tube or
lobes often with some degree of glabrousness.
14. Mature plants 30–60 cm. high; peduncles 4–12 cm.
long; widespread plants of central and north-central
Texas . . . . . 13. *P. pulcherrimum*
14. Mature plants 10–20 cm. high; peduncles 3 cm. long
or less; rare restricted endemic of north-central
Texas . . . . . . 14. *P. reverchonii*
6. Leaves and stems densely short-pubescent to long-hirsute.
15. Flowers pale yellow; spikes 1.7–3.0 cm. wide . . .
. . . . 15. *P. obovatum*
15. Flowers pink; spikes 0.8–1.3 cm. wide.
16. Calyx (including lobes) 4–5 mm. long; spikes 1–1.3 cm.
thick; stems densely pubescent, Panhandle area of Texas
. . . . 16. *P. villosum*
16. Calyx 3–4 mm. long; spikes 1 cm. thick or less; stem
sparsely pubescent; eastern Texas . . 17. *P. griseum*

1. *Petalostemum microphyllum* (Torr. & Gray) Heller, Bull. Torr. Bot. Club 26:593. 1899

   Dalea drummondiana Shinners

   North-central, eastern, and southern Texas mostly on sandy soils along river terraces and in open areas of oak woodlands (Map 101). June–July. Known only from Texas and probably adjacent Louisiana and Oklahoma. Specimens of this species from the northern part of its range in Texas are essentially glabrate; specimens from the southern part of its range (Robertson to Nueces counties) are much more pubescent. More detailed study may justify the recognition of these geographic and morphologic types as separate varieties (see *P. phleoides* for additional comments).

   Chromosome number not determined.

2. *Petalostemum multiflorum* Nutt., Jour. Acad. Phila. 7:92. 1834

   Dalea multiflora (Nutt.) Shinners

   Widespread throughout central Texas, mostly on deep calcareous or rocky limestone soils in open grasslands (Map 102). June–July. Missouri and Kansas to Texas.

   Chromosome number not determined.

3. *Petalostemum phleoides* Torr. & Gray, Fl. N. Am. 1:310. 1838

   Dalea phleoides (Torr. & Gray) Shinners

   Northeastern Texas in sandy soils of pine and oak woodlands; rare (Map 103). June. Arkansas and northeastern Texas according to various authors. *P. phleoides* seems closely related to *P. microphyllum* and *P. glandulosum.* Much additional work is needed to clarify the relationship between these three taxa.

   Chromosome number not determined.

4. *Petalostemum glandulosum* Coult. & Fisher, Bot. Gaz. 18: 299. 1893

   Dalea glandulosa (Coult. & Fisher) Shinners

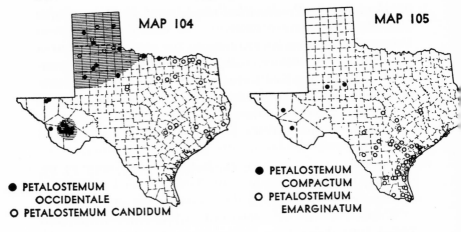

MAP 104

● PETALOSTEMUM
  OCCIDENTALE
○ PETALOSTEMUM CANDIDUM

MAP 105

● PETALOSTEMUM
  COMPACTUM
○ PETALOSTEMUM
  EMARGINATUM

South-central and southeastern Texas in sandy soils (Map 103). May–July. Endemic to Texas. Apparently closely related to *P. microphyllum* and *P. phloeides* (see remarks under these species).

Chromosome number, $n = 7$ (Turner, 1956b).

5. *Petalostemum candidum* (Willd.) Michx., Fl. Bor. Am. 2:49. 1803. WHITE PRAIRIE CLOVER

   Dalea candida Willd.
   Petalostemum occidentale (Gray) Fernald
   Petalostemum truncatum Rydb.

   Trans-Pecos, Panhandle, north-central, and southeastern areas of Texas, in nearly all soil types (Map 104). May–September. A highly variable, widespread species occurring from south-central Canada to Texas. A number of variants of this taxon have been split off as distinct species. In eastern Texas *P. candidum* is represented by populations with thick spikes and long bracts (longer than the subtended calyx); this is the typical form of the species, var. *candidum*. In western Texas these populations are replaced by types with narrower spikes and shorter bracts; these forms have been segregated by some workers as *P.*

occidentale (= *P. oligophyllum* [Torr.] Rydb.; = *Dalea oligophylla* [Torr.] Shinners). All intergrades between these two extremes occur, even in the same general area (e.g., Davis Mountains in Brewster and Jeff Davis counties). *P. truncatus* Rydb. seems to be no more than a form or, at most, a variety of this species. This species-complex is in much need of extensive field study.

Chromosome number, $2n = 14$ (Ledingham, 1957; Turner, unpublished).

6. *Petalostemum compactum* (Spreng.) Swezey, Neb. Fl. Pl. 6. 1891

Dalea compacta Spreng.

Western Texas in sandy soils, apparently infrequent (Map 105). June–July. Wyoming and Nebraska to western Texas.

Chromosome number not determined.

7. *Petalostemum emarginatum* Torr. & Gray, Fl. N. Am. 1:311. 1838

Dalea emarginata (Torr. & Gray) Shinners

South-central and southern Texas in sandy soils (Map 105). March–December. Endemic to Texas and probably adjacent Mexico.

Chromosome number not determined.

8. *Petalostemum decumbens* Nutt., Jour. Acad. Phila. 7:93. 1834

Gulf Coast grassland of southeastern Texas in heavy clay soils; occurring again in southeastern Oklahoma (Map 102). April–June. Oklahoma and Texas. In the sandy pine woodlands of southeastern Texas this species occurs on localized outcrops of black calcareous soils (Polk and Tyler counties).

Chromosome number not determined.

9. *Petalostemum tenuifolium* Gray, Proc. Amer. Acad. 11:73. 1876

Dalea tenuifolia (Gray) Shinners

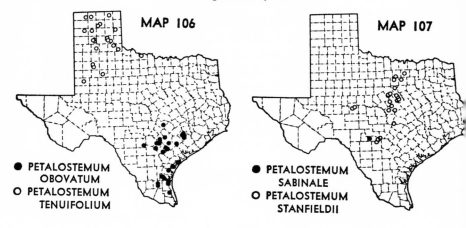

MAP 106

● PETALOSTEMUM
  OBOVATUM
○ PETALOSTEMUM
  TENUIFOLIUM

MAP 107

● PETALOSTEMUM
  SABINALE
○ PETALOSTEMUM
  STANFIELDII

Petalostemum porterianum Small

Panhandle area of Texas, mostly in sandy or silty clay soils (Map 106). May–September. Northeastern New Mexico, adjacent Colorado, Oklahoma, and Texas. The species is closely related to *P. pulcherrimum* and seems to intergrade with that species in parts of its range (e.g., Wichita County, Texas).

Chromosome number not determined.

10. *Petalostemum sabinale* Wats., Proc. Amer. Acad. 21:448. 1886

Dalea sabinalis (Wats.) Shinners

Known by only a few collections from south-central Texas where it occurs in rocky limestone soils (Map 107). May–July. Closely related to *P. stanfieldii* and apparently intergrading with that species.

Chromosome number not determined.

11. *Petalostemum stanfieldii* Small, Fl. S. E. U. S. 631, 1332. 1903

Dalea stanfieldii (Small) Shinners
Petalostemum tenuis (Coult.) Heller

Central Texas in rocky limestone soils (Map 107). May–July. Endemic to Texas. Very closely related to *P. pul-*

cherrimum and *P. sabinale* and apparently intergrading with these species in parts of its range. Seemingly "pure" populations of *P. stanfieldii* occur in the field; however, there is considerable variability from population to population, especially as concerns calyx pubescence.

Chromosome number, $n = 7$ (Turner, 1956b).

12. *Petalostemum purpureum* (Vent.) Rydb., Mem. N. Y. Bot. Gard. 1:238. 1900. PURPLE PRAIRIE CLOVER
    Dalea purpurea Vent.
    Petalostemum pubescens (Gray) Heller
    Petalostemum molle Rydb.
    North-central and trans-Pecos Texas, in calcareous or silty-clay soils (Map 108). June–July. South-central Canada to Texas and Alabama. A widespread, variable species in much need of critical revision. In the southern part of its range it becomes exceedingly complex, possibly as a result of introgression with the closely related species, *P. tenuifolium* and *P. pulcherrimum*. Much additional field work is needed to clarify this complex in Texas.
    Chromosome number, $n = 7$ (Ledingham, 1957).

13. *Petalostemum pulcherrimum* (Heller) Heller, Bull. Torr. Bot. Club 26:593. 1899
    Dalea helleri Shinners
    Central and trans-Pecos Texas, in grasslands on deep calcareous or rocky limestone soils (Map 108). May–July (August). Kansas and Arkansas to Texas. A common but variable species, apparently intergrading with *P. purpureum* in parts of its range.
    Chromosome number, $n = 7$ (Turner, 1956b).

14. *Petalostemum reverchonii* Wats., Proc. Amer. Acad. 21: 449. 1886
    Dalea reverchonii (Wats.) Shinners
    Known only from the type collection (summit of Comanche Peak, Hood County, Texas). June. The species has not been collected since its initial discovery. It is close to

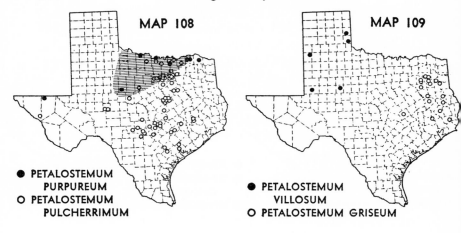

MAP 108

● PETALOSTEMUM
  PURPUREUM
○ PETALOSTEMUM
  PULCHERRIMUM

MAP 109

● PETALOSTEMUM
  VILLOSUM
○ PETALOSTEMUM GRISEUM

P. purpureum and *P. pulcherrimum* but seems to have a combination of characters that mark it distinct. However, detailed study of the entire *P. purpureum* complex may necessitate a change in its status.

Chromosome number not determined.

15. *Petalostemum obovatum* Torr. & Gray, Fl. N. Am. 1:310. 1838. PUSSY FOOT

Dalea obovata (Torr. & Gray) Shinners

Southern Texas in sandy or silty alluvial soils (Map 106). April–July. Endemic to Texas. Superficially, *P. obovatum* resembles *Dalea aurea*, but the floral morphologies are very different in the two species.

Chromosome number not determined.

16. *Petalostemum villosum* Nutt., Gen. 2:85. 1818. SILKY PRAIRIE CLOVER

Dalea villosa (Nutt.) Spreng.

Western Texas in sandy soils (Map 109). June–August. South-central Canada to Texas. *P. villosum* is closely related to *P. griseum* (below), a species of eastern Texas.

Chromosome number, $n = 7$ (Ledingham, 1957).

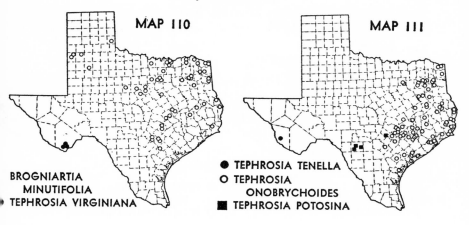

MAP 110

BROGNIARTIA
MINUTIFOLIA
TEPHROSIA VIRGINIANA

MAP 111

● TEPHROSIA TENELLA
○ TEPHROSIA
ONOBRYCHOIDES
■ TEPHROSIA POTOSINA

17. *Petalostemum griseum* Torr. & Gray, Fl. N. Am. 1:310.
1838

Dalea grisea (Torr. & Gray) Shinners

Eastern Texas on sandy soils of pine and oak woodlands
(Map 109). Endemic to Texas and possibly western Louisiana. Closely related to *P. villosum* (above), a species of
the Panhandle area of Texas, and northward.

Chromosome number, $n = 7$ (Turner, unpublished).

35. BRONGNIARTIA

UNARMED suffruticose perennials or shrubs.

LEAVES once compound, odd-pinnate, with 3 to numerous
small leaflets.

FLOWERS purplish to cream-colored, usually large and conspicuous on long, axillary peduncles.

FRUIT a dry, dehiscent legume.

BASIC chromosome number not determined.

A genus with about 30 species in the drier regions of tropical

America. A single species extends into the United States along the Texas–Mexican border. They are of little or no economic importance.

Brongniartia minutifolia Wats., Proc. Amer. Acad. 20:360. 1885

Trans-Pecos Texas (Brewster County) and adjacent Mexico, occurring in dry limestone gravels, at altitudes of 2,500–3,500 feet (Map 110). June–August.

Chromosome number not determined.

36. TEPHROSIA   Tephrosia

UNARMED perennial herbs or shrubs.

LEAVES once compound, odd-pinnate with usually 3 to numerous leaflets (rarely, unifoliate); stipules mostly slender herbaceous, persistent or deciduous; stipels absent.

FLOWERS in terminal or axillary racemes, white, pink, red to purple; stamens monadelphous or diadelphous; anthers all alike.

FRUIT a linear, straight or somewhat curved, flattened, dehiscent legume.

BASIC chromosome number, as determined from counts on 27 species, $x = 11$ (Wood, 1949).

A large genus with about 300 species mostly in the tropical and subtropical areas of both hemispheres, only a few species extending into temperate regions. The genus is without native representatives in Europe. Some of the tropical species are utilized as green manure and cover crops in parts of Central America, Africa, and Asia; otherwise the genus is of little agronomic importance. Various species of *Tephrosia* yield an alkaloid, rotenone, and other related compounds which are used as fish poisons and insecticides in many parts of the world. Wood (1949) has a very excellent account of most of the North American species of this genus (treating all of the Texas species except *T. tenella*).

Key to Species[8]

1. Style glabrous; plants of trans-Pecos Texas . . 1. *T. tenella*
1. Style barbate; plants of Panhandle, central, and eastern areas of Texas.
  2. Leaflets broadly to narrowly linear, three to six times as long as wide.
    3. Racemes short, broad, 3–10 cm. long; stems stiff and erect; leaflets acute at apex . . . . . 2. *T. virginiana*
    3. Racemes narrow, elongate, 10–40 cm. long; stems reclining, not stiffly erect; leaflets obtuse to truncate at apex
    . . . . 3. *T. onobrychoides*
  2. Leaflets obovate to nearly orbicular, one to two times as long as wide.
    4. "Leaflets 5–19, primarily 9–11, densely hirsutulous to nearly glabrous above, but with at least a few appressed hairs near the margins, the margins conspicuously bordered with white hairs; calyx and back of banner with whitish hairs; ovules and seeds 5–6." . 4. *T. lindheimeri*
    4. "Leaflets 3–9, primarily 5–7, completely glabrous above, the margins not conspicuously bordered; indument of calyx and banner golden; ovules and seeds 4–8." . 5. *T. potosina*

1. *Tephrosia tenella* Gray, Pl. Wright. 2:36. 1853

Known to Texas only from collections made in the Chinati Mountains, Presidio County (Map 111). The species occurs from western Texas to Arizona and adjacent Mexico, but apparently is rare in Texas.

Chromosome number not determined.

2. *Tephrosia virginiana* (L.) Pers., Syn. Pl. 2:329. 1807. DEVIL'S SHOESTRING
  Cracca virginiana L.
  Tephrosia leucosericea (Rydb.) Cory

---

[8] Taken in part from that of Wood (1949).

Eastern, north-central, and Panhandle areas of Texas, mostly in sandy soils (Map 110). April–June. New Hampshire to Wisconsin, south to Texas. A widespread, variable species, especially in regard to pubescence.

Chromosome number, $2n = 22$ (Wood, 1949).

3. *Tephrosia onobrychoides* Nutt., Jour. Acad. Phila. 7:104. 1834

Cracca onobrychoides (Nutt.) Kuntze

Tephrosia angustifolia Featherm.

Tephrosia texana (Rydb.) Cory

Eastern Texas, mostly in sandy soils of pine or oak woodlands but sometimes on heavy, calcareous soils of the coastal grassland (Map 111). April–June. Eastern Oklahoma, southern Missouri south to Alabama and southeastern Texas. A variable species, especially in regard to pubescence.

Chromosome number, $2n = 22$ (Wood, 1949).

4. *Tephrosia lindheimeri* Gray, Bost. Jour. Nat. Hist. 6:172. 1850. LINDHEIMER TEPHROSIA

Cracca lindheimeri (Gray) Kuntze

Central and southern Texas, mostly in granitic soils of the central mineral region and in deep calcareous or sandy soils of south-central and southern Texas (Map 112). April–September. The species is closely related to *T. potosina* (below) but may be distinguished by the combination of characters used in the key to species.

Chromosome number, $2n = 22$ (Wood, 1949).

5. *Tephrosia potosina* Brandeg., Univ. Calif. Pub. Bot. 4:272. 1912

South-central Texas and adjacent Mexico in limestone soils; only a few collections from Uvalde and Hays (?) counties have been made in Texas (Map 111). April–August.

Chromosome number, $2n = 22$ (Wood, 1949).

Extralimital Species

Tephrosia spicata (Walt.) Torr. & Gray

This species has been reported for Texas by Cory and Parks (1937). The present writer has not seen specimens from Texas, but it is not improbable that the plant may be found in easternmost Texas, since Wood (1949) cites a collection from Calcasieu Parish in adjacent Louisiana.

Chromosome number, 2n = 22 (Wood, 1949).

37. WISTERIA   Wisteria

UNARMED, woody, twining vines, or, rarely, shrubs or treelike.

LEAVES once compound, odd-pinnate, with 5–15 rather large, thin leaflets; stipels present.

FLOWERS handsome, in large terminal, drooping racemes, white to lilac-purple; stamens diadelphous.

FRUIT a large, linear, flattened, dehiscent or indehiscent pod, the valves often constricted between the seeds.

BASIC chromosome number, as determined from counts on 5 species, $x = 8$ (D. & W.).

A genus with 7 species in the temperate regions of North America, China, and Japan. Some of the species are important ornamentals and have been introduced in gardens throughout the world. The generic name *Wisteria* is conserved over that of *Kraunhia*; *Wisteria* is sometimes spelled *Wistaria*.

KEY TO SPECIES

1. Legume and ovary glabrous; pedicels 5–10 mm. long; native species . . . . 1. *W. macrostachya*
1. Legume and ovary pubescent; pedicels 10–25 mm. long; introduced species . . . . 2. *W. sinensis*

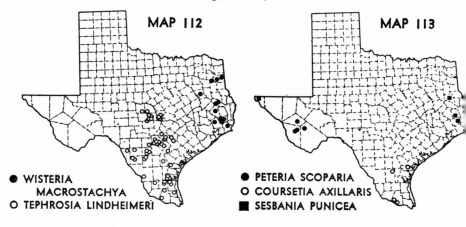

MAP 112

MAP 113

● WISTERIA
  MACROSTACHYA
○ TEPHROSIA LINDHEIMERI

● PETERIA SCOPARIA
○ COURSETIA AXILLARIS
■ SESBANIA PUNICEA

1. *Wisteria macrostachya* Nutt. *ex* Torr. & Gray, Fl. N. Am.
   1:283. 1838. KENTUCKY WISTERIA
   Bradleia macrostachya (Torr. & Gray) Small
   Wisteria frutescens var. *macrostachya* Torr. & Gray
   East Texas in moist or wet woods and along riverbanks
   (Map 112). April–August. Central United States from In-
   diana south to Texas and Louisiana. Very similar to the
   more eastern *W. frutescens* (L.) Poir., and sometimes
   treated as a variety of that species.
   Chromosome number, $2n = 16$ (D. & W.).

2. *Wisteria sinensis* (Sims) Sweet, Hort. Brit., ed. 1:121. 1827.
   CHINESE WISTERIA
   An introduced species commonly cultivated as an orna-
   mental throughout Texas.
   Wisteria floribunda (Willd.) DC., JAPANESE WIS-
   TERIA, is another species frequently cultivated in the state.
   Chromosome number, $2n = 16$ (D. & W.).

Excluded Species

Wisteria frutescens (L.) Poir. AMERICAN WISTERIA
Reported for Texas by Cory and Parks (1937). Possibly on

the basis of cultivated material or misidentified specimens of *W. macrostachya*, a closely related species of the southeastern United States.

38. PETERIA   Peteria

PERENNIAL, herbaceous plants with slender, rather stiff, glabrous stems.

LEAVES once compound, with numerous small leaflets; stipules spiny.

FLOWERS in loose, pedunculate racemes; stamens diadelphous.

FRUIT a narrow, linear, dehiscent legume.

BASIC chromosome number not determined.

A genus with only 4 species, in the drier mountainous areas of the United States and adjacent Mexico (Porter, 1956).

Peteria scoparia Gray, Pl. Wright. 1:50. 1852. CAMOTE DEL MONTE

Trans-Pecos Texas in mostly igneous soils (Map 113). July–August. Texas to Arizona and adjacent Mexico. The species is apparently rare in Texas, occurring in the lower mountain ranges, at altitudes of 4,000–5,000 feet. According to Coulter (1891), the species has small, edible, tuberous rootstocks.

Chromosome number not determined.

39. COURSETIA   Baby Bonnets

ARMED or unarmed shrubs or trees.

LEAVES once compound with usually numerous leaflets; stipels small.

FLOWERS axillary, purplish to white, often with a yellowish

eye; stamens 10, diadelphous or monadelphous to about the middle.

FRUIT a dry, several-seeded, linear, dehiscent legume.

BASIC chromosome number not determined.

A genus with about 15 species in the drier regions of tropical and subtropical America.

Coursetia axillaris Coulter & Rose, Bot. Gaz. 16:180. 1891
Southernmost Texas and adjacent Mexico, locally abundant on shallow, sandy, loam uplands, often underlain by caliche (Map 113). March–June.
Chromosome number not determined.

40. SESBANIA   Sesbania

ANNUAL or perennial, large herbs or semi-woody shrubs, the stems usually green and easily broken.

LEAVES once compound, evenly pinnate with numerous, rather large leaflets; stipules herbaceous, quickly deciduous.

FLOWERS in terminal or axillary racemes, yellowish, red to orange; stamens diadelphous.

FRUIT very variable, a dry, elongate, linear, or 4-sided, winged pod, dehiscent or indehiscent.

BASIC chromosome number, as determined from counts on approximately 14 species, $x = 6$ (Turner, 1955b).

A genus with about 40 species in the tropical and subtropical regions of both hemispheres. Most of the species grow in areas of high rainfall or in wet habitats. In Texas the native species are very common troublesome weeds in the Gulf Coast rice fields. However, *Sesbania macrocarpa* and other foreign species have been used as cover crops in fallow rice fields of tropical and subtropical areas with some success. *S. macro-*

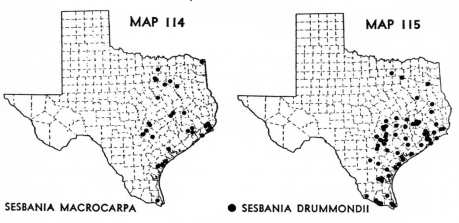

MAP 114

SESBANIA MACROCARPA

MAP 115

● SESBANIA DRUMMONDII

carpa develops numerous, conspicuous nodules and should prove a good plant for soil improvement purposes in the Gulf Coast region.

KEY TO SPECIES

1. Stalk of inflorescence (peduncle) 5–12 cm. long; flowers 6–9 mm. long; pods with 2 seeds . . . . 1. *S. vesicaria*
1. Stalk of inflorescence 1–5 cm. long; flowers 10–20 mm. long; pods with several to many seeds (rarely, 2 by abortion).
    2. Inflorescence (raceme) composed of 2–6 flowers; pods elongate, linear, not winged . . . . 2. *S. macrocarpa*
    2. Inflorescence (raceme) composed of 10–30 flowers; pods short, thickened, 4-winged.
        3. Banner yellow, 12–15 mm. long; native species common in east and southern Texas . . . . 3. *S. drummondii*
        3. Banner orange-red or rose-colored, 15–20 mm. long; introduced species of eastern Texas, rarely escaping cultivation . . . . 4. *S. punicea*

1. *Sesbania vesicaria* (Jacq.) Ell., Bot. S. C. and Ga. 2:222. 1822. BAG-POD SESBANIA

 Glottidium vesicarium (Jacq.) Harper

 Mostly eastern Texas in damp or low sandy soils (Map

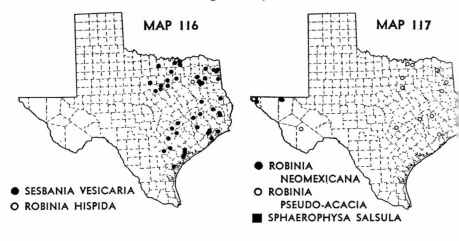

MAP 116

MAP 117

● SESBANIA VESICARIA
○ ROBINIA HISPIDA

● ROBINIA
    NEOMEXICANA
○ ROBINIA
    PSEUDO-ACACIA
■ SPHAEROPHYSA SALSULA

116). August–September. Southeastern United States (South Carolina, Florida to Texas).

Chromosome number, $n = 6$ (Turner, 1955b).

2. *Sesbania macrocarpa* Muhl., Cat. Pl. Amer. Sept. 65. 1813. COFFEE BEAN

Sesban exaltatus (Raf.) Rydb.

Sesbania exaltata (Raf.) Cory

Mostly eastern Texas in damp or low, wet, alluvial or clay soils (Map 114). August–October. Southeastern United States and subtropical areas. This species is a common weed in the rice fields of coastal Texas where it goes by the local name "Indigo." It is sometimes used as a cover crop in soil improvement programs (Briscoe and Andrews, 1938).

Chromosome number, $n = 6$ (Turner, 1955b).

3. *Sesbania drummondii* (Rydb.) Cory, Rhodora 38:406. 1936. DRUMMOND SESBANIA

Daubentonia drummondii Rydb.

Daubentonia longifolia (Cav.) DC., not *S. longifolia* (Ort.) DC.

Eastern and southern Texas in damp sandy or clay soils

(Map 115). June–September. Southeastern United States
to Mexico. This species is common throughout its range in
Texas and goes by the local name "Senna." Where the
plant dominates shallow water depressions these are called
"Senna swamps."

Chromosome number, $n = 6$ (Turner, 1955b).

4. *Sesbania punicea* (Cav.) Benth., *in* Mart. Fl. Bras. 15:43.
1859

    Daubentonia punicea (Cav.) DC.

An introduced species, occasionally cultivated in east
Texas, where it sometimes escapes and establishes itself
along roadsides (Map 113). May. Native to tropical America, but widely cultivated in the southeastern United States
and elsewhere for its attractive flowers. In fruit, very similar to *S. drummondii*, but readily distinguished from that
species in flower.

Chromosome number, $2n = 12$ (D. & W.).

Excluded Species

Sesbania sericea (Willd.) Link., Enum. 2:244. 1822

Rydberg (1924) reports a single collection of this species
from Houston, Texas. The present writer has not seen specimens from Texas. The plant may have been a chance introduction on ballast at Houston and perhaps is no longer represented in our flora.

Chromosome number, $2n = 24$ (D. & W.).

41. ROBINIA   Locust

TREES or shrubs, usually armed with spinescent stipules.

LEAVES once compound, odd-pinnate with several to numerous
entire leaflets; stipels early deciduous.

FLOWERS axillary in short, pendulous, handsome racemes, the
petals white, violet- to rose-colored; stamens diadelphous.

FRUIT a dry, linear, flattened, dehiscent legume, containing several to numerous seeds.

BASIC chromosome number, as determined from counts on 8 species, $x = 10$ (D. & W.).

A genus with about 10 species native to the temperate regions of northern Mexico and the United States, but some of the species widely cultivated elsewhere as ornamentals and for use in soil erosion control.

KEY TO SPECIES

1. Ultimate stems and leaves densely hispid; flowers rose-colored
.   .   .   .   1. *R. hispida*
1. Ultimate stems and leaves glabrous, only the axis of raceme hispid, if at all; flowers white to lavender.
   2. Pod and axis of raceme densely hispid   .   2. *R. neomexicana*
   2. Pod and axis of raceme glabrous   .   .   3. *R. pseudo-acacia*

1. *Robinia hispida* L., Mant. 101. 1767. ROSE ACACIA (Rose Locust)

An introduced species, sometimes persisting in abandoned yards and lots (Map 116). Native to the southern Appalachians and adjacent areas, often cultivated elsewhere as an ornamental.

Chromosome number, $2n = 30$ (D. & W.).

2. *Robinia neomexicana* Gray, Mem. Amer. Acad. ser. 2, 5:314. 1854. NEW MEXICO LOCUST

Trans-Pecos Texas, known only from collections in the Guadalupe Mountains, limestone soil (Map 117). May–June. A variable species occurring throughout the Southwest and adjacent Mexico in mountainous areas, at altitudes of 4,000–8,500 feet. The Texas material examined falls into the var. *luxurians* Dieck. (= *R. luxurians* [Dieck.] Rydb.). It is distinguished from the typical form of the species (var. *neomexicana*) in having glandular-setose pods and oval leaflets; var. *neomexicana*, from southwestern New Mexico, has merely hirsutellous pods and lanceolate or ovate leaflets, though the varieties are apparently linked by intermediates (Sargent, 1933, p. 624).

Chromosome number, $2n = 20$ (for var. *luxurians*; D. & W.).

3. *Robinia pseudo-acacia* L., Sp. Pl. 722. 1753. BLACK LOCUST

Central and eastern Texas, mostly in sandy or silty, alluvial soils along roadsides and stream banks (Map 117). April–July. Native to the eastern United States from Canada to Oklahoma and Louisiana. The species is widely cultivated as a shade tree and for use in soil erosion control. It is doubtful that *R. pseudo-acacia* is native to the state, but it has become well established in certain areas. A number of hybrids between this species and others in the genus are known, some of these being used as nursery stock.

Chromosome number, $2n = 20$ (D. & W.).

42. SPHAEROPHYSA   Sphaerophysa

PERENNIAL, herbaceous plants with erect stems arising from underground, creeping rootstocks.

LEAVES once compound, odd-pinnate with numerous thin leaflets.

FLOWERS brick-red, in loose axillary racemes.

FRUIT an inflated, nearly globose, bladder-like pod with thin, papery walls.

BASIC chromosome number, as determined from counts on a single species, $x = 8$ (D. & W., reported as *Swainsona*).

A genus with about 30 species in Australia, New Zealand, and northern Asia. Some of the species are reportedly toxic to livestock.

Sphaerophysa salsula (Pall.) DC., Prod. 2:271. 1825

   Swainsona salsula (Pall.) Taub.

Known in Texas from only a few collections along the roadside in El Paso County where it has recently been introduced (Map 117). May–July. Native to northern Asia, but occasionally introduced in various parts of western America. *S. salsula* is very similar to the bladdery-fruited *Astragalus* species, but is readily distinguished from these plants by its red flowers.

Chromosome number not determined.

43. ASTRAGALUS[9]   Milk Vetch (Loco Weed)

UNARMED perennial or annual herbs (rarely, spinescent shrubs in Asia).

LEAVES once compound, odd-pinnate with mostly several to many leaflets; leaflets without stipels.

FLOWERS in axillary racemes (rarely, single), white, yellow to purplish; stamens 10, diadelphous; keel petals obtuse to acute.

FRUIT a linear to globose, dry to fleshy, dehiscent or indehiscent pod with 1 to many seeds.

BASIC chromosome number, as determined from counts on approximately 110 species, $x = 8, 11, 12, 13$ (D. & W.; Head, 1957; Ledingham, 1957). Senn (1938a) gives the base number as $x = 8$, species with $n = 11, 13$, or 14, interpreted as being derived hypo- and hyperploids.

A very large genus with about 1,500 species occurring throughout the subtropical and temperate world except for Australia. *Astragalus* species are particularly abundant in

---

[9] Delimitation of species, keys, and nomenclature by Rupert C. Barneby.

Asia, southern Europe, western North America, and the Andean region of South America.

Many species in this genus are toxic to livestock, often causing a disease known as "locoism." As a consequence they have not been widely adopted as desirable forage plants. However, a few species such as *A. chinensis* in eastern Asia, *A. cicer* in Europe, and *A. falcatus* in western Asia have been used successfully as green manures or forage crops. Most of the native Texas species are common spring plants but do not make up an appreciable amount of the vegetation.

KEY TO SPECIES

1. Pubescence of the herbage dolabriform, the hairs attached laterally above their bases, with one ascending, and a shorter, descending arm [2].
    2. Tall, erect, leafy plants, more or less rhizomatous, the stems 4.5–10 dm. long; racemes densely many-flowered, the flowers nodding; pods erect, bilocular; stipules connate .   .
    .   .   .   .   1. *A. canadensis*
    2. Low tufted or loosely matted and prostrate plants, the stems arising together from the root crown or shortly forking caudex; racemes relatively few-flowered, the flowers ascending or spreading; pods 1-locular [3].
        3. Flowers large, the deeply campanulate or cylindric calyx tube 6.5–10.5 mm. long, the keel 12–19 mm. long [4].
            4. Pod straight or nearly so, a little laterally compressed its whole length, carinate by the sutures, persistent on the receptacle until after dehiscence; a widespread plains species, extending south to the Panhandle, trans-Pecos, and north-central areas of Texas   .   .   .
            .   .   .   .   2. *A. missouriensis*
            4. Pod crescent-shaped, laterally compressed at both ends, dorso-ventrally compressed at the middle, readily disjointing from the receptacle and dehiscent on the ground; a western species just entering Texas in El Paso County .   .   .   .   .   .   3. *A. amphioxys*
        3. Flowers smaller, the campanulate calyx tube 3–4.5 mm. long, the keel 4–10 mm. long [5].

5. Stipules connate; slender prostrate caulescent plants of the Davis Mountains, the stems 1–6 dm. long . .
. . . . 4. *A. humistratus*

5. Stipules free; tufted acaulescent or shortly caulescent plants, the stems 0–1 dm. long. Peduncles and racemes often dimorphic, the early peduncles well developed and bearing chasmogamous flowers, the later ones very short, often subradical, and bearing cleistogamous flowers; but sometimes the inflorescences all of either one sort or the other . . . . 5. *A. lotiflorus*

1. Pubescence basifixed, the hairs simple, attached at base [6].

6. Plants perennial (doubtful cases keyed under both alternatives) [7].

7. Flowers large, the calyx tube 5–11.5 mm. long; banner 12–25 mm., the keel 10.5–19 mm. long (keel as little as 9 mm. in densely villous-tomentose *A. mollissimus* var. *earlei* of trans-Pecos Texas) [8].

8. Stipules near the base of the stem connate; pod pendulous-stipitate, the body triquetrous, 1-locular; northwestern Texas (upper Wichita River and Panhandle) . . . . 6. *A. racemosus*

8. Stipules all free; pod sessile, spreading or erect [9].

9. Herbage densely silky-villous or villous-tomentose with shorter, curly and longer, straight, spirally twisted hairs to 1–3 mm. long (the vesture becoming tawny after a short period in the herbarium); stipules silky-pilose dorsally [10].

10. Stems few, erect, 2–6 dm. long; peduncles stiffly erect; flowers nodding; pedicels becoming 4–9 mm. long in fruit; pod persistent on the receptacle until after dehiscence; Davis Mountains, flowering after summer rain . . . . . 8. *A. giganteus*

10. Stems usually numerous, decumbent or closely tufted, 0–1.5(2) dm. long; peduncles humistrate in age; flowers ascending; fruiting pedicels to 3 mm. long; pod readily deciduous, dehiscent on the ground; widespread, Edwards Plateau north and west; flowering in the spring . 9. *A. mollissimus*

9. Herbage variously pubescent to nearly glabrous, but, if the hairs over 1 mm. long, then all of one sort, not

twisted, and the stipules then glabrous or nearly so dorsally [11].
11. Flowers ochroleucous; calyx very sparsely strigulose; pod subunilocular, the septum very narrow and incomplete; coarse ill-scented (seleniferous) plants entering northwestern Texas in Bailey, Martin, and Midland counties . 7. *A. praelongus*
11. Flowers mostly purple; if ochroleucous, then the calyx densely tomentulose and of east Texas; pod fully 2-locular, the septum broad [12].
  12. Pod plumply ovoid, subglobose or, if oblong-cylindroid, then 1–2 cm. in diameter; valves of the pod very thick and succulent when first formed, 1–5 mm. thick when dry; widespread [13].
    13. Ovary and pod glabrous; calyx early circumscissile, leaving the pod naked [14].
      14. Pod broadly oblong-ellipsoid or subglobose, seven eighths to one and one half times as long as its diameter; stipules glabrous or nearly so dorsally; leaflets commonly glabrous or medially glabrescent on the upper surface; widespread . . . . 10. *A. crassicarpus*
      14. Pod cylindroid, three to four times longer than wide; stipules strigulose dorsally, at least above the middle; leaflets equally cinereous- or silvery-strigulose on both sides; confined to gypseous soils of the Pecos Valley in Reeves and Culberson counties and adjoining New Mexico . . . 11. *A. gypsodes*
    13. Ovary and pod pubescent [15].
      15. Stems arising singly or few together from loosely forking subterranean caudex-branches or oblique rootstocks; walls of the ripe pod 1–1.5 mm. thick; calyx persistent about the base of the fruit; widespread and common over the prairies east of the Pecos . . . . . . 12. *A. plattensis*
      15. Stems arising in a clump together from the root crown; pod walls 2–5 mm. thick; calyx early circumscissile, leaving the fruit naked; a rare form (Irion and Brewster counties) of . . . . 10. *A. crassicarpus*
  12. Pod narrowly oblong-ellipsoid, 1.7–3.8 cm. long, 5–8 mm. in diameter, obtusely triquetrous, grooved dorsally, the valves stiffly papery, less than 0.5 mm. thick; trans-Pecos

Texas (Hudspeth, Culberson, and El Paso counties) and apparently isolated on the Edwards Plateau in Reagan County . . . . 13. *A. waterfallii*

7. Flowers small, the calyx tube 1.5–4.5 mm. long; banner mostly 4.5–10 mm. (but to 15.5 mm. in *A. distortus* of east Texas), keel 3.5–10 mm. long [16].

    16. Stipules, at least those at base of the stems, connate; stems partly subterranean, arising from a buried root crown and emerging singly from the ground [17].

        17. Pod small, about 4–8 mm. long, 2.5–3.5 mm. in diameter, solid or nearly so; Panhandle southeast to Knox and Fisher counties . . . . . 14. *A. gracilis*

        17. Pod larger, 1–1.7 cm. long, 4.5–6 mm. in diameter, a little inflated; trans-Pecos Texas . . 15. *A. pictiformis*

    16. Stipules all free; stems arising together from the root crown at soil level [18].

        18. Plants of trans-Pecos Texas; pod globose, ovoid or half-ovoid, bladdery-inflated, the papery-diaphanous valves strigulose [19].

            19. Pod subsymmetrically ovoid or globose, both sutures about equally convex; very common in trans-Pecos Texas . . . . . . 16. *A. wootonii*

            19. Pod strongly asymmetric, half-ovoid or -ellipsoid, the ventral suture nearly straight, the dorsal one strongly convex; just entering Texas in El Paso County . . . . 17. *A. allochrous*

        18. Plants of east Texas; pod narrowly lunate-ellipsoid or half-obovoid, the firmly papery or leathery valves glabrous [20].

            20. Calyx 3–5.5 mm. long, the teeth not over 2 mm. long; petals (in Texas) purplish, the keel 5.5–9.3 mm. long . . . . 18. *A. distortus*

            20. Calyx 6.3–8.9 mm. long, the teeth 2.5–4 mm. long; petals cream-colored or greenish-white; keel 9.4–10.2 mm. long . . . . . 19. *A. soxmaniorum*

6. Plants annual [21].

    21. Pod papery, bladdery-inflated, 1-locular; trans-Pecos Texas; return to choice 19/19.

    21. Pod variable but never much inflated, bilocular except in *A. soxmaniorum* of east Texas [22].

        22. Petals uniformly cream-colored or greenish-white; keel

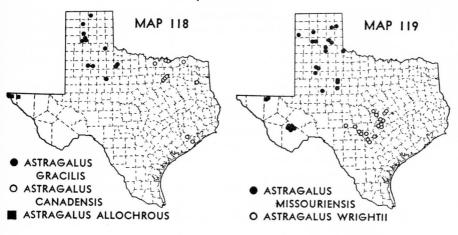

MAP 118

● ASTRAGALUS
  GRACILIS
○ ASTRAGALUS
  CANADENSIS
■ ASTRAGALUS ALLOCHROUS

MAP 119

● ASTRAGALUS
  MISSOURIENSIS
○ ASTRAGALUS WRIGHTII

9.4–10.2 mm. long; pod 1-locular; potentially perennial
but flowering the first season . . 19. *A. soxmaniorum*

22. Petals purple, lilac, or at least lilac-tipped; if appearing
whitish when dried then the keel shorter; pod bilocular;
obligate annuals (*A. emoryanus* exceptionally biennial)
[23].

23. Plant thinly hirsute with widely spreading hairs 1–
1.3 mm. long; petals irregularly graduated, the white
wings much shorter than the violet banner and keel,
the keel-blades lunately lanceolate, gradually taper-
ing into a narrow beaklike apex; pod sessile abruptly
deflexed, triangular-ovate in dorsal view, 5.5–9 mm.
long . . . . 20. *A. reflexus*

23. Plant variously pubescent, but if hirsute, then densely
so and the pod otherwise; petals regularly graduated, even if only slightly so, the banner longest and
keel shortest [24].

24. Pod densely pilose-hirsute, narrowly oblong,
straight, 7–13 mm. long, 2.5–3.5 mm. in diameter; racemes capitately 3–7-flowered, the flowers
and pods erect or nearly so on stiff erect peduncles
. . . . 21. *A. wrightii*

24. Pod glabrous, strigulose or thinly hirsutulous, but
if pubescent either narrower, or spreading, or incurved [25].

25. Racemes 7–25-flowered; pod deflexed, elevated on and readily deciduous from a stipelike gynophore 1.5–2.5 mm. long, the body peltate, subcircular or broader than long in dorsoventral view; ovules 4 . . . . . . 22. *A. brazoensis*

25. Racemes mostly fewer-flowered, but if over 7-flowered, the ovules at least 8; pod sessile or truly stipitate (the stipe continuous with the body), linear to oblong in outline, grooved dorsally [26].

26. Flowers both large and few (2–6), the banner (12)13–18.5 mm. long, the keel 9.5–13 mm. long, its broad blades 7–9.5 mm. long; pod stipitate, the stipe 1–2.5(3) mm. long, the narrowly oblong body 3.5–6 mm. in diameter; style minutely barbellulate below the stigma . 23. *A. lindheimeri*

26. Flowers smaller, the banner not over 12 mm., the keel mostly less than 8 mm. long, its blades 2.3–5 mm. long (but if the keel up to 9.3 mm. or its blades up to 7 mm. long, then the flowers 9 or more to the raceme); style glabrous; pod sessile or nearly so, the stipe less than 1 mm. long and the body then 1.8–3.5 mm. in diameter [27].

27. Pod (sessile, uniformly glabrous) readily deciduous from the receptacle and dehiscent at both ends on the ground; keel-tip broadly rounded, blunt; leaflets of all leaves truncate-emarginate or retuse . . . . 24. *A. emoryanus*

27. Pod (sessile or substipitate, glabrous or pubescent) firmly attached to the receptacle and dehiscent (unless broken off accidentally or in pressing) apically on the raceme; if all leaflets truncate-emarginate or retuse and the keel-tip obtuse, the pod cuneately contracted at base into a short stipe [28].

28. Herbage full, deep green, the margins and lower midrib of the leaflets sparsely strigulose with appressed hairs to 0.3–0.65 mm. long; leaflets of all leaves retuse; calyx sparsely strigulose with hairs to 0.25–0.5 mm. long; keel-tip sharply deltoid or triangular-acute [29].

29. Banner mostly 8–12 mm., keel mostly 6–7.8 mm. long; pod 2–3.5 cm. long, straight or very gently and evenly incurved its whole length . . . . 25. *A. leptocarpus*

29. Banner 5–7.5 mm., keel 4.5–5.8 mm. long; pod

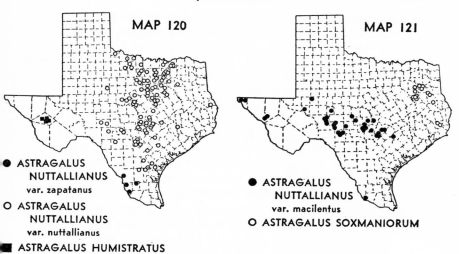

MAP 120

MAP 121

● ASTRAGALUS
   NUTTALLIANUS
   var. zapatanus

O ASTRAGALUS
   NUTTALLIANUS
   var. nuttallianus

◼ ASTRAGALUS HUMISTRATUS

● ASTRAGALUS
   NUTTALLIANUS
   var. macilentus

O ASTRAGALUS SOXMANIORUM

1.2–2.6 cm. long, usually incurved near the base and
straight or nearly so thereafter . . 26. *A. nuttallianus*
28. Herbage more densely pubescent with longer hairs or, if the
hairs no longer, then the leaflets pubescent above, or the ovary
and pod pubescent, or the leaflets elliptic and acute in at least
some upper leaves, or the keel-tip broadly rounded . .
. . . . 26. *A. nuttallianus*

1. *Astragalus canadensis* L., Sp. Pl. 757. 1753. CANADA
MILK VETCH
   Astragalus carolinianus L.
   Northeastern and southeastern Texas, though appar-
ently absent between these geographic extremes (Map
118). May–June. Southern Canada to Colorado, Texas,
New York, and Georgia.
   Chromosome number, $2n = 16$ (D. & W.).

2. *Astragalus missouriensis* Nutt., Gen. Am. 2:99. 1818.
MISSOURI MILK VETCH
   Xylophacos missouriensis (Nutt.) Rydb.
   Panhandle and trans-Pecos areas of Texas, mostly in

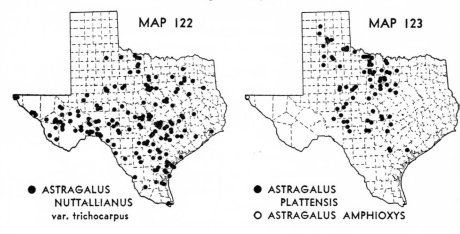

MAP 122

● ASTRAGALUS
NUTTALLIANUS
var. trichocarpus

MAP 123

● ASTRAGALUS
PLATTENSIS
O ASTRAGALUS AMPHIOXYS

sandy or silty-clay soils (Map 119). March–April. Southern Canada (Alberta and Saskatchewan) to New Mexico and Texas.

Chromosome number, $n = 11$ (Ledingham, 1957).

3. *Astragalus amphioxys* Gray, Proc. Amer. Acad. 13:366. 1878

Xylophacos amphioxys (Gray) Rydb.

Known to Texas by a single collection from El Paso County, Texas (Southern Methodist University Herbarium) (Map 123). Texas to southern Nevada, Arizona, and adjacent Mexico.

Chromosome number not determined.

4. *Astragalus humistratus* Gray, Pl. Wright. 2:43. 1853

Batidophaca humistrata (Gray) Rydb.

Jeff Davis Mountains in rocky, igneous soils, at altitudes of 6,500–7,000 feet (Map 120). Southwestern United States from southwestern Nevada and southern Utah to adjacent northern Mexico. The typical variety *humistratus* occurs in Texas, New Mexico, Arizona, and adjacent Mexico; however, var. *sonorae* Jones has been collected just across the New Mexican border in the Organ Mountains and may be found in Texas.

Chromosome number not determined.

5. *Astragalus lotiflorus* Hook., Fl. Bor. Am. 1:152. 1833.
LOW MILK VETCH

> *Astragalus reverchonii* Gray
> *Batidophaca lotiflora* (Hook.) Rydb.
> *Phaca cretacea* Buckl.
> *Batidophaca cretacea* (Buckl.) Rydb.

Central, Panhandle, and trans-Pecos areas of Texas, usually on calcareous or gypsiferous soils (Map 124). April. South-central Canada to Texas and New Mexico. Two varieties of the species are recognized for Texas; these may be distinguished by the following key:

1. Hairs of the herbage mostly appressed or narrowly ascending and to 0.5–1.1 mm. long; pod strigulose, often silky in youth, acuminate distally, mostly more than 2 cm. and to 3.7 cm. long; widespread over calcareous prairies of central and northern Texas . . . . 5a. var. *lotiflorus*
1. Hairs of the herbage mostly spreading or widely ascending and to 1.2–1.7 mm. long; pod villosulous or villous-hirsute, shortly beaked, 1.2–2.7 cm. long; a western form of greater altitudes, just entering west Texas in Bailey, Brewster, Nolan, and Randall counties . . . . . 5b. var. *nebraskensis* Bates

Chromosome number not determined.

6. *Astragalus racemosus* Pursh, Fl. Am. Sept. 740. 1814
> *Tium racemosum* (Pursh) Rydb.

Northwestern Texas, mostly in rocky or silty-clay soils (Map 125). March–June. North Dakota to Texas and New Mexico.

Chromosome number, $2n = 24$ (D. & W.; Ledingham, 1957).

7. *Astragalus praelongus* Sheldon, Minn. Bot. Stud. 1:23. 1894

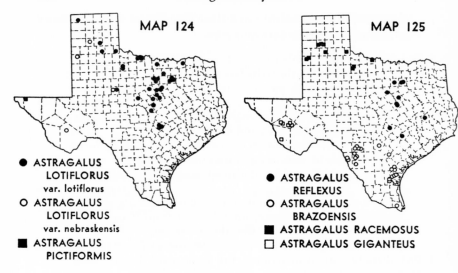

MAP 124

● ASTRAGALUS
LOTIFLORUS
var. lotiflorus
O ASTRAGALUS
LOTIFLORUS
var. nebraskensis
■ ASTRAGALUS
PICTIFORMIS

MAP 125

● ASTRAGALUS
REFLEXUS
O ASTRAGALUS
BRAZOENSIS
■ ASTRAGALUS RACEMOSUS
□ ASTRAGALUS GIGANTEUS

Jonesiella ellisiae Rydb.

Northwestern Texas, mostly in limestone or seleniferous soils (Map 127). March–May. Texas to Arizona, southern Utah, and Nevada. In Texas the species is represented by var. *ellisiae* (Rydb.) Barneby; the typical variety is more western in distribution. Reportedly very toxic to sheep.

Chromosome number, $2n = 24$ (Delay, 1950).

8. *Astragalus giganteus* Wats., Proc. Amer. Acad. 17:370. 1882. GIANT MILK VETCH

Trans-Pecos Texas in mountainous areas, at altitudes of 6,000–7,000 feet, igneous soils (Map 125). June–August. Texas, New Mexico, and adjacent Mexico.

Chromosome number not determined.

9. *Astragalus mollissimus* Torr., Ann. Lyc. N. Y. 2:178. 1827. CRAZY-WEED

Western Texas, in nearly all soil types (Map 126). March–May. Nebraska and Wyoming to southern Nevada, Texas, and southern Mexico. A variable species composed of several intergrading varieties. The Texas varieties may be identified by the following key:

1. Pod glabrous, thinly puberulent when young or, if permanently pubescent throughout, the hairs less than 1 mm. long.
  2. Petals cream-colored, immaculate; western Edwards Plateau
    . . . . 9a. var. *coryi* Tidestr.
  2. Petals purple throughout or marginally suffused with purple; distribution more northern and western.
    3. Calyx tube 3.4–4.5 mm. in diameter; flowers usually large, the keel 14–18 mm. long; intergrading with the variety below (as indicated by the lined area on Map 126) .
    . . . . 9b. var. *mollissimus*
    3. Calyx tube 0.8–3 mm. in diameter; flowers mostly smaller, the keel 9–13 mm. long; abundant in trans-Pecos Texas, passing northward into the above variety . . .
    . . . . 9c. var. *earlei* (Rydb.) Tidestr.
1. Pod densely villous-tomentose, the hairs over 1 mm. long; western trans-Pecos Texas.
  4. Calyx 10 mm. long or more; banner 16–25 mm. long; pod 1–1.5 cm. long; ovules 20–30 . . . . .
  . . . . . . 9d. var. *bigelovii* (Gray) Barneby
  4. Calyx 7–9.5 mm. long; banner 12–16 mm. long; pod 1 cm. long or less; ovules 12–16 . . . . . .
  . . . . . . 9e. var. *marcidus* (Rydb.) Barneby

A. argillophilus Cory is treated here as a synonym of var. *coryi*. *A. earlei* Greene *ex* Rydb., *A. bigelovii* Gray, and *A. marcidus* Greene *ex* Rydb. are treated as varieties of *A. mollissimus*, as indicated above.

Chromosome number, $2n = 24$ (for var. *earlei*; Head, 1957).

10. *Astragalus crassicarpus* Nutt., Fraser Cat. 1. 1813.
GROUND PLUM
    Astragalus carnosus Pursh
    Geoprumnon crassicarpum (Nutt.) Rydb.
    Central, northern, and western Texas in nearly all soil types (Map 128). March–April. Southern Canada to Texas and northeastern Arizona. The round, fleshy fruits

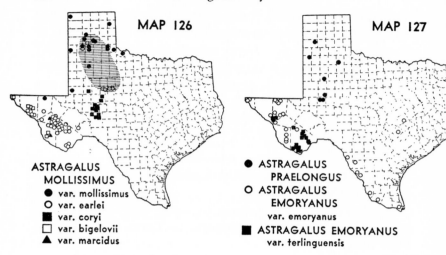

ASTRAGALUS
MOLLISSIMUS
● var. mollissimus
○ var. earlei
■ var. coryi
□ var. bigelovii
▲ var. marcidus

● ASTRAGALUS
   PRAELONGUS
○ ASTRAGALUS
   EMORYANUS
   var. emoryanus
■ ASTRAGALUS EMORYANUS
   var. terlinguensis

of this species were eaten by the Indians and early settlers of the Midwest. Three varieties of this species are recognized for Texas; they may be identified by the following key:

1. Calyx pilose or pilosulus with mixed black and white or largely black hairs (rarely, all white); petals purple or purple-tinged; peduncles mostly 2–6.5 cm. long.
   2. Stems arising together from the crown of the taproot, or very shortly forming from the root at or just below the soil level; mostly north-central and western Texas . . . .
      . . . . 10a. var. *crassicarpus*
   2. Stems arising singly or few together from slender, widely forking underground stem-branches, forming loosely matted growths; mostly central Texas . . . . . .
      . . . . 10b. var. *berlandieri* Barneby
1. Calyx (and pedicels) densely villosulous-tomentulose (at least at base, commonly throughout) with short entangled and some longer ascending cream-colored or brownish hairs; petals greenish-white or cream-colored; peduncles mostly 6–15 cm. long; northeastern Texas . . . .
      . . . . 10c. var. *trichocalyx* (Nutt.) Barneby *ex* Gleason

A. mexicanus DC. (= *Geoprumnon mexicanum* [DC.] Rydb.) is here treated as a synonym of var. *berlandieri*. *A. trichocalyx* Nutt. (= *Geoprumnon trichocalyx* [Nutt.] Rydb.) is treated as a variety as indicated above. In western Texas, occasional specimens of *A. crassicarpus* are found with pubescent pods. Rydberg treated most of the present taxa as species of a different genus (*Geoprumnon*).

Chromosome number, $2n = 22$ (D. & W., for var. *crassicarpus*).

11. *Astragalus gypsodes* Barneby, Amer. Midl. Natur. 55:499. 1956. GYP MILK VETCH

Trans-Pecos Texas, known to occur only on gypseous soils (Map 129). May. Endemic to Texas and adjacent New Mexico.

Chromosome number, $2n = 24$ (Head, 1957).

12. *Astragalus plattensis* Nutt. *ex* Torr. & Gray, Fl. N. Am. 1:332. 1838.

Astragalus pachycarpus Torr. & Gray
Geoprumnon plattense (Nutt.) Rydb.
Geoprumnon pachycarpum (Torr. & Gray) Rydb.

Central and northern Texas, mostly in calcareous soils (Map 123). March–April. South Dakota, south to Texas and Alabama.

Chromosome number not determined.

13. *Astragalus waterfallii* Barneby, Leafl. West. Bot. 7:31. 1953. WATERFALL MILK VETCH

Western Texas in rocky limestone soils (Map 130). March. Endemic to Texas and adjacent New Mexico.

Chromosome number not determined.

14. *Astragalus gracilis* Nutt., Gen. Am. 2:100. 1818

Astragalus microphacos Cory
Astragalus parviflorus (Pursh) MacM.
Microphacos gracilis (Nutt.) Rydb.
Microphacos parviflorus (Pursh) Rydb.

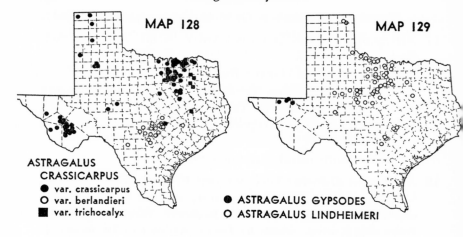

MAP 128

MAP 129

ASTRAGALUS
CRASSICARPUS
● var. crassicarpus
O var. berlandieri
■ var. trichocalyx

● ASTRAGALUS GYPSODES
O ASTRAGALUS LINDHEIMERI

Northwestern Texas usually in calcareous soils (Map 118). April–June. Southwestern North Dakota and eastern Montana, south to northeastern New Mexico and Texas. A widespread variable species.

Chromosome number not determined.

15. *Astragalus pictiformis* Barneby, Leafl. West. Bot. 8:20. 1956

Trans-Pecos Texas in mostly limestone soils often associated with *Juniperus* spp. (Map 124). Texas and eastern New Mexico. Texas plants referable to this species were treated by Rydberg (1929) as *Pisophaca greenei*.

Chromosome number not determined.

16. *Astragalus wootonii* Sheld., Minn. Geol. and Nat. Hist. Survey Bot. Studies 1:138. 1894. GARBANCILLO

Phaca wootonii (Sheld.) Rydb.

Astragalus tracyi (Rydb.) Cory

Phaca tracyi Rydb.

Trans-Pecos Texas in sandy or silty-clay soils (Map 131). March–April. Texas to southeastern California and central Mexico. The species produces loco disease in horses, cattle, and sheep.

Chromosome number, $2n = 24$ (Turner, unpublished).

17. *Astragalus allochrous* Gray, Amer. Acad. Arts and Sci. Proc. 13:366. 1878

   Phaca allochroa (Gray) Rydb.

   Western trans-Pecos Texas, mostly in rocky or sandy soils (Map 118). April. Texas to Arizona and adjacent Mexico. The species reportedly causes loco disease in horses.

   Chromosome number not determined.

18. *Astragalus distortus* Torr. & Gray, Fl. N. Am. 1:333. 1838

   Eastern Texas, mostly in sandy soils of pine and oak woodlands (Map 130). March–April. West Virginia to Iowa and Kansas, south to Texas. All of the Texas specimens thus far examined fall into the var. *engelmannii* (Sheld.) Jones (= *Holcophacos engelmannii* Sheld.); however, the typical var. *distortus* may yet be collected in Texas since it occurs in southeastern Oklahoma. The varieties may be distinguished by the following character combinations (though individual characters often break down):

1. Pod deeply sulcate on both ventral and dorsal surfaces, didymous in cross section; ovules mostly 28–37; banner 11–15.5 mm. long; keel 7.5–9.5 mm. long . . . . 18a. var. *distortus*
1. Pod shallowly sulcate dorsally but not, or obscurely so, ventrally; obcordate to nearly round in cross section; ovules 15–28; banner mostly 6.5–11.5 mm. long; keel 5.5–7 mm. long .
    . . . . 18b. var. *engelmannii*

   The two varieties reportedly intergrade northward where their ranges meet.

   Chromosome number, $n = 13$ (for var. *engelmannii*; Turner and Fearing, unpublished).

19. *Astragalus soxmaniorum* Lundell, Field & Lab. 13:3. 1945

   Eastern Texas in mostly white sandy soils of pine and oak woodlands (Map 121). March–April. Endemic to

Texas. Often growing near *A. distortus*, but this latter species usually on heavier, silty-sandy soils.

Chromosome number not determined.

20. *Astragalus reflexus* Torr. & Gray, Fl. N. Am. 1:334. 1838
    Hamosa reflexa (Torr. & Gray) Rydb.
    Central and north-central Texas in black clay soils (Map 125). April. Endemic to Texas.
    Chromosome number not determined.

21. *Astragalus wrightii* Gray, Bost. Jour. Nat. Hist. 6:176. 1850. WRIGHT MILK VETCH
    Central Texas in rocky limestone soils (Map 119). April–May. Endemic to Texas. This species has no close relatives in America, but it appears to be closely related to a group of species occurring in the Orient and Mediterranean regions.
    Chromosome number not determined.

22. *Astragalus brazoensis* Buckl., Proc. Acad. Phila. 1861:452. 1862. BRAZOS MILK VETCH
    Hesperastragalus brazoensis (Buckl.) Rydb.
    Southern Texas, mostly in silty-clay or sandy soils (Map 125). February–April. Endemic to Texas and adjacent Mexico.
    Chromosome number, $2n = 22$ (Turner and Fearing, unpublished).

23. *Astragalus lindheimeri* Gray, Pl. Wright. 1:52. 1852. LINDHEIMER MILK VETCH
    Hamosa lindheimeri (Gray) Rydb.
    Astragalus lindheimeri var. *bellus* Shinners
    Central and north-central Texas in sandy or clay soils (Map 129). March–May. Endemic to Texas and adjacent Oklahoma. *A. lindheimeri* var. *bellus* Shinners is a populational "form" of the species with larger flowers and less leafy stems.
    Chromosome number not determined.

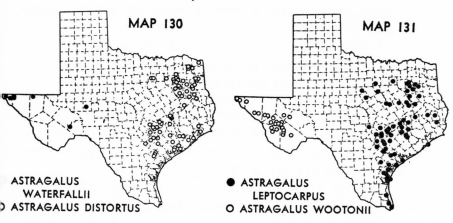

MAP 130

ASTRAGALUS
  WATERFALLII
ASTRAGALUS DISTORTUS

MAP 131

● ASTRAGALUS
   LEPTOCARPUS
○ ASTRAGALUS WOOTONII

s emoryanus (Rydb.) Cory, Rhodora 38:406.

ORY MILK VETCH

a emoryana Rydb.

l, southern, and trans-Pecos areas of Texas, sandy or silty-clay soils (Map 127). February– xas, New Mexico, and northern Mexico. Two are recognized for Texas and may be distin- the following key:

long, very gently to strongly, but then evenly, in- 2.2) cm. long, (2)2.2–3.3 mm. in diameter, five half times as long as its diameter; widespread . . . . . . 24a. var. *emoryanus*

1 broadly and plumply lance-oblong, nearly straight or very slightly incurved, 0.8–1.4 cm. long, (2.5)3–3.7 mm. in diameter, three to four and one third times as long as its diameter; locally common in the Big Bend country (Brewster County to southern Hudspeth County) . . . . 24b. var. *terlinguensis* (Cory) Barneby

Occasional intergrades between these taxa have been seen from Brewster County. Var. *terlinguensis* is sometimes treated as a species (*A. terlinguensis* Cory).

Chromosome number not determined.

25. *Astragalus leptocarpus* Torr. & Gray, Fl. N. Am. 1:334. 1838

> *Hamosa leptocarpa* (Torr. & Gray) Rydb.
> *Hamosa leptocarpoides* (Jones) Rydb.
> *Astragalus leptocarpoides* (Jones) Cory

Eastern Texas, mostly in sandy soils (Map 131). March–April. Endemic to Texas and possibly adjacent Louisiana. Resembling *A. nuttallianus*, but readily distinguished by the larger flowers and straight, elongate pods. Chromosome number, $n = 13$ (Turner, 1956b).

26. *Astragalus nuttallianus* DC., Prodr. 2:289. 1825. TUR-KEY-PEA (Pea-Vine)

> *Hamosa nuttalliana* (DC.) Rydb.

Throughout most of Texas in nearly all soil types (Maps 120, 121, 122). March–April. Oklahoma and Texas to Utah, southeastern California, Baja California, and southern Mexico. A widespread variable species encompassing several intraspecific taxa. The following is a key to those varieties recognized in the present treatment:

1. Keel sharply deltoid or narrowly triangular at apex, the tip acute or acutish; racemes subcapitately 1- to 9(12)-flowered, the axis not at all or scarcely elongating 0–8(12) mm. long in fruit. Pod either glabrous or pubescent [2].
  2. Leaflets of all (both lowest and uppermost) leaves truncate-emarginate or retuse [3].
    3. Ovary and pod glabrous; herbage sparsely strigulose with appressed hairs or nearly glabrous; widespread in eastern Texas, south to Uvalde, Bexar, Duval, and Nueces counties . . . . 25a. var. *nuttallianus*
    3. Ovary and pod pubescent; leaflets and leaf rachis pilosulous with widely spreading incurved hairs; local in lower Rio Grande Valley (Webb, Zapata, and Jim Hogg counties and adjacent Mexico) . . . 25b. var. *zapatanus* Barneby
  2. Leaflets of at least the upper, often of all leaves, elliptic and acute or acutish, polymorphic; pod either glabrous, strigulose, or pilosulous; herbage commonly silvery- or gray-strigulose or -pilosulous; abundant nearly throughout Texas

except the lower Rio Grande Valley and Panhandle areas
.   .   .   .   .   .   25c. var. *trichocarpus* Torr. & Gray
1. Keel broadly rounded and obtuse at apex; racemes 3- to 27-
flowered, the axis more or less elongating and (0.5)1–3 cm.
long in fruit; pod glabrous; leaflets variable in number (9–23)
and outline, either acute or emarginate in all leaves or dimorphic, those of only the upper leaves acute; eastern and
central to trans-Pecos areas of Texas   .   .   .   .   .
.   .   .   .   .   .   25d. var. *macilentus* (Small) Barneby

The varieties recognized above are for the most part easily
separated, though occasional specimens may appear somewhat intermediate. Of the infraspecific taxa listed, var. *trichocarpus* (= *Hamosa austrina* Small; *Astragalus austrinus*
[Small] Schulz; *A. austrinus* var. *pleianthus* Shinners; *Hamosa davisiana* Rydb.) is the most variable. It is likely that
more intensive field and experimental work will result in the
recognition of several additional specific taxa from this
variety. Var. *macilentus* has been treated as a distinct species
(*Hamosa macilenta* Small). The *A. nuttallianus* complex is
in much need of populational and experimental study.
    Chromosome number not determined.

44. OXYTROPIS   Crazy-weed

PERENNIAL, caulescent, or acaulescent herbs often arising
from underground rhizomes.

LEAVES once compound, odd-pinnate with several to numerous
leaflets; stipules broad, often membranous and adnate to the
petiole; leaflets asymmetric at base.

FLOWERS in terminal racemes, white, yellow to various shades
of purple; keel usually beaked; stamens diadelphous.

FRUIT a narrowly ellipsoid to subglobose pod, dry and dehiscent or turgid and indehiscent, mostly with several to numerous seeds.

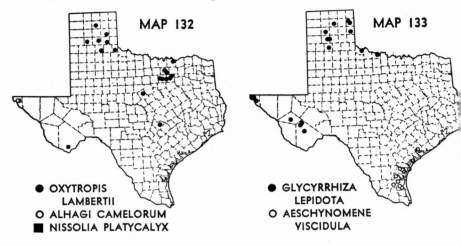

● OXYTROPIS
   LAMBERTII
○ ALHAGI CAMELORUM
■ NISSOLIA PLATYCALYX

● GLYCYRRHIZA
   LEPIDOTA
○ AESCHYNOMENE
   VISCIDULA

BASIC chromosome number, as determined from counts on about 10 species, $x = 8$ (D. & W.; Ledingham, 1957).

A genus with about 125 species in the northern, temperate regions of North America, Europe, and Asia. *Oxytropis* is sometimes included in the larger genus, *Astragalus*, where it is usually retained as a distinct subgenus. The two genera are superficially very similar and are apt to be mistaken at first sight by the novice in the field. The species are of little economic importance, though some of them are highly poisonous to livestock.

Oxytropis lambertii Pursh, Fl. Am. Sept. 740. 1814. LAMBERT CRAZY-WEED
   Astragalus lambertii (Pursh) Spreng.
   Central and Panhandle Texas, usually on gypseous or limestone soils (Map 132). April–June. A widespread, highly variable species occurring from south-central Canada to northern Mexico. In Texas and Oklahoma the species is represented by the var. *articulata* (Greene) Barneby. The typical var. *lambertii* is found from Kansas northward and can be

distinguished by its larger corolla and calyx (Barneby, 1952). The name *Astragalus lambertii* var. *abbreviatus* (Greene) Shinners has been used to cover material which the present writer includes in the var. *articulata*. The species is an extremely poisonous and habit-forming plant to livestock. In Arizona the var. *bigelovii* is known as "White Loco" and is reportedly one of the most dangerous of their poisonous plants, being readily eaten by horses, cattle, and sheep.

Chromosome number, $n = 24$ (Ledingham, 1957, for var. *lambertii*).

45. GLYCYRRHIZA   Licorice

PERENNIAL herbaceous plants with tall, erect stems arising from stout roots.

LEAVES once compound, odd-pinnate with glandular-viscid leaflets; stipules slender, small.

FLOWERS in spikelike, axillary racemes, the petals mostly whitish; stamens diadelphous, the alternate ones with reduced anthers.

FRUIT dry and indehiscent, the valves densely covered with short, hooked prickles.

BASIC chromosome number, as determined from counts on 6 species, $x = 8$ (D. & W.).

A genus with about 15 species in the temperate and subtropical regions of both hemispheres. The well-known flavoring, licorice, is obtained from the root of *G. glabra* L.; otherwise the species are of little economic importance.

Glycyrrhiza lepidota Pursh, Fl. Am. Sept. 480: 1814. AMERICAN LICORICE

North-central and western Texas, mostly in alluvial soils along stream beds or in damp roadside ditches and waste areas

(Map 133). April–July. A widespread species occurring throughout most of the United States.

Chromosome number, $n = 8$ (D. & W.).

46. ALHAGI   Camel-thorn

MUCH-BRANCHED, thorny, glabrous shrubs.

LEAVES small, simple.

FLOWERS numerous in short panicles or racemes, purplish-pink.

FRUIT a flattened pod with 1 to several joints, the segments not separating at maturity.

BASIC chromosome number not determined.

A small genus with only 3 species native to the desert regions of central and western Asia. The single species below has been introduced in the southwestern United States, where it has apparently become established (Kearney and Peebles, 1942).

Alhagi camelorum Fisch., Hort. Gorenk., ed. 2, 72. 1812. CAMEL-THORN

Introduced only recently in El Paso County, Texas, where it has become established along drainage ditches (Map 132). June–July. The species is reportedly of great value as a browse plant in the desert regions of central Asia, but according to Kearney and Peebles (1942), the plant may prove an undesirable introduction in cultivated areas since, once established, it is extremely difficult to eradicate.

Chromosome number not determined.

47. AESCHYNOMENE   Joint Vetch

HERBS, shrubs, or, rarely, trees, with erect or prostrate stems.

LEAVES once compound, odd-pinnate with few to numerous leaflets.

FLOWERS in axillary racemes or terminal clusters, yellow or yellowish-orange, sometimes flecked with other colors; stamens diadelphous in 2 sets of 5 each.

FRUIT a flattened pod, breaking transversely into 1-seeded segments at maturity.

BASIC chromosome number, as determined from counts on 2 species, $x = 10$ (D. & W.; Turner, unpublished).

A genus with about 100 species native to the warmer regions of Australia, America, Africa, and Asia. Some of the species are reportedly used as green manures and soil cover crops in tropical areas.

KEY TO SPECIES

1. Leaflets 2–5 pairs; stems prostrate or spreading   .   .   .
.   .   .   .   1. *A. viscidula*
1. Leaflets 9–31 pairs; stems erect   .   .   .   .   2. *A. indica*

1. *Aeschynomene viscidula* Michx., Fl. Bor. Am. 2:75. 1803.
STICKY JOINT VETCH
    Secula viscidula (Michx.) Small
    Coastal areas of southern Texas in sandy soils (Map 133). April–September. Southeastern United States to tropical South America.
    Chromosome number, $n = 10$ (Turner, unpublished).

2. *Aeschynomene indica* L., Sp. Pl. 713. 1753
    Coastal and eastern Texas in mostly wet, alluvial soils (Map 134). August–September. Southeastern United States along the coast from North Carolina to Texas; known

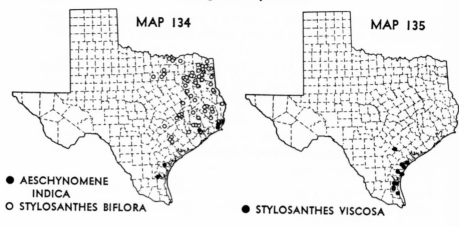

● AESCHYNOMENE
   INDICA
○ STYLOSANTHES BIFLORA   ● STYLOSANTHES VISCOSA

also as a weed in the West Indies, Asia, Australia, and
Africa. Rudd (1955) has treated some of the specimens
from southernmost Texas as *A. evenia* Wright var. *evenia*.
However, as noted by Rudd in her treatment, these specimens, in general, appear like *A. indica*. In the present
paper these specimens are treated as individuals of this
latter taxon since the total characters and distribution of
this material seem to fall more logically into the circumscription of *A. indica* than that of *A. evenia*.

Chromosome number, $2n = 40$ (D. & W.).

48. NISSOLIA   Nissolia

STEMS herbaceous, prostrate, twining, or, rarely, semishrubby.

LEAVES odd-pinnate; leaflets usually 5.

FLOWERS yellow, racemose or verticillate in the leaf axils.

FRUIT indehiscent, of few short, broad joints, the terminal
joint with a large thick terminal wing (aborted in *H. wislizenii*).

BASIC chromosome number not determined.

A genus with about 12 species in the mountainous and semidesert areas of North and South America (Rudd, 1956).

Nissolia platycalyx S. Wats., Proc. Amer. Acad. 17:344. 1882

Known to Texas by only two collections (Map 132), both from mid-elevations (5,000 feet) in the Chisos Mountains, Big Bend National Park (Rudd, 1956). July. Northern Mexico and adjacent Texas.

Chromosome number not determined.

49. STYLOSANTHES   Pencil-flower

PERENNIAL HERBS or small shrubs, often with prostrate or semierect, wiry stems.

LEAVES 3-foliate, the leaflets linear, lanceolate or oval; stipels absent; stipules conspicuous, connate, forming a sheath about the stem.

FLOWERS yellow or yellow-orange, in terminal heads or short spikes; stamens monadelphous, the anthers of two types.

FRUIT a dry, mostly indehiscent loment with 1 to several seeds, the terminal portion often beaked.

BASIC chromosome number, as determined from counts on 2 species, $x = 10$ (D. & W.).

A genus with about 25 species mostly in the tropical and subtropical regions of Asia, Africa, South America, and North America (Mohlenbrock, 1957). Some of the species are reportedly important pasture and range legumes, especially in tropical areas (Whyte *et al.*, 1953).

KEY TO SPECIES

1. Flowers in terminal bracted spikes 1–3 cm. long (somewhat less at early anthesis); branches glandular-pubescent; plants of southern Texas . . . . 1. *S. viscosa*
1. Flowers in short terminal heads or spikes 1 cm. long or less;

branches not at all glandular-pubescent (may be densely hispid); plants mostly of eastern Texas　.　.　.　2. *S. biflora*

1. *Stylosanthes viscosa* Sw., Prod. Veg. Ind. Occ. 108. 1788
　　Southern Texas, mostly in deep sandy soils (Map 135).
May–September. Mexico and Cuba to Central America.
This species has passed for *S. hamata* (L.) Taub. in Cory
and Parks (1937).
　　Chromosome number not determined.

2. *Stylosanthes biflora* (L.) B. S. P., Prelim. Cat. N. Y. Pl. 13.
1888. PENCIL-FLOWER
　　Eastern Texas, mostly in sandy soils (Map 134). April–
November. Central and eastern United States from Illinois
and New York south to Florida. Two forms of this species
occur in Texas: (1) var. *hispidissima* (Michx.) P. & B.,
with the internodal regions of the stem densely hispid and
(2) the typical form of the species (var. *biflora*), with
merely an appressed pubescence on the internodal regions
of the stem. However, there is much intergradation between
these morphologic types, the two forms often occurring together in the same population. *S. riparia* Kearney, a closely
related species with about the same range as *S. biflora*, has
been reported for Texas by Fernald (1950). The present
writer has not seen specimens of this species from Texas,
though some of the characters attributable to the species
(e.g., asymmetric pods) have been seen in what otherwise
appears to be *S. biflora* (other characters taken into consideration).
　　Chromosome number not determined.

50. ZORNIA　　Zornia

ANNUAL or perennial herbs with mostly prostrate or semierect, slender stems.

LEAVES palmately compound with 2–4 leaflets, these often
glandular-punctate.

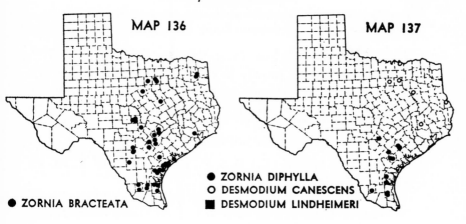

MAP 136

MAP 137

● ZORNIA DIPHYLLA
○ DESMODIUM CANESCENS
■ DESMODIUM LINDHEIMERI

● ZORNIA BRACTEATA

FLOWERS of various colors, commonly yellow, in axillary or terminal bracted spikes; stamens monadelphous.

FRUIT a flattened, several-jointed loment, the articles persistent at maturity, not disarticulating.

BASIC chromosome number, as determined from counts on a single species, $x = 10$ (D. & W.).

A genus with about 15 species, mostly in the tropical and subtropical regions of North and South America, but a few species occurring in the Old World. Species related to *Z. diphylla* are reportedly important range legumes and fodder plants in parts of Africa and South America.

KEY TO SPECIES

1. Leaflets 2 . . . . 1. *Z. diphylla*
1. Leaflets 3 or 4 . . . . 2. *Z. bracteata*

1. *Zornia diphylla* (L.) Pers., Syn. 2:318. 1807

Southern Texas, mostly in sandy or gravelly soils (Map 137). June–September. Tropical and subtropical areas of both hemispheres. A widespread, highly variable species with a number of varieties in tropical America. In Africa closely related taxa have been reported as important grassland legumes and are said to be of considerable importance as fodder plants. In Texas the plant is infrequent. According to Milne-Redhead (1954), typical *Z. diphylla* is a plant of limited distribution in tropical Asia, thus the North American material of this complex may eventually be recognized as a separate taxon.

Chromosome number not determined.

2. *Zornia bracteata* (Walt.) Gmel., Syst. 1096. 1791

Central and southern Texas mostly in sandy or gravelly soils (Map 136). April–July. Southeastern United States. Chromosome number, $2n = 20$ (D. & W.).

51. DESMODIUM   Tick Clover (Beggar-ticks)

UNARMED, annual or perennial herbs, less often shrubby to nearly arborescent (in tropical regions).

LEAVES trifoliate (rarely, 1- or 5-foliate); stipules present; stipels present, persistent.

FLOWERS white to purplish, in axillary or terminal racemes, often paniculately compound; stamens diadelphous (rarely, monadelphous); the anthers all alike.

BASIC chromosome number, as determined from counts on 22 species, $x = 11$ (D. & W.; rarely, $x = 10$, Turner and Fearing, unpublished).

A large genus with approximately 200 species in the tropical and temperate regions of North America, South America, Africa, and Australia. A number of the species are used as fodder and as soil cover and green manure crops. *Desmodium purpureum* is recommended for cultivation in the southeastern United States; it appears to thrive in this area, often persisting along roadsides and in abandoned fields. Most of the native Texas species occur in sandy soils in the eastern

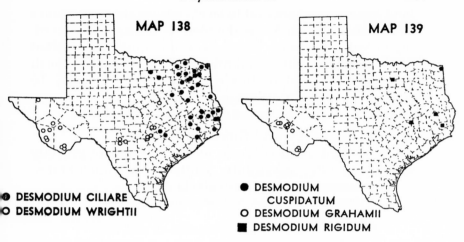

MAP 138

● DESMODIUM CILIARE
○ DESMODIUM WRIGHTII

MAP 139

● DESMODIUM
   CUSPIDATUM
○ DESMODIUM GRAHAMII
■ DESMODIUM RIGIDUM

part of the state, but a few species such as *D. paniculatum* and *D. tweedyi* are adapted to dry calcareous soils and might prove valuable in any planned selective or genetical work for drought-resistant legume types.

The generic name *Meibomia* has been utilized for *Desmodium* by some American workers, but the latter genus is now conserved over the former. For a brief review of the nomenclature involved see Isely (1955).

KEY TO SPECIES

1. Leaves unifoliate . . . . 1. *D. wrightii*
1. Leaves trifoliate.
   2. Plants of mountainous areas in trans-Pecos Texas.
      3. Plants delicate annuals . . . 2. *D. neomexicanum*
      3. Plants perennial . . . . . . 3. *D. grahamii*
   2. Plants of central and eastern Texas.
      4. Stipe of loment three times the length of calyx or more; calyx glabrous, regular, scarcely, if at all, lobed.
         5. Inflorescence axillary and terminal; flowers white; stipe 10 mm. long or less . . . . 4. *D. pauciflorum*
         5. Inflorescence terminal only; stipe 5–22 mm. long.

6. Inflorescence borne at apex of a leafy stem; terminal leaflet (of well-developed leaves) 7–15 cm. long   .
    .   .   .   .   5. *D. glutinosum*
6. Inflorescence borne on a leafless scape from base of plant; terminal leaflet 4–7 cm. long   .   .   6. *D. nudiflorum*
4. Stipe of loment two to two and one half times the length of calyx or less; calyx irregular, decidedly lobed.
  7. Leaflets pubescent beneath with principally uncinate (hooked) hairs, at least along the midrib and veins (easily seen under 10x lens).
    8. Stipules 2–4 mm. long   .   .   .   .   7. *D. fernaldii*
    8. Stipules 8–25 mm. long.
      9. Leaflets with large pale blotches along either side of midrib; stipels (at base of terminal leaflet) 1–2.5 mm. long .   .   .   .   .   .   8. *D. tweedyi*
      9. Leaflets uniformly green; stipels 2–12 mm. long.
        10. Pedicels (most of them) 3–7 mm. long; stipules of mid-stem leaves 1–3 mm. wide at base   .   .
          .   .   .   .   9. *D. canadense*
        10. Pedicels (most of them) 8–24 mm. long; stipules 3–8 mm. wide at base.
          11. Flowers 10–14 mm. long; loment articles 6–11 mm. long .   .   .   .   10. *D. canescens*
          11. Flowers 3–6 mm. long; loment articles 3–5 mm. long   .   .   .   .   .   11. *D. purpureum*
  7. Leaflets without hooked hairs beneath, or if present, these few, inconspicuous, and only on the lower part of the midrib and main veins, mostly hidden among the more conspicuous straight hairs.
    12. Valves of the loment glabrate, the sutures pubescent; rare plants of limestone canyons in central Texas   .
      .   .   .   .   12. *D. lindheimeri*
    12. Valves of the loment distinctly pubescent as well as the sutures.
      13. Stipules ovate (5–12 mm. long) or lance-linear (8–12 mm. long); terminal leaflets 3–10 cm. in length.
        14. Leaflets densely soft pubescent beneath, soft and velvety to the touch; stipules ovate, two to three times as long as wide; mid-stem leaves with petioles 2–3 cm. long.
          15. Stems prostrate, trailing; leaves rotund or

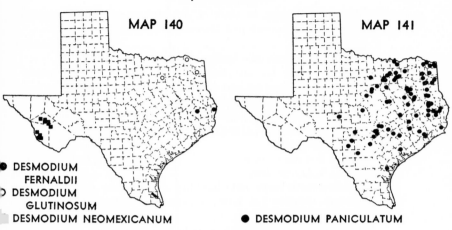

MAP 140

MAP 141

● DESMODIUM
   FERNALDII
◑ DESMODIUM
   GLUTINOSUM
▪ DESMODIUM NEOMEXICANUM

● DESMODIUM PANICULATUM

broadly ovate, as broad as long or broader   .   .
  .   .   .   .   .   .   13. *D. rotundifolium*
15. Stems stiffly erect, not trailing; leaves broadly ovate
    to elliptic.
    16. Terminal leaflets one to one and eight tenths
        times as long as wide, truncate or broadly obtuse
        at base; loment articles 5–8 mm. long, the dorsal
        suture straight or nearly so   .   .   .   .
        .   .   .   . 14. *D. viridiflorum*
    16. Terminal leaflets one and one half to two and
        one half times as long as wide, at least some of
        them acute or narrowly obtuse at base; loment
        articles 3–5(6) mm. long, the dorsal suture
        rounded   .   .   .   .   . 15. *D. nuttallii*
14. Leaflets glabrous to sparsely pubescent beneath, not soft
    or velvety to touch; stipules lance-linear, four to eight
    times as long as wide; mid-stem leaves with petioles
    4–6 cm. long   .   .   .   .   . 16. *D. cuspidatum*
13. Stipules small, linear to subulate, 2–6(8) mm. long; termi-
    nal leaflets 0.5–10 cm. in length.
    17. Terminal leaflets broadly ovate to oval, 0.5–3 cm. long,
        two times as long as wide or less (if longer, then the
        leaves 2.5 cm. long or less); petioles of mid-stem leaves
        2–20 mm. long.

18. Stems weak, prostrate . . . . . **17. *D. lineatum***
18. Stems stiffly erect.
  19. Pedicels 5–9(10) mm. long; stems densely and conspicuously pubescent; petioles 3–10 mm. long; leaflets thickened, strongly reticulate-veined (intergrades with *D. marilandicum*, below) . . . . **18. *D. ciliare***
  19. Pedicels (9)10–15 mm. long; stems with a scattered pubescence, often nearly glabrate; petioles (some of them) 12–25 mm. long; leaflets thin, not conspicuously reticulate-veined . . . . **19. *D. marilandicum***
17. Terminal leaflets linear to ovate, two to ten times longer than wide (rarely, less), at least some of them 3 cm. long or more; petioles of middle stem leaves 10–60 mm. long.
  20. Petioles of mid-stem leaves 2–20 mm. long.
    21. Leaflets pubescent beneath; 6–25 mm. wide.
      22. Leaflets (terminal ones) oblong to ovate, two to four times as long as wide . . . **20. *D. rigidum***
      22. Leaflets ovate to linear-ovate, four to ten times as long as wide. . . . . **21. *D. sessilifolium***
    21. Leaflets essentially glabrous, 5–8 mm. wide . .
    . . . . **22. *D. strictum***
  20. Petioles of mid-stem leaves, at least some of them, (15)20–60 mm. long.
    23. Leaflets 5–8 mm. wide, essentially glabrate beneath
    . . . . **22. *D. strictum***
    23. Leaflets wider, glabrous to densely pubescent beneath.
      24. Terminal leaflets linear to ovate, most of them 3(4) cm. wide or less, pubescent beneath; stipe of the fruit 2–5 mm. long . . . **23. *D. paniculatum***
      24. Terminal leaflets ovate; glabrous beneath (rarely, minutely scattered-pubescent); stipe of the fruit 4–7 mm. long . . . . . **24. *D. laevigatum***

1. *Desmodium wrightii* Gray, Bost. Jour. Nat. Hist. 6:177. 1850. WRIGHT TICK CLOVER
    Central and trans-Pecos Texas in rocky limestone soils (Map 138). August. Texas to Arizona and adjacent Mexico.
    Chromosome number, $2n = 22$ (Turner and Fearing, unpublished).

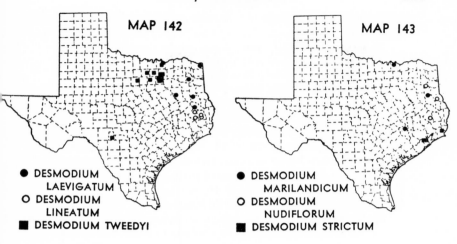

MAP 142

MAP 143

● DESMODIUM
   LAEVIGATUM
○ DESMODIUM
   LINEATUM
■ DESMODIUM TWEEDYI

● DESMODIUM
   MARILANDICUM
○ DESMODIUM
   NUDIFLORUM
■ DESMODIUM STRICTUM

2. *Desmodium neomexicanum* Gray, Pl. Wright. 1:53. 1852

Trans-Pecos Texas in rocky igneous soils of mountainous areas in Brewster, Jeff Davis, and Presidio counties (Map 140). August. Texas to Arizona and adjacent Mexico, occurring again in South America.

Chromosome number not determined.

3. *Desmodium grahamii* Gray, Pl. Wright. 2:48. 1853. GRAHAM TICK CLOVER

Trans-Pecos Texas in igneous soils of the Davis and Chisos mountains (Map 139). June. Texas to Arizona and adjacent Mexico.

Chromosome number not determined.

4. *Desmodium pauciflorum* (Nutt.) DC., Prod. 2:330. 1825

Northeastern Texas in sandy soils of pine and oak woodlands, infrequent (Map 144). July. Central and southeastern United States.

Chromosome number not determined.

5. *Desmodium glutinosum* (Muhl. *ex* Willd.) Wood, Classbook, 120. 1845

Desmodium acuminatum (Michx.) DC.

Northeastern Texas in sandy or silty alluvial soils of pine and oak woodlands (Map 140). June. Widespread throughout the central and eastern United States.

Chromosome number, $n = 11$ (Young, 1940; as *D. grandiflorum*, according to Isely, 1955).

6. *Desmodium nudiflorum* (L.) DC., Prodr. 2:330. 1825

Eastern Texas in damp sandy soils of pine or oak woodlands (Map 143). September. Central and eastern United States.

Chromosome number, $n = 11$ (Young, 1940).

7. *Desmodium fernaldii* Schub., Rhodora 52:147. 1950

Southeastern Texas in sandy soils of pine and oak woodlands, apparently infrequent (Map 140). June. Southeastern United States.

Chromosome number not determined.

8. *Desmodium tweedyi* Britt., Trans. N. Y. Acad. Sci. 9:183. 1889

Central and north-central Texas in sandy or silty alluvial soils along stream bottoms (Map 142). June–July. Texas and adjacent Oklahoma. *D. tweedyi* has been listed as a synonym of *D. illinoense* Gray by Schubert in Fernald's recent treatment in *Gray's Manual of Botany* (1950). However, the two taxa appear distinct, both morphologically and geographically. *D. illinoense* is not known from Texas, but it is reported from the adjacent state of Oklahoma.

Chromosome number not determined.

9. *Desmodium canadense* (L.) DC., Prodr. 2:328. 1825. CANADA TICK CLOVER

Not collected in Texas as yet, but to be expected since it occurs in the adjoining state of Oklahoma. July. Widespread species occurring from southern Canada to Oklahoma and east to North Carolina.

Chromosome number, $n = 11$ (Young, 1940).

10. *Desmodium canescens* (L.) DC., Prodr. 2:328. 1825. HOARY TICK CLOVER

Eastern Texas mostly in sandy soils of pine or oak woodlands (Map 137). September. Widespread species occurring from southern Canada to Texas and east to Florida.

Chromosome number, $2n = 22$ (Young, 1940).

11. *Desmodium purpureum* (Mill.) Fawc. & Rendle, Fl. Jamaica 4:36. 1920. BEGGARWEED

Desmodium tortuosum (Sw.) DC.

Southeastern Texas in sandy soils of pine and oak woodlands (Map 144). August–September. Southeastern United States from Texas to Florida and tropical America. The species is cultivated in parts of the South as a soil cover crop on marginal lands.

Chromosome number, $n = 11$ (D. & W.; as *D. tortuosum*).

12. *Desmodium lindheimeri* Vail, Bull. Torr. Bot. Club 18: 120. 1891

South-central Texas in rocky limestone soils along creek bottoms (Map 137); known to this writer only by the type collection from New Braunfels, Comal County, Texas (*Lindheimer 765a*, Nov., 1850; isotype University of Texas Herbarium).

Chromosome number not determined.

13. *Desmodium rotundifolium* DC., Prodr. 2:330. 1825. PROSTRATE TICK CLOVER

Southeastern Texas in rich, sandy, loamy soils of oak and pine woodlands (Map 144). June. Central and eastern United States from Michigan to Florida.

Chromosome number, $n = 11$ (Young, 1940).

14. *Desmodium viridiflorum* (L.) DC., Prod. 2:329. 1825. VELVET-LEAF TICK CLOVER

Eastern Texas in sandy soils of pine and oak woodlands (Map 145). September–October. Southeastern United

States from Oklahoma to Florida. *D. viridiflorum* is closely related to the species below and is separated from that taxon with some difficulty. Isely (1953) recognizes the taxa as specifically distinct. In Texas the characters which mark the species appear to intergrade.

Chromosome number, $n = 11$ (Young, 1940).

15. *Desmodium nuttallii* (Schindl.) Schub., Rhodora 52:142. 1950. NUTTALL TICK CLOVER

Northeastern Texas in sandy soils of pine and oak woodlands (Map 145). September. Central and eastern United States, more northern in range than the species above. *D. nuttallii* is closely related to *D. viridiflorum* and in Texas appears to intergrade with that species (see comments above).

Chromosome number not determined.

16. *Desmodium cuspidatum* (Muhl.) Loud., Hort. Brit. 309. 1830

Desmodium bracteosum (Michx.) DC.

Northeastern Texas in sandy soils of pine and oak woodlands (Map 139). September. Central and eastern United States from Maine and Minnesota to Florida.

Chromosome number not determined.

17. *Desmodium lineatum* (Michx.) DC., Prod. 2:330. 1825

Southeastern Texas in sandy soils of pine woodlands (Map 142). July–September. Southeastern United States from Texas to Florida and Maryland.

Chromosome number not determined.

18. *Desmodium ciliare* (Muhl.) DC., Prodr. 2:329. 1825

Desmodium obtusum (Muhl.) DC.

Mostly eastern Texas in sandy or gravelly soils of pine and oak woodlands (Map 138). August–October. Southern Canada to Texas and Florida. Intergrades in Texas with the species below.

Chromosome number, $n = 11$ (Young, 1940; as *D. obtusum*).

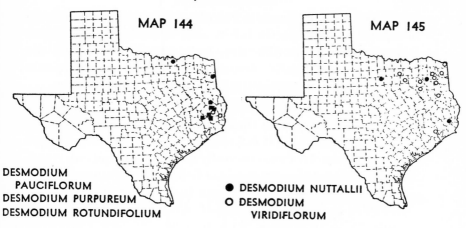

MAP 144

MAP 145

DESMODIUM
PAUCIFLORUM
DESMODIUM PURPUREUM
DESMODIUM ROTUNDIFOLIUM

● DESMODIUM NUTTALLII
O DESMODIUM
VIRIDIFLORUM

19. *Desmodium marilandicum* (L.) DC., Prod. 2:228. 1825.
MARYLAND TICK CLOVER
Infrequent in sandy soils of pine and oak woodlands in
eastern Texas (Map 143). August–October. Eastern
United States south to Texas and Alabama. Most of the
Texas material referred here is not typical of the species
as it appears farther north but shows features which link
it to *D. ciliare*. Isely (1955) has listed a number of characters which can be used to separate the species; these have
been used, with some modification, in the present key.
Chromosome number, $n = 11$ (Young, 1940).

20. *Desmodium rigidum* (Ell.) DC., Prodr. 2:330. 1825.
RIGID TICK CLOVER
Mostly eastern Texas in sandy soils of pine and oak
woodlands (Map 139). October. Eastern United States
from New Hampshire to Michigan, south to Florida and
Mexico. Resembling *D. marilandicum*, but larger in all of
its parts.
Chromosome number, $n = 11$ (Young, 1940).

21. *Desmodium sessilifolium* (Torr.) Torr. & Gray, Fl. N. Am.
1:363. 1838. SESSILE-LEAVED TICK CLOVER

Very common in sandy or gravelly soils of central and northern Texas (Map 146). June–September. Eastern United States from Massachusetts and Michigan south to Louisiana.

Chromosome number, $n = 11$ (Turner, 1956b).

22. *Desmodium strictum* (Pursh) DC., Prod. 2:337. 1825

Known only from a few collections in southeastern Texas (Map 143). July–August. Southeastern United States on the Atlantic and Gulf Coast plains.

Chromosome number, $n = 11$ (D. & W.).

23. *Desmodium paniculatum* (L.) DC., Prodr. 2:329. 1825. PANICLED TICK CLOVER

Desmodium dichromum Shinners

Widespread throughout central and eastern Texas in sandy, gravelly, or calcareous soils (Map 141). May–October. A variable species occurring from the north-central United States to Texas and Florida. The present interpretation of the species is the same as that of Isely (1953). Some of the forms of this species have been segregated as distinct varieties or species such as *D. paniculatum* var. *dillenii* (Darl.) Isely (= *D. dillenii* Darl.), a form with thicker, broader leaflets and shorter petioles than is typical for the species. Reference should be made to Isely's treatment and that of Schubert (1950) for the list of confusing synonyms compiled for this taxon.

Some populations of *D. paniculatum* occur naturally on limestone soils of central Texas. Seed collections from such races were planted in the experimental gardens at Austin, Texas, and grown to maturity. Response to cultivation was excellent, the perennial shoots showing vigorous summer growth in spite of near-drought conditions. Further agronomic work on the species seems desirable.

Desmodium dichromum appears to be a form of the species with shorter pedicels and somewhat broader leaves.

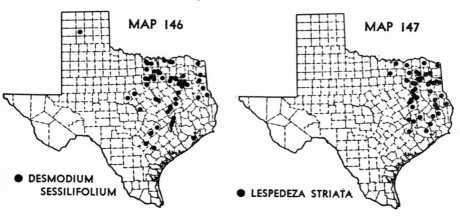

The plant is known only by a single collection from Palo Pinto County.

Chromosome number, $n = 11$ (Young, 1940).

24. *Desmodium laevigatum* (Nutt.) DC., Prodr. 2:329. 1825. SMOOTH TICK CLOVER

Eastern Texas in sandy soil of pine and oak woodlands (Map 142). September. Eastern and central United States from New York and Illinois to Texas and Florida.

Chromosome number, $n = 11$ (Young, 1940).

Extralimital Species

Desmodium spirale (Sw.) DC.

This species has been listed for Texas by Cory and Parks (1937), but according to Schubert (1950), this name is synonymous with *D. procumbens* (Mill.) Hitchc., a species of Arizona, New Mexico, Mexico, and southward. The Texas report is probably based on misidentified material of *D. neomexicanum* Gray.

52. LESPEDEZA   Bush Clover

UNARMED, herbaceous or shrubby perennials, or rarely, annuals.

LEAVES pinnately 3-foliolate, the leaflets without stipels; stipules present, persistent.

FLOWERS white, yellow, red to purplish, in loose or contracted racemes, often cleistogamous; stamens diadelphous, anthers all alike.

FRUIT a single, 1-seeded, oval to rounded, flattened, indehiscent pod.

BASIC chromosome number, as determined from counts on approximately 24 species, $x = 9, 10, 11$ (D. & W.).

A genus with approximately 100 species mainly confined to the temperate regions of eastern Asia, Australia, and eastern North America. At the present time only 3 of the species are of any real value to agriculture; these are the annual species, *L. striata* and *L. stipulacea*, and the perennial species, *L. cuneata* (all are introduced in Texas). However, extensive experimental work is being initiated with the perennial taxa, and it is not unlikely that important agronomic types will be developed in the near future (Hanson and Cope, 1955). The species reseed themselves profusely, a desirable feature of pasture and green manure plants. Of the species native to Texas, the closely related taxa, *L. texana, L. repens,* and *L. procumbens,* should prove valuable research material for future breeding work in this genus. *Lespedeza* is in need of detailed field and experimental work. Many of the species apparently hybridize; this, along with their partially cleistogamous nature, makes classical taxonomic evaluation and circumscription extremely difficult, if not impossible.

KEY TO SPECIES

1. Stipules ovate to ovate-lanceolate, membranous; stems short, 5–30(45) cm. long, procumbent or weakly ascending; plants annual.
    2. Stipules 3–5 mm. long, 1–3 mm. wide; stem hairs pointed downward (retrose); leaflets 2–6 mm. wide . . 1. *L. striata*
    2. Stipules 6–10 mm. long, 3–5 mm. wide; stem hairs pointed upward (antrose); leaflets 5–12 mm. wide . . .
        . . . . 2. *L. stipulacea*
1. Stipules subulate or setaceous, not membranous; stems elongate, 20–120 cm. long, erect or procumbent; plants perennial.
    3. Stems procumbent, trailing or very weakly ascending; flowers purple or violet.
        4. Mature fruit 5–7 mm. long; plants of rocky limestone soils.
            5. Leaf petioles (of lower and mid-stem leaves) 2–4 cm. long; main stem mostly much-branched (i.e., with numerous well-developed lateral branches); stem nearly glabrate or pubescent with appressed hairs; plants of north-central Texas (intergrades with *L. texana* southward) . . . . 9. *L. violacea*
            5. Leaf petioles 0.5–2 cm. long; main stem mostly unbranched (without lateral leafy branches); stem pubescent with appressed or spreading hairs; plants of rocky limestone soil in central Texas (intergrades with *L. violacea* northward) . . . . . 3. *L. texana*
        4. Mature fruit 3–5(6) mm. long; plants of sandy soils in east and north-central Texas.
            6. Stems and petioles densely pubescent with spreading hairs . . . . 4. *L. procumbens*
            6. Stems and petioles with an appressed pubescence or nearly glabrate . . . . . . 5. *L. repens*
    3. Stems stiffly erect; flowers violet, purple, or yellowish-white.
        7. Calyx lobes 5–10 mm. long; flowers yellowish.
            8. Leaflets one to two times as long as wide (rarely, more); inflorescence usually definitely spicate, at least some of the peduncles 1–5 cm. long . . . . 6. *L. hirta*
            8. Leaflets mostly two and one third to four times as long as wide; inflorescence globose or short-ovoid, the peduncles 0.2–1 cm. long . . . . . . 7. *L. capitata*
        7. Calyx lobes 1.5–3.5 mm. long; flowers purplish or white marked with purple.

9. Leaflets ovate-oblong to elliptic or obovate, one to three times as long as wide.
   10. Wing petals as long as the keel or nearly so; mature fruit 6–9 mm. long; leaflets pubescent beneath with spreading hairs; stems stout, at maturity 2–6 mm. in diameter .
  .   .   .   .   8. *L. stuevei*
   10. Wing petals distinctly shorter than the keel; mature fruit 4–6 mm. long; leaflets pubescent beneath with appressed hairs; stems delicate, scarcely 2 mm. in diameter at maturity .   .   .   .   9. *L. violacea*
9. Leaflets linear to narrowly oblong or linear-cuneate, three to eight times as long as wide.
   11. Leaflets truncate to broadly obtuse and mucronate at the apex; none of the calyx lobes united; mature fruit 3 mm. long; introduced species, sometimes escaping cultivation
  .   .   .   .   10. *L. cuneata*
   11. Leaflets acute to obtuse at the apex; the upper two calyx lobes united for about half their length; mature fruit 4–7 mm. long; native species, widely distributed in sandy or gravelly soils of central and eastern Texas .   .   .
  .   .   .   .   11. *L. virginica*

1. *Lespedeza striata* (Thunb.) H. & A., Bot. Beech. Voy. 262. 1841. JAPANESE BUSH CLOVER (Common Lespedeza)
  Kummerowia striata (Thunb.) Schindl.

Eastern Texas in sandy soils of oak and pine woodlands (Map 147). June–September. Native to eastern Asia, but widely introduced and escaped throughout much of the central and eastern United States. Closely related to the species below but much more common in Texas. *L. striata* reseeds itself successfully and appears to do well in disturbed areas of central Texas.

Chromosome number, $2n = 22$ (D. &. W., 1956; reported also under *Kummerowia striata*; Fearing, unpublished; earlier reports of $2n = 20$ are apparently erroneous).

2. *Lespedeza stipulacea* Maxim., Prim. Fl. Amur. 85. 1859. KOREAN BUSH CLOVER (Korean Lespedeza)

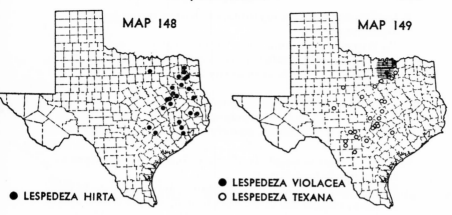

MAP 148 — ● LESPEDEZA HIRTA

MAP 149 — ● LESPEDEZA VIOLACEA / O LESPEDEZA TEXANA

Known to Texas by only a few collections from eastern Texas (Map 154). June–September. Native of eastern Asia, but recently introduced in the central and eastern United States where it appears to have become naturalized, persisting as a weed along roadsides and in waste places.

Chromosome number, $2n = 22$ (Young, 1940).

3. *Lespedeza texana* Britt. *ex* Small, Fl. Southeastern U. S. 641; 1332. 1903. TEXAS BUSH CLOVER

Central Texas usually in rocky, limestone, or heavy calcareous soils (Map 149). June–September. Endemic to Texas. Closely related to *L. violacea*, *L. procumbens*, and *L. repens*. It differs from the latter two species by its larger fruits and its restriction to rocky calcareous soils. *L. repens* and *L. procumbens* are mainly confined to gravelly or sandy soils. *L. texana* appears to offer much promise as breeding stock for the development of successful central Texas perennial legumes. It is drought resistant and produces best growth in late summer in this area. Crosses with *L. violacea*, *L. repens*, or *L. procumbens* might prove significant in any planned agronomic work using this species.

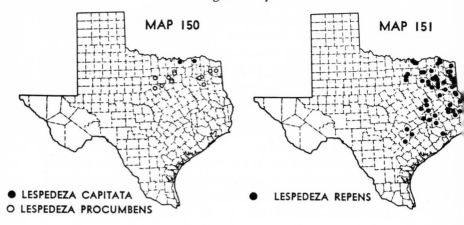

MAP 150

MAP 151

● LESPEDEZA CAPITATA
○ LESPEDEZA PROCUMBENS

● LESPEDEZA REPENS

Chromosome number not determined.

4. *Lespedeza procumbens* Michx., Fl. Bor. Am. 2:71. 1803.
TRAILING BUSH CLOVER
Northeastern Texas, mostly in sandy soils of pine or oak woodlands (Map 150). July–September. A widespread species occurring throughout the eastern United States. *L. procumbens* is closely related to the species below and is perhaps best treated as a variety of that species. *L. procumbens* reportedly hybridizes with a number of perennial species in the genus *Lespedeza* (Fernald, 1950). Much experimental work is needed to clarify the relationships of this species in the genus.
Chromosome number, $2n = 20$ (D. & W.).

5. *Lespedeza repens* (L.) Bart., Prodr. Fl. Philad. 2:77. 1818.
CREEPING BUSH CLOVER
Eastern Texas in sandy or gravelly soils of pine and oak woodlands (Map 151). April–September. A widespread variable species occurring throughout most of the eastern United States. It reportedly hybridizes with the above taxon and *L. hirta*, and possibly other related species. *L. repens* is very close to *L. procumbens*, and perhaps these

two taxa are no more than extremes of a single polymorphic species (see comment above). Occasional large-fruited forms of this species are found in the sandy lands of northeastern Texas, perhaps as a result of "gene contamination" from *L. stuevei*.

Chromosome number, $2n = 20$ (D. & W.).

6. *Lespedeza hirta* (L.) Hornem., Hort. Hafn. 699. 1807. HAIRY BUSH CLOVER

Central and eastern Texas mostly in sandy or gravelly soils of pine and oak woodlands (Map 148). June–September. Eastern United States from Maine to Minnesota, south to Texas and Florida. A widespread, variable species. Part of the variability found in *L. hirta*, at least in Texas, is due to occasional hybridization with *L. stuevei*. Intermediates between these taxa have been seen from several localities. In addition, *L. hirta* reportedly hybridizes with *L. capitata*, *L. virginica*, *L. repens*, and *L. procumbens* (Fernald, 1950). Several infraspecific taxa have been proposed for the extreme forms of the species or to recombination types from hybrids mentioned above. However, it seems best, with present knowledge, to consider the species as a widespread, variable taxon whose morphological characters are sometimes obscured by occasional hybridization with related species.

Chromosome number, $2n = 20$ (D. & W.).

7. *Lespedeza capitata* Michx., Fl. Bor. Am. 2:71. 1803

Northeastern Texas in silty-clay soils (Map 150). July–August. A widespread, variable species ranging from southern Canada, south throughout the eastern United States to Texas and Florida. Several infraspecific taxa have been proposed for the extreme forms of the species, but these appear to have little morphological-geographical correlation. Hybrids between *L. capitata* and other species of the genus are reported in the literature (Fernald, 1950). Reports of *L. capitata* from south-central Texas are ap-

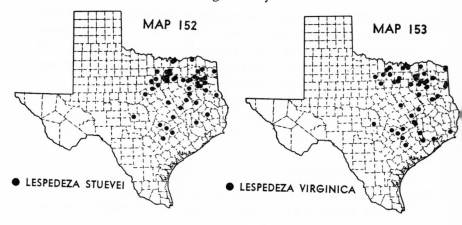

MAP 152 · LESPEDEZA STUEVEI

MAP 153 · LESPEDEZA VIRGINICA

parently erroneous and probably refer to forms of *L. hirta* which superficially resemble *L. capitata*.

Chromosome number, $2n = 20$ (D. & W.).

8. *Lespedeza stuevei* Nutt., Gen. Am. 2:107. 1818. STUEVE BUSH CLOVER

Lespedeza simulata Mackenzie & Bush

Eastern Texas in sandy or gravelly soils of pine and oak woodlands (Map 152). May–October. Eastern United States from New York to Illinois, south to Texas and Alabama. A variable species, reportedly hybridizing with a number of related taxa (Fernald, 1950). In Texas, the species apparently hybridizes with *L. hirta*, often making specific determinations of intermediate types difficult (see remarks under *L. hirta*). Several infraspecific taxa have been recognized for this species, but it seems best, with present knowledge, to treat the taxon as a single variable species.

Chromosome number, $2n = 20$ (D. & W.).

9. *Lespedeza violacea* (L.) Pers., Syn. 2:318. 1807

Lespedeza prairea (Mackenzie & Bush) Britt.

North-central Texas in sandy or gravelly soils of oak woodlands, apparently rare (Map 149). July. Eastern United States from New Hampshire to Minnesota and south to Texas and Florida. Closely resembles *L. texana*, *L. repens*, and *L. procumbens*; this whole complex is in need of critical revisionary and field study. In central Texas, *L. violacea* appears to be replaced by weakly ascending populations on calcareous soils, here treated as *L. texana*.

Chromosome number, $2n = 20$ (D. & W.).

10. *Lespedeza cuneata* (DuMont) G. Don., Gen. Hist. Dichlam. Pl. 2:307. 1832. CHINESE BUSH CLOVER (Sericea Lespedeza)

Lespedeza sericea (Thunb.) Benth. (See Isely, 1955, for a discussion of the nomenclature involved.)

The *L. cuneata* complex is in much need of revisionary study. A number of races of this taxon introduced into America have been treated as distinct species, varieties, or forms. Until the confusion is cleared up it seems best to treat these morphologically related types as members of a single species (Map 154).

Chromosome number, $2n = 18$ (D. & W., as *Lespedeza sericea*).

11. *Lespedeza virginica* (L.) Britt., Trans. N. Y. Acad. Sci. 12: 64. 1893. SLENDER BUSH CLOVER

Eastern Texas, mostly in sandy or gravelly soils of pine and oak woodlands (Map 153). August–October. Eastern United States from New Hampshire to Wisconsin, south to Texas and Florida. A common species in Texas. The species reportedly hybridizes with *L. stuevei* and *L. procumbens*. Several varieties of *L. virginica* have been proposed, but it seems best, with present knowledge to treat the species as a single, variable taxon.

Chromosome number, $2n = 20$ (D. & W.).

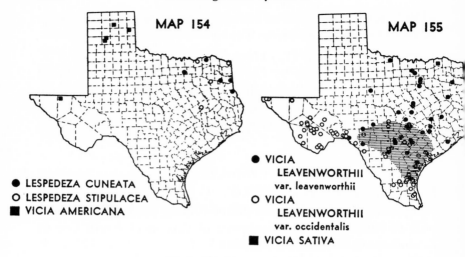

MAP 154

● LESPEDEZA CUNEATA
O LESPEDEZA STIPULACEA
■ VICIA AMERICANA

MAP 155

● VICIA
  LEAVENWORTHII
  var. leavenworthii
O VICIA
  LEAVENWORTHII
  var. occidentalis
■ VICIA SATIVA

Species Recently Reported for Texas
but Excluded in this Treatment

Lespedeza manniana Mackenzie & Bush

Reported for Texas by Fernald (1950); Gleason (1952) recognizes the taxon as a variety of *L. nuttallii*, but does not list Texas in its range. See Isely (1955) for a discussion of its relationship to other species. Specimens from Texas referable to either *L. nuttallii* or to *L. manniana* were not seen by the present writer.

Lespedeza intermedia (Wats.) Britt.

Reported for Texas by Fernald (1950), Gleason (1952), Gambill (1953), and Isely (1955). Indubitable specimens from Texas referable to *L. intermedia* were not seen by the present writer. Most of the Texas material which these workers referred to *L. intermedia* is perhaps included with *L. stuevei* in the present treatment.

Lespedeza angustifolia (Pursh) Ell.

Reported for Texas by Cory and Parks (1937). Small

(1903) gives Louisiana as its easternmost range. This writer has not seen specimens from Texas.

Lespedeza frutescens (L.) Horn.

Reported for Texas by Cory and Parks (1937) and Small (1903). Blake (1924) has discussed the status of this name. Specimens referred to this species by the authors mentioned are probably misidentifications for *L. stuevei* (as treated in the present paper).

Occasionally Introduced Species

Lespedeza bicolor Turcz.

Apparently only recently planted along roadsides in sandy soils of eastern Texas. Specimens of this species will key to *L. violacea* in the above treatment.

Chromosome number, $2n = 22$ (D. & W.).

53. VICIA   Vetch

ANNUAL or perennial, unarmed, herbaceous, trailing, or climbing vines.

LEAVES once compound, odd-pinnate, with tendrils terminating the leaf apex, leaflets few to many; stipules herbaceous, persistent.

FLOWERS white, blue, violet, or yellow, few and sessile in the leaf axils, or 1 to numerous on elongate peduncles; stamens diadelphous, anthers all alike; style with a ring of hairs below the apex.

FRUIT a dry, flattened to terete, mostly dehiscent, 2-valved pod with 2 to numerous seeds.

BASIC chromosome number, as determined from counts on approximately 55 species, $x = 6, 7$ (D. & W.; Turner, 1956b).

A large genus with about 150 species widely distributed in

the temperate regions of both hemispheres. Some of the species are important silage, pasture, and green manure legumes. Introduced species such as *V. sativa*, *V. angustifolia*, *V. dasycarpa*, and *V. villosa* are grown as winter annuals in parts of Texas.

The native species are important early spring rangeland legumes in eastern and central Texas. They commonly furnish the first green forage following winter rains. During June the plants disappear rapidly, furnishing little or no summer forage.

The species of *Vicia* are self-fertile. Attempts to hybridize various related species have met with failure by most workers.

KEY TO SPECIES

1. Flowers 1–3 in the leaf axils, sessile or nearly so.
    2. Pod and seeds compressed; flowers 1.8–3.0 cm. long .   .
        .   .   .   .   1. *V. sativa*
    2. Pod terete and seeds subglobose; flowers 1.2–1.8 cm. long
        .   .   .   .   2. *V. angustifolia*
1. Flowers 1 to numerous on a common, elongate peduncle, 1.5–6 cm. long.
    3. Racemes 1- to 5-flowered, the flowers arranged along the upper 1 cm. of the peduncle.
        4. Flowers 15–20 mm. long; stipules irregularly toothed; perennials of the Panhandle area of Texas   .   .   .
            .   .   .   .   3. *V. americana*
        4. Flowers 12 mm. long or less; stipules entire or with 1 prominent lobe; plants elsewhere.
            5. Pedicel of mature pod 2–3 mm. long; leaflets mostly 3–7; pods 4–5 mm. wide, sabre-shaped   .   .   .
                .   .   .   .   4. *V. minutiflora*
            5. Pedicel of pod 0.5–2 mm. long; leaflets mostly 5–16; pods 5–6.5 mm. wide, rhombic-oblong   .   .   .   .
                .   .   .   .   5. *V. leavenworthii*
    3. Racemes 5- to 30-flowered, the flowers arranged along the upper 0.5–5 cm. of the peduncle.
        6. Calyx gibbous at base; pods 8–10 mm. wide; introduced or cultivated species.

7. Stems glabrous or sparsely pubescent with appressed
   hairs .   .   .   .   6. *V. dasycarpa*
7. Stems densely pubescent with widely spreading hairs
   . . . . 7. *V. villosa*
  6. Calyx not gibbous at base; pod 4–7.5 mm. wide; native
    species.
    8. Lower calyx teeth broad, triangular, shorter than the
      tube; pods tapering to both ends, 2.5–3.5 cm. long   .
      . . . . 8. *V. caroliniana*
    8. Lower calyx teeth slender, attenuate, as long as the tube
      or longer; pods abruptly narrowed at both ends, 2–2.5
      cm. long . . . . . . 9. *V. ludoviciana*

1. *Vicia sativa* L., Sp. Pl. 736. 1753. COMMON VETCH

An introduced species, occasionally escaping cultivation in eastern Texas (Map 155). May–June. Native to Europe, but widely established elsewhere as a weed. The species is very variable; a number of intergrading varieties have been described, many of these assuming importance in cultivation.

Chromosome number, $2n = 12, 14$ (D. & W.).

2. *Vicia angustifolia* (L.) Reich., Fl. Moen. Franc. 2:44. 1778. NARROW-LEAVED VETCH

Cultivated species, to be expected as an occasional escape in eastern Texas. Native to Europe but widely introduced elsewhere as a weed. The species is very similar to *V. sativa* and is sometimes included as a variety of that species.

Chromosome number, $2n = 12$ (D. & W.).

3. *Vicia americana* Muhl. *ex* Willd., Sp. Pl. 3:1096. 1803. AMERICAN VETCH

Panhandle area of Texas, mostly in sandy soils (Map 154). May–June. Widespread throughout the northern United States and adjacent Canada. The species is very variable and is in need of detailed revisionary study. In Texas the species is represented by the var. *linearis* (Nutt.) Wats., which has shorter stems and narrower, thicker leaves than is typical for the species; Shinners (1948) treated this taxon as *V. linearis* (Nutt.) Greene. The variety appears to intergrade with other taxa of *V. americana* in parts of Colorado, New Mexico, and Wyoming.

Chromosome number, $n = 7$ (Ledingham, 1957).

4. *Vicia minutiflora* Dietr., Sym. Pl. 4:1107. 1847. SMALL-FLOWERED VETCH

Vicia micrantha Nutt.; not *V. micrantha* H. & A.

Eastern and north-central Texas in sandy soils of pine and oak woodlands (Map 158). March–April. Endemic to Texas, Oklahoma, and probably Arkansas and Louisiana. Forms of this species with densely pubescent pods have been called *V. reverchonii* Wats.

Chromosome number not determined.

5. *Vicia leavenworthii* Torr. & Gray, Fl. N. Am. 1:271. 1838. LEAVENWORTH VETCH

Southern, central, and trans-Pecos regions of Texas, mostly in open areas on calcareous or sandy soils (Map 155). March–May. Oklahoma, Texas, and adjacent Mexico. Two intergrading varieties of this species are recognized for Texas and may be distinguished by the following key:

1 Leaflets of mid-stem leaves 1–3 mm. wide, five to ten times as long as wide; plants of southern, south-central, and trans-Pecos areas of Texas   .   .   .   .   .   var. *occidentalis* Shinners
1 Leaflets of mid-stem leaves (2.5)3–5 mm. wide, four to six times as long as wide; plants of central and north-central Texas   .
·   .   .   .   .   var. *leavenworthii*

Shinners treated the few-flowered, narrow-leaved populations of *V. leavenworthii* from southern Texas as *V. ludoviciana* var. *texana* (Torr. & Gray) Shinners, restricting *V. leavenworthii* var. *occidentalis* to trans-Pecos Texas. The former variety is based on a collection by Leavenworth from eastern Texas (as indicated by Shinners) and probably represents a fragmentary specimen of *V. leavenworthii*

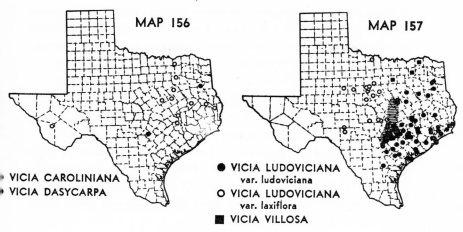

VICIA CAROLINIANA
VICIA DASYCARPA

● VICIA LUDOVICIANA
var. ludoviciana
○ VICIA LUDOVICIANA
var. laxiflora
■ VICIA VILLOSA

var. *leavenworthii*. The *V. leavenworthii* and *V. ludoviciana* complexes are in need of detailed populational and experimental study.

Chromosome number, $2n = 14$ (Turner, 1956b, for var. *leavenworthii*; $n = 7$ for var. *occidentalis*, Johnston, unpublished).

6. *Vicia dasycarpa* Ten., Viagg. Abruzz. 81. 1829. WINTER VETCH (Woolly-pod Vetch)

Introduced in Texas where it frequently escapes cultivation and becomes a roadside weed (Map 156). April–August. Native to southern Europe, but now introduced in many parts of the United States.

Chromosome number, $2n = 14$ (D. & W.).

7. *Vicia villosa* Roth., Tent. Fl. Germ. 2:182. 1789. HAIRY VETCH (Russian Vetch)

Introduced in Texas where it occasionally escapes cultivation, becoming a weed along roadsides (Map 157). April–August. Native to Europe, but now widely introduced as a forage and green manure crop in much of the temperate world.

Chromosome number, $2n = 14$ (D. & W.).

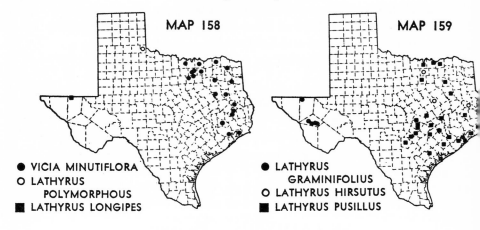

MAP 158

MAP 159

● VICIA MINUTIFLORA
O LATHYRUS
   POLYMORPHOUS
■ LATHYRUS LONGIPES

● LATHYRUS
   GRAMINIFOLIUS
O LATHYRUS HIRSUTUS
■ LATHYRUS PUSILLUS

8. *Vicia caroliniana* Walt., Fl. Car. 182. 1788. CAROLINA VETCH

Apparently rare in eastern Texas. The present writer has seen only a few collections from Texas (Map 156). April–June. Moist woods and thickets from New York to Wisconsin and south to Texas and Florida.

Chromosome number not determined.

9. *Vicia ludoviciana* Nutt. *ex* Torr. & Gray, Fl. N. Am. 1:271. 1838

Central and eastern Texas in sandy soils of pine and oak woodlands and on calcareous soils of the Gulf Coast grassland and central Texas (Map 157). March–May. Texas, adjacent Louisiana, and Oklahoma.

Two intergrading varieties of the species are recognized for Texas: (1) var. *ludoviciana*, with flowers bunched 0.5–1.5 cm. along the upper portion of the peduncle, occurring mostly in sandy soils of eastern Texas; and (2) var. *laxiflora* Shinners, with flowers loosely arranged 1.2–3 cm. along the upper portion of the peduncle, occurring in limestone soils of central and north-central Texas.

V. ludoviciana appears to intergrade with *V. leaven-*

worthii in south-central Texas and perhaps other areas; the biologic relationships of these two species are in need of detailed experimental and field study.

Chromosome number, $n = 7$ (Turner, 1956b, for var. *ludoviciana*).

Excluded Species

Vicia exigua Nutt.

Reported for Texas by Cory and Parks (1937), probably a misidentification of *V. leavenworthii* var. *occidentalis*, as noted by Shinners (1948).

54. LATHYRUS Pea-vine

ANNUAL or perennial, usually weak-stemmed, herbaceous plants.

LEAVES once compound, with 2–18 leaflets (rarely, absent), the terminal portion modified into a simple or branched tendril (rarely, reduced to a short bristle); stipules conspicuous, usually hastate or sagittate-lobed.

FLOWERS single to numerous in axillary racemes, white, pink, red to purplish; stamens diadelphous; style pubescent on its inner surface for about half its length.

FRUIT an ovate to linear, usually flattened, dehiscent legume.

BASIC chromosome number, as determined from counts on approximately 40 species, $x = 7$ (D. & W.).

A large genus with about 120 species in the temperate regions of North America, South America, Africa, and Eurasia. Some of the species, such as *L. hirsutus*, are important agricultural crops and are widely used in the southeastern United States for pasture, hay, winter cover, and soil improvement. The species of *Lathyrus* are mostly adapted to temperate, moist climates and hence show little promise as rangeland legumes in the warmer, arid parts of Texas.

KEY TO SPECIES

1. Leaflets 2.
  2. Annuals; flowers 1.5 cm. long or less; pods 2–4 cm. long.
    3. Pods and ovary pubescent, 5–8 mm. broad; introduced (cultivated) species .   .   .   .   .   1. *L. hirsutus*
    3. Pods and ovary glabrous, 2–4 mm. broad; native species
    .   .   .   .   2. *L. pusillus*
  2. Perennials; flowers 1.5 cm. long or more; pods 6–10 cm. long
  .   .   .   .   3. *L. latifolius*
1. Leaflets 4–12.
  4. Tendrils bristle-like, simple, not at all prehensile   .   .
  .   .   .   .   4. *L. polymorphous*
  4. Tendrils well developed, prehensile, forked.
    5. Leaflets 4–10, ten times as long as wide; plants of trans-Pecos Texas .   .   .   .   .   .   5. *L. graminifolius*
    5. Leaflets (8)10–14, two to five times as long as wide; plants of east and north-central Texas .   .   .   6. *L. venosus*

1. *Lathyrus hirsutus* L., Sp. Pl. 732. 1753. SINGLETARY PEA
    An introduced species occasionally escaping cultivation or persisting as a volunteer in abandoned fields (Map 159). The present writer has seen only a few collections from north-central Texas. The species is a native of Europe.
    Chromosome number, $2n = 14$ (D. & W.).

2. *Lathyrus pusillus* Ell., Bot. S. C. & Ga. 2:223. 1824
    Eastern and central Texas, usually in sandy or deep clay soils (Map 159). March–May. South-central and southeastern United States to northeastern Mexico. A native species of common occurrence during the spring months, particularly in heavy clay soils along the upper Gulf Coast.
    Chromosome number, $n = 7$ (Turner, 1956b).

3. *Lathyrus latifolius* L., Sp. Pl. 733. 1753. EVERLASTING PEA
    Native to Europe; not collected in Texas as an escapee, but to be expected since it is widely naturalized in adjacent northern states and has escaped cultivation there. The spe-

cies is reportedly cultivated in north and central Texas (Shinners, 1948).

Chromosome number, $2n = 14$ (D. & W.).

4. *Lathyrus polymorphous* Nutt., Gen. N. Am. Pl. 2:96. 1818. SHOWY PEA-VINE

Panhandle area of Texas, cited by Hitchcock (1952). This writer has seen a single collection (Childress County, March 4, 1932, specific locality not given) in the University of Texas Herbarium (Map 158). In Texas the species is represented by the subspecies *incanus* (Smith & Rydb.) Hitchcock, which is distinguished from the more northeastern subspecies *polymorphous* in being glabrous or nearly so.

Chromosome number not determined.

5. *Lathyrus graminifolius* (Wats.) White, Bull. Torr. Bot. Club 21:454. 1894. GRASS-LEAF PEA-VINE

Trans-Pecos Texas on igneous soils in the Davis Mountains, at altitudes of 5,500–8,000 feet (Map 159). April–May. Southwestern United States from Texas to Arizona and adjacent Mexico.

Chromosome number, $n = 7$ (Hitchcock, 1952).

6. *Lathyrus venosus* Muhl. *ex* Willd., Sp. Pl. 3:1092. 1803

Collections of this species from Texas have not been seen by the present writer, but Hitchcock (1952, p. 15) cites Texas in his range for the variety *intonsus* Butters & St. John (his dot map does not indicate this, however). *L. venosus* is found near the Texas border in Oklahoma and Arkansas and possibly may occur in the northeasternmost corner of the state. The species has its main center of distribution in the north-central and northeastern United States.

Chromosome number, $2n = 28$ (D. & W.).

Cultivated Species

Lathyrus odoratus L. SWEET PEA

This species is commonly cultivated in Texas as an ornamental in yards. The plant is an annual and may be distinguished by its large sweet-scented flowers and pubescent pods. Probably native to southern Europe.

Chromosome number, $2n = 14, 28$ (D. & W.).

55. CLITORIA Pigeon Wings (Butterfly Pea)

PERENNIAL, erect herbs or twining vines.

LEAVES once compound, odd-pinnate with 3 to numerous leaflets, stipules conspicuous, persistent; stipels present.

FLOWERS 1 to several on axillary peduncles, large and showy, bluish-purple, red to nearly white; stamens diadelphous.

FRUIT a several-seeded, linear, dry, dehiscent legume.

BASIC chromosome number, as determined from counts on 4 species, $x = 8, 12$ (D. & W.; Turner and Fearing, unpublished).

A genus with about 35 species mostly in the tropical and subtropical regions of both hemispheres. The individual flowers of some of the species are among the largest in the family Leguminosae.

KEY TO SPECIES

1. Leaflets 3; native species . . . . . 1. *C. mariana*
1. Leaflets 5–7; cultivated or introduced species . . .
. . . . 2. *C. ternata*

1. *Clitoria mariana* L., Sp. Pl. 753. 1753. SPOON-FLOWER
    Central and eastern Texas in sandy or gravelly soils in open areas of pine and oak woodlands (Map 160). May–September. Northeastern and central United States to Florida.
    Chromosome number not determined.

2. *Clitoria ternata* L., Sp. Pl. 753. 1753
    Cultivated in the eastern and southern parts of the state

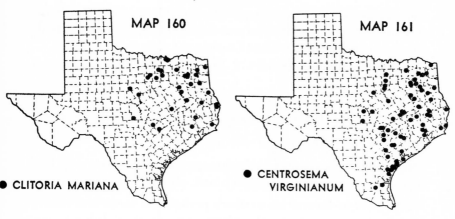

MAP 160

CLITORIA MARIANA

MAP 161

CENTROSEMA VIRGINIANUM

and, perhaps, occasionally escaping (the label on a specimen in the University of Texas Herbarium notes the plant as "cultivated; well established" in upland areas about Austin, 1943; more recent collections have not been seen). Widely distributed in the tropical regions of both hemispheres, but probably Asian in origin.

Chromosome number, $2n = 16$ (D. & W.).

56. CENTROSEMA   Butterfly Pea

PERENNIAL, prostrate, or high-climbing, twining vines with mostly herbaceous stems.

LEAVES once compound, predominantly 3-foliolate, rarely, 5- to 7-foliolate; stipules conspicuous, persistent; stipels present.

FLOWERS purplish to nearly white, solitary or several together in the leaf axils, usually large and showy; stamens diadelphous.

FRUIT a several-seeded, linear, dry, dehiscent legume.

BASIC chromosome number, as determined from counts on a single species, $x = 10$ (D. & W.).

A genus with about 30 species, mostly in the tropical and subtropical regions of North and South America.

Centrosema virginianum (L.) Benth., Ann. Wien. Mus. 2:120. 1838. BUTTERFLY PEA
Bradburya virginiana (L.) Kuntze
Central and eastern Texas in sandy or gravelly soils (Map 161). March–November. Northeastern United States to Florida and tropical America.
Chromosome number not determined.

57. AMPHICARPA Hog Peanut

TWINING, perennial vines with slender, herbaceous stems.

LEAVES pinnately 3-foliate, the leaflets rhombic-ovate; stipels present.

FLOWERS of the upper branches in definite racemes, having well-developed white or lilac petals; flowers of the lower, creeping branches, when present, without well-developed petals; stamens diadelphous.

FRUIT from the upper, perfect flowers, a flattened, dry, dehiscent legume; fruit from lower flowers, when present, subterranean, fleshy, and indehiscent.

BASIC chromosome number, as determined from counts on 2 species, $x = 10$ (Fearing, unpublished).

A genus with about 3 species of subtropical and temperate regions of eastern Asia and North America. The genus is sometimes spelled *Amphicarpaea*.

Amphicarpa bracteata (L.) Fern., Rhodora 35:276. 1933. HOG PEANUT
Amphicarpa monoica (L.) Ell.
Falcata pitcheri (Torr. & Gray) Kuntze
Falcata comosa (L.) Kuntze

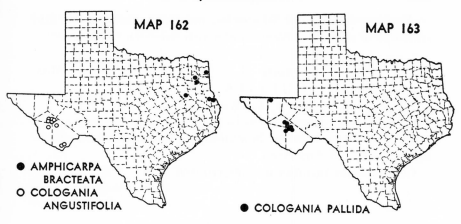

MAP 162

MAP 163

● AMPHICARPA
   BRACTEATA
○ COLOGANIA
   ANGUSTIFOLIA

● COLOGANIA PALLIDA

Easternmost Texas on sandy or alluvial soils in damp woodlands (Map 162). May–September. A widespread, variable
species occurring from Canada through the central and eastern United States to Florida. Two varieties of this species are
found in Texas: (1) var. *bracteata*, whose stems are clothed
with whitish, retrose or appressed hairs, having leaves with
terminal leaflets 2–6 cm. long, and (2) var. *comosa* (L.) Fern.
(=*A. pitcheri* Torr. & Gray), whose stems are clothed with
tawny, spreading hairs, having leaves with terminal leaflets
(6)7–10 cm. long. These two varieties intergrade to a large
degree throughout their ranges and are probably the extremes
of a single variable species (Fearing and Turner, unpublished).

Chromosome number, $2n = 20$ (D. & W., as *Amphicarpa
monoica*).

58. COLOGANIA   Cologania

UNARMED, perennial herbs with semierect, trailing or twining, herbaceous stems.

LEAVES once compound, odd-pinnate with 3 (rarely, 5) leaflets; stipules herbaceous, striate; stipels present.

FLOWERS solitary, or 2 to several, in the leaf axils; corolla pink or purplish; calyx tubular, 4-toothed; stamens diadelphous.

FRUIT a linear, dry, dehiscent, straight or curved legume with several to numerous seeds.

BASIC chromosome number, as determined from counts on 3 species, $x = 11$ (Fearing, unpublished).

A small genus with about 10 species in the mountainous and subtropical regions of North America and South America, a few species extending into the temperate regions of the southwestern United States and Argentina (Fearing, unpublished). The genus seems to be centered in Mexico where some 15 species occur. Nothing is known about the agronomic potential of this group, but in Texas the species inhabit rocky, igneous soils in native grassland stands, occurring with *Bouteloua hirsuta* and *B. gracilis*.

The genus has been lumped with *Amphicarpaea* (Taubert, 1894), but Fearing (unpublished) has presented evidence for generic recognition. Most American workers have recognized the genera as distinct.

KEY TO SPECIES

1. Leaflets ovate to lanceolate, one to five times as long as wide
.   .   .   .   1. *C. pallida*
1. Leaflets linear, five to twenty times longer than wide   .   .
.   .   .   .   2. *C. angustifolia*

1. *Cologania pallida* Rose, Contr. U. S. Nat. Herb. 8:38. 1903
     Trans-Pecos Texas in igneous soils of the Davis Mountains, at altitudes of 2,500–5,000 feet (Map 163). July–October. Southwestern United States and adjacent Mexico. A widespread, highly variable species with numerous intergrading forms. In Texas the species appears to hybridize with *C. angustifolia* (below) since a number of intermediates seem to link the species in this area (specimens deposited in the University of Texas Herbarium). *C. pallida*

is closely related to *C. pulchella*, a species of more southern distribution.

Chromosome number, $2n = 44$ (Fearing, unpublished).

2. *Cologania angustifolia* H. B. K., Nov. Gen. & Sp. Plant. 6: 414. 1823

    C. longifolia Gray

    C. confusa Rose

Trans-Pecos Texas in igneous soils of the Davis and Chisos mountains (the type locality of *C. confusa* was doubtfully listed by Rose [1903] as "near El Paso"), at altitudes of 4,500–6,500 feet (Map 162). July–October. Southwestern Texas and adjacent Mexico. A variable species, perhaps hybridizing with *C. pallida* in the Davis Mountain region of Texas (see above species). *C. confusa* seems to be intermediate between these two species, having the leaf shape of *C. angustifolia* but the falcate legume and smaller flower size of *C. pallida*. Much field work and experimental garden work is needed to clarify this complex in western Texas.

Chromosome number, $2n = 44$ (Fearing, unpublished).

59. APIOS   Potato Bean (Ground Nut)

PERENNIAL, twining vines with herbaceous stems which arise from slender rhizomes bearing tuberous enlargements.

LEAVES once compound, odd-pinnate with (3)5–9 leaflets; stipules slender, persistent; stipels small, inconspicuous.

FLOWERS in axillary peduncled racemes, brownish-red to nearly white; keel contorting; stamens diadelphous.

FRUIT a linear, several-seeded, dehiscent legume.

BASIC chromosome number not determined, but Atchison (1949) reports an approximate count for a single species as $2n = 40$.

A genus with about 8 species in the temperate regions of eastern North America and eastern Asia.

Apios americana Medic., *in* Vorles. Churpf. Phys. Ges. 2:355. 1787. AMERICAN POTATO BEAN
   Glycine apios L.
   Apios tuberosa Moench.

Eastern and central Texas mostly in sandy oak and pine woodlands (Map 164). May–September. Canada, central and eastern United States to Florida. Two varieties of this species are recognized for Texas: (1) var. *americana*, with compact racemes which are rounded at the apex and (2) var. *turrigera* Fern., with slender, loose racemes, having lanceolate or prolonged tips. The varieties in Texas are not well marked, either morphologically or geographically, though most of the material collected falls into var. *turrigera*.

Chromosome number, as approximated by Atchison (1949), $2n = 40$.

60. ERYTHRINA   Coral Bean

TREES, shrubs, or, rarely, perennial herbs, often armed with spiny branches.

LEAVES pinnately 3-foliate, the leaflets broad and stipellate.

FLOWERS in axillary or terminal racemes, red or reddish, very conspicuous; banner large and elongate, the remaining petals mostly small or absent; stamens diadelphous.

FRUIT a linear, dehiscent, stipitate legume containing several bright red seeds.

BASIC chromosome number, as determined from counts on 37 species, $x = 21$ (D. & W.).

A genus with about 40 species in the tropical and subtropi-

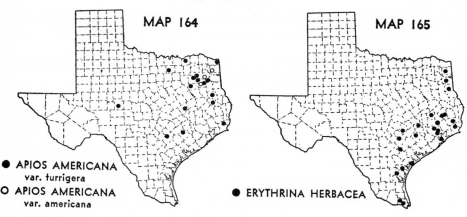

MAP 164

MAP 165

● APIOS AMERICANA
   var. turrigera
○ APIOS AMERICANA
   var. americana

● ERYTHRINA HERBACEA

cal regions of both hemispheres. Seeds of the various species are reportedly very poisonous, these being used to poison small animals in some areas. An extract from the leaves and bark is sometimes used to stupefy fish in parts of tropical America; in addition, Standley (1922) reports a variety of medicinal uses of the plant by the natives of Mexico.

Erythrina herbacea L., Sp. Pl. 706. 1753. CORAL BEAN
   Eastern and southern Texas in sandy soils (Map 165). April–June. North Carolina to Florida, Texas, and Mexico. In the southeastern United States this species is commonly a small shrub or herbaceous perennial; however, exceptional woody forms of the species from southern Florida, Texas, and Mexico have been called *E. arborea* (Chapm.) Small. (= *E. herbacea* var. *arborea* Chapm.). *E. herbacea* is often cultivated as an ornamental in yards. The seeds are reportedly poisonous, being used to poison rats and dogs in tropical areas.
   Chromosome number, $2n = 42$ (D. & W.).

61. GALACTIA   Milk Pea

UNARMED, perennial herbs with erect, trailing or twining stems.

LEAVES simple or once compound with 3–7 entire leaflets; stipules small, early deciduous.

FLOWERS in axillary peduncled racemes, or 1–2 in the leaf axils, white, violet, or red; stamens diadelphous or monadelphous to the middle.

FRUIT an elongate, linear, dehiscent legume with several to numerous seeds.

BASIC chromosome number, as determined from counts on 4 species, $x = 10$ (D. & W.; Turner, 1956b; Turner and Fearing, unpublished).

A genus with about 50 species in the tropical, subtropical, and warmer temperate regions of North America, South America, Asia, and Australia. The majority of the species appear to be centered in the New World. The North American species are in need of critical revisionary study.

KEY TO SPECIES

1. Leaves simple .   .   .   .   1. *G. marginalis*
1. Leaves compound, 3- to 5-foliate.
  2. Leaves nearly sessile, the petioles 1–3 mm. long   .   .
  .   .   .   .   2. *G. longifolia*
  2. Leaves with well-developed petioles, these 6 mm. long or more.
    3. Leaflets 4 or 5 on at least some of the leaves   .   3. *G. grayi*
    3. Leaflets 3, never 4 or 5.
      4. Stems short, erect, 1 foot tall or less, not at all trailing or twining; flowers white   .   .   .   .   .   4. *G. erecta*
      4. Stems elongate, trailing or twining; flowers lavender to reddish.
        5. Pods both subterranean and aerial; stems trailing but

not twining; racemes 2–7 at the nodes; leaflets thick, leathery, the veins conspicuous and reticulate beneath . .
. . . . 5. *G. canescens*
5. Pods never developing below soil surface; stems usually conspicuously twining, at least at the tips; racemes 1–2 at the nodes, seldom more; leaflets thin, not leathery or conspicuously reticulate beneath, except in *G. texana*.
  6. Peduncle and raceme slender, elongate, the well-developed ones 10 cm. long or more . . . 6. *G. macreei*
  6. Peduncle and raceme short, mostly 10 cm. long or less.
    7. Leaflets elliptic-linear to linear-oblong, two to five times longer than wide; flowers 10–14 mm. long; plants of trans-Pecos Texas . . . 7. *G. wrightii*
    7. Leaflets commonly ovate to oval, rarely elliptical-linear, mostly one to two (sometimes four) times as long as wide, flowers 6–12 mm. long; plants of central and east Texas.
      8. Legume distinctly falcate; leaves thick and leathery, conspicuously reticulate-veined beneath; plants of rocky limestone soils in south-central Texas .
. . . . 8. *G. texana*
      8. Legume straight or nearly so, the base or tip sometimes curved, but the whole legume scarcely falcate; leaves thin, not conspicuously reticulate-veined beneath; plants of sandy or gravelly soils in eastern Texas, rarely occurring on adjacent calcareous soils . . . . . 9. *G. volubilis*

1. *Galactia marginalis* Benth., Ann. Wien. Mus. 2:126. 1838
  Galactia heterophylla (Gillies) Vail; not *G. heterophylla* Gray
South-central Texas in sandy or gravelly soils (Map 166). March–September. Mexico to Central and South America.
Chromosome number not determined.

2. *Galactia longifolia* Benth. *ex* Hoehne, Comm. Linh. Telegr. Estrat. Matto-Grosso (Publ. 74), Annexo 5, Bot. pt. 12:26. 1922

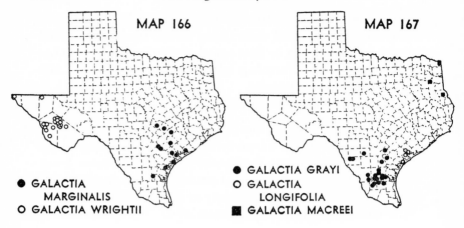

Known only by a few collections from the coastal area of south-central Texas (Map 167). July–September. The species is bicentric in distribution, occurring again in South America.

Chromosome number not determined.

3. *Galactia grayi* Vail, Bull. Torr. Bot. Club 22:503. 1895. GRAY MILK PEA

Galactia heterophylla Gray; not *G. heterophylla* (Gillies) Vail

Endemic to southern Texas, occurring mostly in sandy soils (Map 167). April–September.

Chromosome number, $n = 10$ (Turner, 1956b).

4. *Galactia erecta* (Walt.) Vail, Bull. Torr. Bot. Club. 22:502. 1895. ERECT MILK PEA

Southeastern Texas, known only from a few recent collections in Polk and Tyler counties where it occurs in deep pine duff beneath large, well-spaced trees of *Pinus palustris* (Map 168). May–June. Southeastern United States from Texas to Florida and North Carolina.

Chromosome number not determined.

5. *Galactia canescens* Benth., Ann. Wien. Mus. 2:126. 1838

Endemic to south-central and southern Texas, mostly on sandy or silty-alluvial soils (Map 168). April–July. This species is interesting in that some of the fruits develop beneath the ground, forming edible "nuts" much like the common cultivated peanut.

Chromosome number, $n = 10$ (Turner, 1956b).

6. *Galactia macreei* Curtis, Bost. Jour. Nat. Hist. 1:120. 1837

Northeastern Texas in sandy soils of wooded areas (Map 167). July–September. Southeastern United States from Texas to Virginia. This species seems scarcely distinct and perhaps is best treated as a variety or form of *G. volubilis*.

Chromosome number not determined.

7. *Galactia wrightii* Gray, Pl. Wright. 1:44. 1852. WRIGHT MILK PEA

Trans-Pecos Texas mostly on igneous soils in mountainous areas, at altitudes of 4,500–5,500 feet (Map 166). May–September. Texas to Arizona and adjacent Mexico. Apparently closely related to *G. volubilis* and distinguished from that species with difficulty.

Chromosome number not determined.

8. *Galactia texana* (Scheele) Gray, Bost. Jour. Nat. Hist. 6:170. 1850. TEXAS MILK PEA

Endemic to south-central Texas and known only from a few collections on dry, rocky, limestone soils (Map 169). June. This species appears to be closely related to *G. volubilis* and in many respects seems intermediate between that species and *G. canescens*. It has the vegetative characters of the latter species, but the narrower, more falcate pods, fewer racemes to a node, and lack of subterranean fruit mark it as distinct.

Chromosome number, $2n = 20$ (Turner and Fearing, unpublished).

9. *Galactia volubilis* (L.) Britt., Mem. Torr. Bot. Club 5:208. 1894. DOWNY MILK PEA

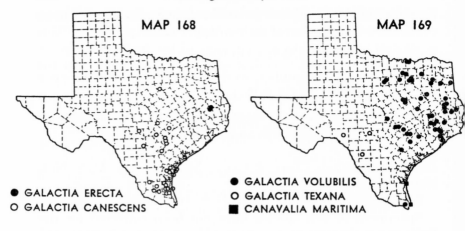

MAP 168

MAP 169

● GALACTIA ERECTA
○ GALACTIA CANESCENS

● GALACTIA VOLUBILIS
○ GALACTIA TEXANA
■ CANAVALIA MARITIMA

Eastern Texas, mostly in sandy or gravelly soils of pine and oak woodlands (Map 169). June–August. Central and eastern United States from Ohio to New York and south to Florida and Texas. A widespread, highly polymorphic species in much need of extensive field work and critical study. Most of the Texas specimens examined have oval or elliptic, softly pubescent leaves, though all intermediates between this type and specimens with more linear, nearly glabrate leaves are found. Along the Gulf Coast in Texas, populations occur which have very small leaves, short peduncles, and distinct claviform taproots; such extremes also intergrade with the above forms. Some of the east Texas collections included in this taxon show characters of *G. regularis*, a species of more eastern distribution, perhaps indicating a breakdown of the characters that mark these two species.

Chromosome number, $2n = 20$ (D. & W.).

62. DIOCLEA

Semiwoody or woody, high-climbing, twining vines.

Leaves large, pinnately 3-foliate; stipules minute.

FLOWERS blue or purplish in axillary, pedunculate racemes; calyx lobes 4 (by fusion of the two upper lobes).

FRUIT a dry, flattened, dehiscent legume.

BASIC chromosome number, as determined from counts on a single species, $x = 12$ (D. & W.).

A genus with about 25 species, mostly in the tropical and subtropical regions of North and South America.

Dioclea multiflora (Torr. & Gray) Mohr., Contr. U. S. Nat. Herb. 6:580. 1901

   Dioclea boykinii Gray

Specimens of this species have not been collected for the state as yet, but are to be expected in deep east Texas since Cocks (1910) reports a collection from Louisiana on the "banks of Red River near Shreveport."

   Chromosome number, $2n = 24$ (D. & W.).

63. PUERARIA   Kudzu

TRAILING or twining, high-climbing, coarse, perennial vines.

LEAVES pinnately trifoliate, with large densely pubescent leaflets; stipels present.

FLOWERS reddish-purple in long axillary racemes, mostly hidden amongst the leaves; stamens 10, monadelphous.

FRUIT a dry, linear, many-seeded, mostly dehiscent legume.

BASIC chromosome number, as determined from counts on 2 species, $x = 12$ (D. & W.).

A genus with about 15 species, native to eastern and tropical Asia but widely introduced elsewhere as an ornamental. *P. lobata* is used extensively in the southern United States in soil erosion control and as a forage crop in some areas. It has become a common roadside plant in parts of eastern Texas, particularly where it has been planted along bare, sandy road-cuts.

Pueraria lobata (Willd.) Ohwi, Bull. Tokyo Sci. Mus. 18:16. 1947. KUDZU-VINE

    Pueraria thunbergiana (Sieb. & Zucc.) Benth.

Introduced in Texas, often persisting along road shoulders where it has been planted to reduce erosion. Native to eastern Asia, but now widely cultivated as an ornamental and forage crop.

Flowering specimens are not known from Texas; collections grown from seed in the experimental garden at the University of Texas have not produced flowers after 4 years of culture. The best method for vegetative propagation in this area can be obtained by planting the crowns from 2- to 4-year-old plants (Whyte *et al.*, 1953). A crown is the lowermost portion of the stem with the several fleshy roots attached. Kudzu-vine is a fast-growing, coarse perennial, and, once established, is able to persist through relatively dry summers and cold winters.

Chromosome number, $2n = 22, 24$ (D. & W., as *Pueraria thunbergiana*).

64. CANAVALIA   Jack Bean (Sword Bean)

ANNUAL or perennial herbs and shrubs, stems usually twining.

LEAVES trifoliate, the terminal leaflet stalked; stipules thin, membranous, not striate, early deciduous.

FLOWERS of various colors, numerous in raceme-like thyrses; stamens monadelphous (the vexillar stamen partly or, rarely, entirely free); anthers all alike.

FRUIT a linear, several- to many-seeded, mostly dehiscent, stipitate pod.

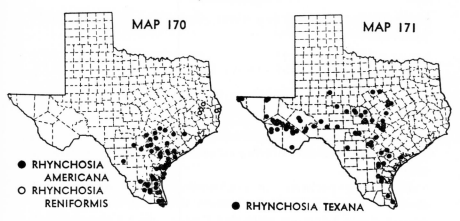

MAP 170

● RHYNCHOSIA
  AMERICANA
○ RHYNCHOSIA
  RENIFORMIS

MAP 171

● RHYNCHOSIA TEXANA

BASIC chromosome number, as determined from counts on 3 species, $x = 11$ (D. & W.).

A genus with about 40 species in the tropical and subtropical regions of both hemispheres. Some of the species such as *C. ensiformis* and *C. gladiata* are used as green manure and soil cover crops in parts of tropical America, Africa, and Asia.

Canavalia maritima (Aubl.) Thou., Jour. Bot. Desv. 1:80. 1813
   Canavalia lineata (Thunb.) DC.
   Canavalia obtusifolia (Lam.) DC.
   Southern Texas on sandy dune soil along the seashore (Map 168). Widespread along the seashores of Louisiana (Piper, 1925), Florida, the West Indies, Mexico, and South America.
   Chromosome number not determined.

65. RHYNCHOSIA Rhynchosia

UNARMED perennial herbs or shrubs, the stems erect, trailing or twining.

LEAVES simple or 3-foliolate, the leaflets usually punctate with resinous dots (often inconspicuous); stipules persistent.

FLOWERS in axillary or terminal racemes, yellow or tinged with red; stamens diadelphous; anthers all alike.

FRUIT a flattened, orbicular to oblong, dehiscent, legume, containing 1 to 3 seeds.

BASIC chromosome number, as determined from counts on 6 species, $x = 11$ (D. & W.; Turner, 1956b).

A genus with about 100 species in the tropical, subtropical, and warmer regions of both hemispheres. Some of the species are used as a source of food in parts of Africa and Asia. *R. minima* is reportedly an important rangeland legume in many parts of the world (see below). *R. texana* appears to be an important range legume in the drier native grasslands of central and west Texas. A number of the species are common in the sandy soils of the southeastern United States and undoubtedly serve as important soil builders in this area. For the most part little is known about their agronomic potential; seed selection and breeding work with members of the genus should prove fruitful to future workers interested in rangeland legumes.

KEY TO SPECIES

1. Leaves simple.
  2. Stems short, erect, 5–20 cm. tall; plants of extreme east Texas
    .   .   .   . 1. *R. reniformis*

  2. Stems elongate, prostrate or twining, to 100 cm. long; plants
    of central and south-central Texas   .   . 2. *R. americana*
1. Leaves, most of them, trifoliate.
  3. Flowers 1–3 in the leaf axils   .   .   .   . 3. *R. texana*
  3. Flowers 4 to many in terminal or lateral (often congested) racemes.
    4. Stems stiffly erect, tomentulose-pilose with mostly appressed-ascending hairs; racemes 1–4 cm. long; calyx lobes 5–6 mm. long   .   .   .   .   .   . 4. *R. tomentosa*
    4. Stems trailing or twining (often erect in *R. difformis*), glabrate or with spreading or reflexed hairs.

5. Calyx 3–4 mm. long .   .   .   .   .   5. *R. minima*
5. Calyx 8–12 mm. long.
  6. Racemes elongate, 5–30 cm. long . . 6. *R. latifolia*
  6. Racemes congested, 1–4 cm. long (at maturity) .
    . . . . 7. *R. difformis*

1. *Rhynchosia reniformis* (Pursh) DC., Prod. 2:384. 1825. DOLLAR-LEAF RHYNCHOSIA

Rhynchosia simplicifolia (Walt.) Wood; not *R. simplicifolia* DC.

Dolicholus simplicifolius (Walt.) Vail

Southeastern Texas in sandy soils of pine and oak woodlands (Map 170). June–September. Southeastern United States from North Carolina to Florida and Texas.

Chromosome number not determined.

2. *Rhynchosia americana* (Mill.) Metz, Contr. Biol. Lab., Catholic Univ. Amer. 16:126. 1934. AMERICA RHYNCHOSIA

Dolicholus americanus (Mill.) Vail

South-central and southern Texas in sandy or gravelly soils (Map 170). March–October. Texas and adjacent Mexico.

Chromosome number, $n = 11$ (Turner, 1956b).

3. *Rhynchosia texana* Torr. & Gray, Fl. N. Am. 1:387. 1838. TEXAS RHYNCHOSIA

Dolicholus texensis (Torr. & Gray) Vail

Southern, central, and trans-Pecos areas of Texas, mostly on dry, limestone, or igneous soils in native grasslands (Map 171). April–October. A widespread, variable species occurring from Texas to Arizona and adjacent Mexico; also native to Brazil and Argentina. Forms of *R. texana* with narrow leaflets have been called var. *angustifolia* Gray. The species is common in much of the drier rangeland of southwestern Texas. Experimental breeding work with the forms

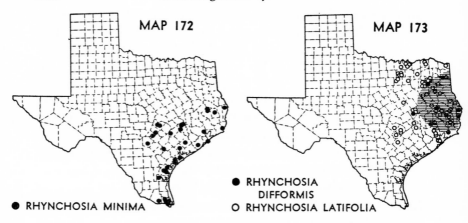

MAP 172

● RHYNCHOSIA MINIMA

MAP 173

● RHYNCHOSIA
DIFFORMIS
○ RHYNCHOSIA LATIFOLIA

from South America might prove profitable in any planned agronomic development of the Texas ecotypes.

Chromosome number, $n = 11$ (Turner, unpublished).

4. *Rhynchosia tomentosa* (L.) H. & A., Comp. Bot. Mag. 1:23. 1835

Dolicholus tomentosus (L.) Vail

East Texas in sandy soils. The species is reported for Texas by Fernald (1950). The present writer has seen a single collection from Texas (Charles Wright; without locality; deposited in the University of Texas Herbarium). Southeastern United States, Virginia to Florida and Texas. The species is closely related to *R. difformis* and probably intergrades with that species in parts of its range. In Texas, very definitely erect plants of *R. difformis* are not uncommon and, except for the pubescence and somewhat larger flowers, look very much like specimens of *R. tomentosa*.

Chromosome number, $2n = 22$ (D. & W., as *R. erecta*).

5. *Rhynchosia minima* (L.) DC., Prodr. 2:385. 1825

Dolicholus minimus (L.) Medic.

Southern and southeastern Texas, mostly on silty-clay or

alluvial soils (Map 172). April–December. A widespread, cosmopolitan species occurring from southeastern United States, south to Brazil, also in tropical Africa and Australia. This species appears to do well in disturbed, clay soils of south-central Texas and is worthy of extensive experimental study. *R. minima* is reportedly an important grassland legume in native pastures throughout most of its range. Breeding work with many of these geographical types with Texas material might prove worthwhile in any rangeland legume improvement program.

Chromosome number, $2n = 22$ (D. & W.).

6. *Rhynchosia latifolia* Nutt. *ex* Torr. & Gray, Fl. N. Am. 1: 285. 1838. BROAD-LEAF RHYNCHOSIA

Dolicholus latifolius (Nutt.) Vail
Rhynchosia torreyi Vail
Dolicholus torreyi (Vail) Vail

Eastern Texas mostly in sandy or gravelly soils of pine and oak woodlands (Map 173). May–August. South-central United States from Missouri to Louisiana and Texas. This species is very common in Texas and throughout most of its range is easily recognized by its long, large-flowered racemes and conspicuously trailing or twining stems. However, in east Texas the species seems to intergrade completely with *R. difformis* (below). *R. torreyi* Vail is apparently an intermediate form between these two taxa.

Chromosome number, $n = 11$ (Turner, unpublished).

7. *Rhynchosia difformis* (Ell.) DC., Prod. 2:384. 1825

Easternmost Texas in sandy soils of piny woodlands and fallow fields (Map 173). South-central and southeastern United States. A widespread species, apparently intergrading with *R. latifolia* in eastern Texas (see above) and possibly with *R. tomentosa* in parts of its range.

Chromosome number, $2n = 22$ (Turner and Fearing, unpublished).

66. STROPHOSTYLES   Wild Bean

ANNUAL or perennial, twining or trailing vines, the stems herbaceous.

LEAVES trifoliate, the terminal leaflet stalked; stipules striate, herbaceous, usually persistent.

FLOWERS terminal on elongate peduncles, purplish to cream-colored; keel strongly incurved; stamens diadelphous.

FRUIT a linear, dry, dehiscent legume with several to numerous seeds.

BASIC chromosome number, as determined from counts on 2 species, $x = 11$ (Turner, 1956b).

A genus with about 4 species in the temperate regions of central and eastern North America. The genus is sometimes considered no more than a section of the larger genus *Phaseolus*.

KEY TO SPECIES

1. Flowers 5–8 mm. long; stalk of inflorescence (peduncle) slender, rarely exceeding 10 cm. in length; seeds 2–3 mm. long   .
 . .   .   .   1. *S. leiosperma*
1. Flowers 9–15 mm. long; stalk of inflorescence stout, mostly 15 cm. or more in length; seeds 3–10 mm. long.
  2. Bracts at base of individual flowers blunt, half as long as the calyx tube or less; leaflets without conspicuous lobes at base, three to eight times as long as wide   .   .   2. *S. umbellata*
  2. Bracts at base of individual flowers acute, as long as the calyx tube or longer; leaflets lobed at base, or if not lobed, the leaves one to three times as long as wide   .   .   .   3. *S. helvola*

1. *Strophostyles leiosperma* (Torr. & Gray) Piper, Contr. U. S. Nat. Herb. 22:668. 1926
    Strophostyles pauciflora (Benth.) Wats.
    Phaseolus leiospermus Torr. & Gray

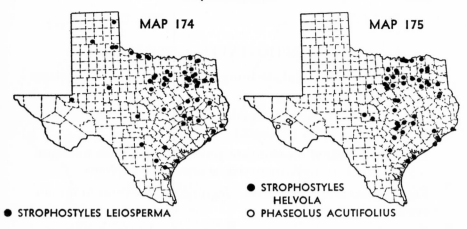

MAP 174

MAP 175

● STROPHOSTYLES
HELVOLA
○ PHASEOLUS ACUTIFOLIUS

● STROPHOSTYLES LEIOSPERMA

Eastern, central, southern, and Panhandle areas of Texas, mostly in sandy or silty-clay soils (Map 174). May–September. Central and southeastern United States. The species is often found growing intertwined with *S. helvola* without any indication of natural hybridization.

Chromosome number not determined.

2. *Strophostyles umbellata* (Muhl. *ex* Willd.) Britt., Britt. & Brown, Illus. Fl. 2:339. 1897

Phaseolus umbellatus (Willd.) Britt.

Easternmost Texas, mostly in sandy soils of pine woodlands (Map 176). June–September. Central and eastern United States from New York to Texas. Closely resembling *S. helvola*, but distinguished by the characters used in the key.

Chromosome number, $n = 11$ (Turner, 1956b).

3. *Strophostyles helvola* (L.) Ell., Sketch 2:230. 1822. AMBERIQUE BEAN

Phaseolus helvolus L.

Central, southern, and eastern Texas, mostly in sandy or gravelly soils of oak woodlands or in clay soils of the coastal grassland (Map 175). June–September. A widespread, vari-

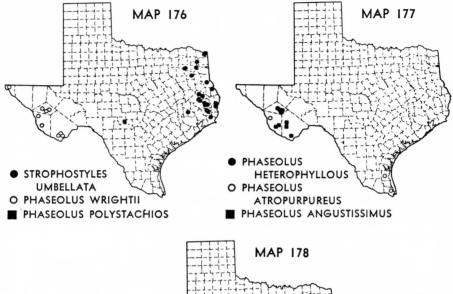

MAP 176

● STROPHOSTYLES
   UMBELLATA
○ PHASEOLUS WRIGHTII
■ PHASEOLUS POLYSTACHIOS

MAP 177

● PHASEOLUS
   HETEROPHYLLOUS
○ PHASEOLUS
   ATROPURPUREUS
■ PHASEOLUS ANGUSTISSIMUS

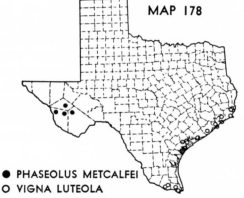

MAP 178

● PHASEOLUS METCALFEI
○ VIGNA LUTEOLA

able species occurring from southern Canada through the central and eastern United States to Florida and Texas. The stems usually grow prostrate along the ground, forming large, radiate patches to 15 feet across.

Chromosome number, $n = 11$ (D. & W., as *Phaseolus helvolus*).

67. PHASEOLUS   Bean

HERBACEOUS, perennial or annual, twining or trailing vines.

LEAVES 3-foliate, the terminal leaflet stalked; stipules persistent; stipels present.

FLOWERS axillary, white, red to purplish; usually in elongate, narrow racemes, keel twisted or contorted; stamens diadelphous.

FRUIT a dry, linear, dehiscent, typical legume with several to numerous seeds.

BASIC chromosome number, as determined from counts on approximately 15 species, x = 11 (12?) (D. & W.).

A large genus with about 200 species, mostly in the tropical and subtropical regions of both hemispheres, but a few species extending into temperate areas. There are a number of economically important species in this genus, such as *P. vulgaris*, the common garden or kidney bean, *P. limensis*, lima bean, and *P. aconitifolius*, moth or mat bean. In addition to the edible species, a number of the species in *Phaseolus* are used as fodder, green manure, and cover crops, particularly in parts of tropical America and Asia.

The species native to Texas appear to offer valuable breeding stock for future agronomic workers in this genus. For the most part, they are perennial, fall bloomers, drought resistant, and appear to do well when grown free from competition in garden plots. For additional comments concerning our native types, reference should be made to the discussion under the appropriate species listed below.

KEY TO SPECIES

1. Plant annual; inflorescence 2- to 4-flowered   .   1. *P. acutifolius*
1. Plant perennial; inflorescence 5- to many-flowered.

2. Leaflets linear to triangular-elongate, five to twenty times as
   long as wide   .   .   .   .   .   .   2. *P. angustissimus*
2. Leaflets of a broader type, less than 5 times as long as wide.
   3. Pods narrow, less than 5 mm. wide; stems and leaves conspicuously pubescent.
      4. Legumes short, curved, 2–3 cm. long, calyx (including
      lobes) 3–5 mm. long; flowers brick-red   .   .   .
      .   .   .   .   .   .   3. *P. heterophyllous*
      4. Legumes linear, nearly straight, 4–8 cm. long; calyx 5–8
      mm. long; flowers dark purple   .   .   4. *P. atropurpureus*
   3. Pods broad, 5 mm. wide or more; stems and leaves glabrous
   to minutely pubescent.
      5. Leaflets triangular with conspicuous lobes at the base;
      legume 3.5 cm. long or less   .   .   .   5. *P. wrightii*
      5. Leaflets triangular-ovate to oval, without conspicuous
      lobes at the base; legume 3.5–8 cm. long.
         6. Stipules subulate 3 mm. long or less; leaflets mostly
         acute at tip; calyx glabrous or essentially so; plants of
         central and east Texas   .   .   .   6. *P. polystachios*
         6. Stipules ovate, 4–8 mm. long; leaflets mostly obtuse or
         retuse, shortly apiculate at tip; calyx conspicuously
         short-pubescent; plants of igneous soils of trans-Pecos
         Texas   .   .   .   .   7. *P. metcalfei*

1. *Phaseolus acutifolius* Gray, Pl. Wright. 1:43. 1852.
TEPARY BEAN

    Native to trans-Pecos Texas, and known in Texas only by
a few collections from Presidio and Jeff Davis counties,
where it grows in igneous or limestone soils at altitudes of
4,000–5,000 feet (Map 175). July–September. In its wild
form this variable species ranges from the southwestern
United States to central Mexico. A broad-leafleted form of
P. acutifolius (var. *latifolius* Freeman) is commonly cultivated in parts of the southern United States and Mexico
under the trade name "Tepary Bean." Narrow-leafleted
forms, which pass into the typical form of the species, have
been called var. *tenuifolius* Gray.

    Chromosome number, $2n = 22$ (D. & W.).

2. *Phaseolus angustissimus* Gray, Pl. Wright. 2:33. 1853

Trans-Pecos Texas in Brewster and Presidio counties mostly on limestone soils, at altitudes of 4,000–5,000 feet (Map 177). Southwestern United States and adjacent Mexico. September–October.

Chromosome number not determined.

3. *Phaseolus heterophyllous* H. & B. *ex* Willd., Enum. Pl. Hort. Bot. Berol. 2:753. 1809

Known in Texas only from Jeff Davis County on igneous soil in the Davis Mountains, at altitudes of 4,000–6,000 feet (Map 177). Southwestern United States, Mexico to Guatemala. Forms of this species with rounded leaves and more pubescent pods have been called var. *rotundifolius* (Gray) Piper (=*P. rotundifolius* Gray), but, as Piper (1926) noted, the characters used to distinguish the variety are weak. Specimens with both rounded- and oblong-lobed leaflets on the same plant have been seen by the present writer.

Chromosome number not determined.

4. *Phaseolus atropurpureus* DC., Prodr. 2:395. 1825. PURPLE BEAN

Trans-Pecos Texas in igneous soils, at altitudes of 5,000–6,000 feet, occurring in southernmost Texas in deep sandy soil along the Gulf Coast (Map 177). June–September. A widespread, very variable species ranging from the southwestern United States to Central and South America. In Texas the plant is apparently rare, only a few specimens having been seen by the present writer. Collections from southern Texas, vegetatively (and superficially in flower) look very much like *Strophostyles helvola*, except that the leaves and stems are densely pubescent.

Chromosome number not determined.

5. *Phaseolus wrightii* Gray, Pl. Wright. 1:43. 1852. WRIGHT BEAN

Trans-Pecos Texas, usually in igneous soils, at altitudes of 3,000–5,000 feet (Map 176). August–November.

Chromosome number not determined.

6. *Phaseolus polystachios* (L.) B.S.P., Prelim. Cat. N. Y. Pl. 15. 1888. THICKET BEAN

Only a few collections of this plant have been seen from Texas (Map 176). Central and eastern United States, from Illinois to New York south to Florida. The species characteristically grows in wooded areas and is a twining vine on low shrubs and trees.

Chromosome number, $2n = 22$ (D. & W., as *Phaseolus polystachys*).

7. *Phaseolus metcalfei* W. & S., Contr. U. S. Nat. Herb. 16:140. 1913. METCALFE BEAN

Trans-Pecos Texas in mountainous areas, at altitudes of 4,000–7,300 feet, usually on igneous soils (Map 178). July–September. Texas to Arizona and south to southern Mexico. The species in its native habitat forms large trailing vines in protected canyons. In cultivation near Austin, Texas, it appears to be highly resistant to drought, persisting in an arrested, leafy, vegetative state during much of the summer but growing rapidly when moisture is available during late summer and fall.

Chromosome number, $n = 11$ (Turner, 1956b).

68. VIGNA   Cowpea (Black-eyed Pea)

ANNUAL or perennial vines, with prostrate or high-climbing, herbaceous, twining stems.

LEAVES 3-foliate, the terminal leaflet stalked; stipules persistent.

FLOWERS yellow, white, or purplish in clustered racemes which terminate elongate, axillary peduncles; keel not twisted or curled; stamens diadelphous, anthers all alike.

FRUIT a linear, somewhat rounded, dry to fleshy, many-seeded pod.

BASIC chromosome number, as determined from counts on 8 species, $x = 10, 11, 12$ (D. & W.).

A genus with about 60 species in the tropical and subtropical regions of both hemispheres. Some of the species are important crop plants, such as *V. unguiculata* (Cowpea) which is grown for its edible seed and soil improvement qualities. *V. luteola*, a deep-rooted perennial, is the only species of the genus native to Texas. It grows best in sandy soils and might prove a valuable soil-improvement legume, especially on marginal soils of southeastern Texas.

KEY TO SPECIES

1. Stipules small, inconspicuous, 2–5 mm. long; pods 3–7 cm. long;
   native species . . . . 1. *V. luteola*
1. Stipules conspicuous, 7–15 mm. long; pods 10 cm. long or more;
   cultivated species . . . . . . 2. *V. unguiculata*

1. *Vigna luteola* (Jacq.) Benth. *in* Mart., Flora Brasil. 5:194. 1859
   Vigna repens (L.) Kuntze, not *Vigna repens* (Grah.) Bak.
   Coastal Texas, mostly in sandy soils (Map 178). March–November. A widespread variable species occurring throughout tropical America and northward to the Gulf Coast from Texas to Florida.
   Chromosome number, $2n = 22$ (D. & W.).

2. *Vigna unguiculata* (L.) Walp., Rep. 1:779. 1842. COWPEA
   Vigna sinensis (L.) Endl. *ex* Hassk.
   Cultivated in parts of Texas and rarely persisting in abandoned fields. The species is native to the Old World tropics but has been widely introduced elsewhere. It is grown primarily for its edible seeds.
   Chromosome number, $2n = 22, 24$ (D. & W.).

New Scientific Names

Indigofera miniata var. *texana* (Buckley) Turner—p. 131

Dalea enneandra var. *pumila* (Shinners) Turner—p. 153

Literature Cited

Abrams, Leroy. 1944. Fabaceae. *In:* Illustrated Flora of the Pacific States. Vol. 2. Stanford (Calif.): Stanford University Press. 635 pp.

Anderson, E. A. 1953. Introgressive hybridization. Biol. Rev. 28:280–307.

Atchison, E. 1949. Studies in the Leguminosae. IV. Chromosome numbers and geographical relationships of miscellaneous Leguminosae. Jour. Elisha Mitchell Sci. Soc. 65:118–122.

————. 1951. Studies in the Leguminosae. VI. Chromosome numbers among tropical woody species. Amer. Jour. Bot. 38:538–546.

Baldwin, J. T. 1939. Chromosomes from leaves. Science 90:240.

Barneby, R. C. 1952. A revision of the North American species of *Oxytropis* DC. Proc. Calif. Acad. Sci. 27:177–312.

Benson, Lyman. 1941. The mesquites and screw-beans of the United States (*Prosopis*). Amer. Jour. Bot. 28:748–754.

————. 1943. Revisions of status of southwestern desert trees and shrubs. Amer. Jour. Bot. 30:230–240.

Blake, S. F. 1924. Notes on American Lespedezas. Rhodora 26:25–34.

Brenan, J. P. M. 1958. New and noteworthy Cassias from tropical Africa. Kew. Bull. 231–252.

Briscoe, C. F., and W. B. Andrews. 1938. Inoculation of Sesban (*Sesbania exaltata*). Jour. Amer. Soc. Agron. 30:135–138.

Britton, N. L., and J. N. Rose. 1928. Mimosaceae. N. Amer. Fl. 23:1–194.

————. 1930. Caesalpiniaceae. N. Amer. Fl. 23:201–349.

Burkart, A. 1949. Leguminosas nuevas o criticas. III. Darwiniana 9: 63–96.

————. 1952. Las Leguminosas Argentinas. 2d ed. Buenos Aires: Acme Agency. 567 pp.

Clapham, A. R., T. G. Tutin, and E. F. Warburg. 1952. Flora of the British Isles. London: Cambridge University Press. 1591 pp.

Cocks, R. S. 1910. Leguminosae of Louisiana. Bull. La. State Mus. Nat. Hist. Surv. 1:1–22.

Cooper, J. G. 1859. On the distribution of the forests and trees of North America, with notes on its physical geography. Rep. Smithson. Inst. 1858:246–280.

Cory, V. L., and H. B. Parks. 1937. Catalogue of the flora of the state of Texas. Bull. Texas Agric. Exp. Sta. 550. 130 pp.

Coulter, J. M. 1891–94. Botany of western Texas. Contr. U. S. Nat. Herb., Vol. 2. 588 pp. (Issued in three numbers.)

Covas, G. 1950. Número de cromosomes en seis Dicotiledóneas Argentinas. Bol. Soc. Argent. Bot. 3:83–84.

Darlington, C. D., and A. P. Wylie. 1956. Chromosome atlas of flowering plants. New York: The Macmillan Company. 519 pp.

Delay, C. 1950–51. Nombres chromosomiques chez les Phanéro-games. Rev. Cyt. Biol. Végét. 12:1–368.

Dice, L. R. 1943. The biotic provinces of North America. Ann Arbor: University of Michigan. 78 pp.

Erbe, L. 1957. Studies on the crossability of *Lupinus texensis* and *Lupinus subcarnosus*. Madroño 14:17.

Ewan, J. 1943. The correct name for the Pacific involucrate *Tri-folium*. Leafl. West. Bot. 3:222–224.

Fassett, N. C. 1939. The Leguminous Plants of Wisconsin. Madison: University of Wisconsin Press. 157 pp.

Fernald, M. L. 1950. Gray's Manual of Botany. 8th ed. New York: The Macmillan Company. 1632 pp.

Fisher, E. M. 1892. Revision of the North American species of *Hoffmanseggia*. Contr. U. S. Nat. Herb. 1:143–150.

Forbes, R. H. 1895. The Mesquite tree: its products and uses. Arizona Agric. Exp. Sta. Bull. 13.

Frahm-Leliveld, J. A. 1953. Some chromosome numbers in tropical leguminous plants. Euphytica 2:46–48.

Gambill, W. C., Jr. 1953. The Leguminosae of Illinois. Urbana: University of Illinois Press. 117 pp.

Gleason, H. A. 1952. New Britton and Brown Illustrated Flora of the Northeastern United States and Adjacent Canada. Vol. 2. Lancaster (Pa.): Lancaster Press. 655 pp.

Hanson, C. H., and W. A. Cope. 1955. Interspecific hybridization in *Lespedeza*. Jour. Hered. 46:233–238.

Harper, R. M. 1950. A statistical summary of the flora of Texas. Bull. Torr. Bot. Club 77:192–203.

Head, S. C. 1957. Mitotic chromosome studies in the genus *Astragalus*. Madroño 14:95–106.

Hennen, J. F. 1950. The true clovers (*Trifolium*) of Texas. Field & Lab. 18:159–164.

————. 1951. The sweet clovers (*Melilotus*) of Texas. Field & Lab. 19:87–89.

Herman, F. J. 1953. A botanical synopsis of the cultivated clovers (*Trifolium*). U. S. Dep. Agric. Monogr. 22. 45 pp.

Hitchcock, C. L. 1952. A revision of the North American species of *Lathyrus*. Univ. Wash. Publ. Biol. 15:1–104.

Hopkins, Milton. 1942. *Cercis* in North America. Rhodora 44:193–211.

Howell, J. T. 1955. A tabulation of Californian endemics. Leafl. West. Bot. 7:257–264.

Hutchinson, John. 1926. The families of flowering plants. I. Dicotyledons. London: Macmillan and Co., Ltd. 328 pp.

Isely, D. 1951. The Leguminosae of the north-central United States. I. Loteae and Trifolieae. Iowa State Coll. Jour. Sci. 25:439–482.

————. 1953. *Desmodium paniculatum* (L.) DC. and *D. viridiflorum*. Amer. Midl. Nat. 49:920–933.

————. 1955. The Leguminosae of the north-central United States. II. Hedysareae. Iowa State Coll. Jour. Sci. 30:33–118.

James, L. E. 1951. Observations on the taxonomy of *Astragalus*, subgenus *Hesperastragalus*. Contr. Dudley Herb. 4:63–72.

Johnston, I. M. 1924. *Parkinsonia* and *Cercidium*. Contr. Gray Herb. n.s. 70:61–68.

Kearney, T. H., and R. H. Peebles. 1942. Leguminosae. *In:* Flowering Plants and Ferns of Arizona. U. S. Dep. Agric. Misc. Publ. 423:412–505.

Larisey, M. M. 1940a. Analysis of a hybrid complex between *Baptisia leucantha* and *Baptisia viridis* in Texas. Amer. Jour. Bot. 27:624–628.

————. 1940b. A monograph of the genus *Baptisia*. Ann. Missouri Bot. Gard. 27:119–244.

Ledingham, G. F. 1957. Chromosome numbers of some Saskatchewan Leguminosae with particular reference to *Astragalus* and *Oxytropis*. Canad. Jour. Bot. 35:657–666.

Macbride, J. F. 1919. Notes on certain Leguminosae. Contr. Gray Herb. n.s. 59:1–27.

Milne-Redhead, E. 1954. *Zornia* in tropical Africa. Bol. Soc. Broteriana 28:79–104.

Mohlenbrock, R. H. 1957. A revision of the genus *Stylosanthes*. Ann. Missouri Bot. Gard. 44:299–355.

Moore, J. A. 1936. The vascular anatomy of the flower in the papilionaceous Leguminosae. I. Amer. Jour. Bot. 23:279–290.

Ottley, A. M. 1944. The American Loti with special consideration of a proposed new section, Simpeteria. Brittonia 5:81–123.

Palmer, E. J. 1931. Conspectus of the genus *Amorpha*. Jour. Arnold Arb. 12:157–197.

Pennell, F. W. 1919. *Eysenhardtia*. N. Amer. Fl. 24:34–40.

Piper, C. V. 1925. The American species of *Canavalia* and *Wenderothia*. Contr. U. S. Nat. Herb. 20:555–588.

————. 1926. Studies in American Phaseolineae. Contr. U. S. Nat. Herb. 22:669–699.

Porter, C. L. 1956. The genus *Peteria* (Leguminosae). Rhodora 58:344–354.

Robinson, B. L. 1898. Revision of the North American and Mexican species of *Mimosa*. Proc. Amer. Acad. Arts and Sci. 33:303–331; Contr. Gray Herb. n.s. 13.

Rose, J. N. 1903. Synopsis of the species of *Cologania*. Contr. U. S. Nat. Herb. 8:34–42.

Rudd, V. E. 1955. The American species of *Aeschynomene*. Contr. U. S. Nat. Herb. 32:1–172.

————. 1956. A revision of the genus *Nissolia*. Contr. U. S. Nat. Herb. 32: 173–206.

Rydberg, P. A. 1923. Indigofereae, Galegeae (*pars*). N. Amer. Fl. 24:137–250.

————. 1924. Sesbanianae. N. Amer. Fl. 24:202–209.

————. 1929. Galegeae (*pars*). N. Amer. Fl. 24:251–462.

Sargent, C. S. 1933. Manual of the Trees of North America. 2d ed. Boston: Houghton Mifflin Company. 910 pp.

Schubert, B. G. 1950. *Desmodium:* preliminary studies. III. Rhodora 52: 135–155.

Sharp, A. J. 1951. The relation of the Eocene Wilcox flora to some modern floras. Evolution 5: 1–5.

Senn, H. A. 1938a. Chromosome number relationships of the Leguminosae. Bibliogr. Genet. 12: 175–337.

———. 1938b. Cytological evidence on the status of the genus *Chamaecrista* Moench. Jour. Arnold Arb. 19: 153–157.

———. 1939. The North American species of *Crotalaria.* Rhodora 41: 317–367.

Shinners, L. H. 1948. The vetches and pea vines (*Vicia* and *Lathyrus*) of Texas. Field & Lab. 16: 18–29.

———. 1949. The genus *Dalea* (including *Petalostemum*) in north-central Texas. Field & Lab. 17: 85–89.

———. 1951. The Texas species of *Psoralea.* Field & Lab. 19: 14–25.

———. 1953. The bluebonnets (*Lupinus*) of Texas. Field & Lab. 21: 149–153.

———. 1954. *Trifolium glomeratum* in Texas. Leafl. West. Bot. 7: 132.

———. 1956. Authorship and nomenclature of bur clovers (*Medicago*) found wild in the United States. Rhodora 58: 1–13.

Small, J. K. 1903. Flora of the Southeastern United States. 2d ed. New York: Published by the author. 1375 pp.

Standley, P. C. 1922. Trees and shrubs of Mexico (Leguminosae). Contr. U. S. Nat. Herb. 23: 348–515.

Taubert, P. 1894. Leguminosae. Die natürlichen Pflanzenfamilien 3³: 70–396.

Tharp, B. C. 1952. Texas Range Grasses. Austin: University of Texas Press. 125 pp.

———. 1939. The Vegetation of Texas. Austin: Texas Academy of Science, Nontechnical Publication Series.

Turner, B. L. 1950a. Vegetative Key to Texas *Desmanthus* and similar genera. Field & Lab. 18: 54–65.

———. 1950b. Mexican species of *Desmanthus.* Field & Lab. 18: 119–130.

――――. 1951. Revision of the United States species of *Neptunia* (Leguminosae). Amer. Midl. Naturalist 46:82–92.

――――. 1955a. The *Cassia fasciculata* complex (Leguminosae) in Texas. Field & Lab. 23:87–91.

――――. 1955b. Chromosome numbers in the genus *Sesbania* (Leguminosae): evidence for a conservative treatment. Rhodora 57:213–218.

――――. 1956a. New names for Texas Leguminosae. Field & Lab. 24:15–17.

――――. 1956b. Chromosome numbers in the Leguminosae. I. Amer. Jour. Bot. 43:577–581.

――――. 1957. Chromosomal and distributional relationships of *Lupinus texensis* and *L. subcarnosus* (Leguminosae). Madroño 14:13–16.

――――. 1958. Chromosome numbers in the genus *Krameria*: evidence for familial status. Rhodora 60:101–106.

Turner, B. L., and J. H. Beaman. 1953. Chromosome complements in *Desmanthus* (Leguminosae). Field & Lab. 21:47–50.

Wagner, F. H. 1948. The bur clovers (*Medicago*) of Texas. Field & Lab. 16:3–7.

Walton, G. P. 1923. A chemical and structural study of mesquite, carob, and honey locust beans. U. S. Dep. Agric. Bull. 1194: 1–19.

Whyte, R. O., G. Nilsson-Leissner, and H. C. Trumble. 1953. Legumes in Agriculture. Food and Agric. Org. Agric. Study 21 (Rome). 367 pp.

Wiggins, I. L. 1942. *Acacia angustissima* (Mill.) Kuntze and its near relatives. Contr. Dudley Herb. 3:227–239.

Wood, C. E. 1949. The American barbistyled species of *Tephrosia*. Rhodora 51: 193–231, 233–302, 305–364, 369–384.

Young, J. O. 1940. Cytological investigations in *Desmodium* and *Lespedeza*. Bot. Gaz. 101:839–850.

Young, V. A., *et al.* 1948. Brush problems on Texas ranges. Texas Agric. Exp. Sta. Misc. Pub. 21:1–19.

Index